# ⊚ Harden's

# London
# Restaurants
2006

© Harden's Limited 2005

ISBN 1-873721-72-2

British Library Cataloguing-in-Publication data:
a catalogue record for this book is available from
the British Library.

Printed in Italy by Legoprint

Research Assistants: Lois Lee, Sarah Ashpole, Alham Usman,
Joanne Nonkoh

Harden's Limited
14 Buckingham Street
London WC2N 6DF

# CONTENTS

**Ratings & prices**
**How this guide is written**

|                                    | Page |
|------------------------------------|------|
| **Survey results**                 |      |
| Most mentioned                     | 9    |
| Nominations                        | 10   |
| Highest ratings                    | 12   |
| Best by cuisine                    | 14   |
| **Top special deals**              | 16   |
| **The restaurant scene**           | 18   |
| **Openings and closures**          | 20   |
| **Eating in London – FAQs**        | 23   |
| **Directory**                      | 28   |
| **Indexes**                        |      |
| Breakfast                          | 214  |
| Brunch menus                       | 216  |
| Business                           | 217  |
| BYO                                | 218  |
| Children                           | 219  |
| Entertainment                      | 227  |
| Late                               | 229  |
| No-smoking areas                   | 230  |
| Outside tables                     | 234  |
| Private rooms                      | 240  |
| Romantic                           | 245  |
| Rooms with a view                  | 246  |
| Notable wine lists                 | 246  |
| **Cuisine lists**                  | 248  |
| **Area overviews**                 | 268  |
| **Maps**                           | 302  |
| 1 – London overview                |      |
| 2 – West End overview              |      |
| 3 – Mayfair, St James's & West Soho |     |
| 4 – East Soho, Chinatown & Covent Garden | |
| 5 – Knightsbridge, Chelsea & South Kensington | |
| 6 – Notting Hill & Bayswater       |      |
| 7 – Hammersmith & Chiswick         |      |
| 8 – Hampstead, Camden Town & Islington | |
| 9 – The City                       |      |
| 10 – South London (& Fulham)       |      |
| 11 – East End & Docklands          |      |

# RATINGS & PRICES

## Ratings

Our rating system is unlike those found in other guides (most of which tell you nothing more helpful than that expensive restaurants are, as a general rule, better than cheap ones).

What we do is to compare each restaurant's performance – as judged by the average grades awarded by reporters in the survey – with other restaurants in the same price-bracket.

This approach has the advantage that it helps you find – whatever your budget for any particular meal – where you will get the best 'bang for your buck'.

The following qualities are assessed:

> **F** — Food
> **S** — Service
> **A** — Ambience

The rating indicates that, *in comparison with other restaurants in the same price-bracket*, performance is ...

> **❶** — Exceptional
> **❷** — Very good
> **❸** — Good
> ④ — Average
> ⑤ — Poor

## Prices

The price shown for each restaurant is the cost for one (1) person of an average three-course *dinner* with half a bottle of house wine and coffee, any cover charge, service and VAT. Lunch is often cheaper. With BYO restaurants, we have assumed that two people share a £5 bottle of off-licence wine.

---

*Telephone number – all numbers should be prefixed with '020' if dialling from outside the London area.*

*Map reference – shown immediately after the telephone number.*

*Rated on Editors' visit – indicates ratings have been determined by the Editors personally, based on their visit, rather than derived from the survey.*

*Website – the first entry in the small print (after any note about Editors' visit)*

*Last orders time – the first entry in the small print, after the website (if applicable); Sunday may be up to 90 minutes earlier.*

*Opening hours – unless otherwise stated, restaurants are open for lunch and dinner seven days a week.*

*Credit and debit cards – unless otherwise stated, Mastercard, Visa, Amex and Maestro are accepted.*

*Dress – where appropriate, the management's preferences concerning patrons' dress are given.*

*Smoking – cigarette smoking restrictions are noted. Pipe or cigar smokers should always check ahead.*

*Special menus – if we know of a particularly good value set menu we note this (e.g. "set weekday L"), together with its formula price (FP) calculated exactly as in 'Prices' above. Details change, so always check ahead.*

# HOW THIS GUIDE IS WRITTEN

## Survey

This guide is based on our fifteenth annual survey of what Londoners think of their restaurants; it is by far the largest annual survey of its type. Since 1998, we have also surveyed restaurant-goers across the rest of the UK. The out-of-town results are published in our guide 'UK Restaurants', published in association with Rémy Martin Fine Champagne Cognac. This year the total number of reporters in our combined London/UK survey, conducted mainly online, was over 8,000, and, between them, they contributed over 90,000 individual reports.

## How we determine the ratings

In most cases, ratings are arrived at statistically. This essentially involves 'ranking' the average rating each restaurant achieves in the survey – for food, for service and for ambience – against the the average ratings of the other establishments in the same price-bracket.

A few restaurants – usually too recently opened for the survey – are rated by the editors themselves. To emphasise the personal basis of such assessments, we include a small-print note – "Rated on Editors' visit".

## How we write the reviews

The tenor of each review is broadly determined by the ratings of the establishment concerned (determined as described above). We also pay some regard to the proportion of positive nominations (such as for 'favourite restaurant') compared to negative nominations (such as for 'most overpriced'). To explain *why* a restaurant has been rated as it has, we extract snippets from survey comments ("enclosed in double quotes"). A short review cannot possibly reflect all the nuances from, sometimes, several hundred reports, and what we try to do is to illustrate the key themes which emerge.

## Editors' visits

We have, anonymously and at our own expense, visited the great majority of the restaurants listed in this book. However (except in the case of new restaurants, as noted above), we use these experiences only to help us to interpret reporters' views. We do *not* superimpose our own opinions: how well (or poorly) a restaurant is rated is determined by the survey results.

**Please help us to make the next edition even more accurate.** Register for free updates at www.hardens.com and you will be invited to take part in our next survey in the spring of 2006. **If you take part in the survey, you will, on publication, receive a complimentary copy of *Harden's London Restaurants 2007*.**

**Richard Harden**                    **Peter Harden**

# SURVEY – MOST MENTIONED

*These are the restaurants which were most frequently mentioned by reporters. (Last year's position is given in brackets.) An asterisk\* indicates the first appearance in the list of a recently-opened restaurant.*

1   J Sheekey (1)
2   Hakkasan (4)
3   The Ivy (2)
4   Gordon Ramsay (3)
5   The Wolseley (11)
6   Bleeding Heart (7)
7   Nobu (5)
8   Gordon Ramsay at Claridge's (9)
9   Chez Bruce (8)
10  Oxo Tower (6)

11  La Poule au Pot (12)
12  Andrew Edmunds (10)
13  Le Gavroche (17)
14  Yauatcha\*
15  The Cinnamon Club (19)
16  Le Caprice (14)
17  Locanda Locatelli (13)
18  Zuma (26)
19  Tom Aikens (24)
20  La Trompette (22)

21  The Square (19)
22  Mirabelle (16)
23  Pétrus (21)
24  Club Gascon (15)
25  The River Café (27)
26  Blue Elephant (23)
27  Connaught (Angela Hartnett) (35)
28  Le Pont de la Tour (28)
29  Chutney Mary (34)
30  The Don (-)

31  Racine (31)
32  Moro (30)
33= The Anchor & Hope\*
33= Savoy Grill (28)
35  Coq d'Argent (25)
36  Zafferano (32)
37  Café du Marché (37)
38  Sketch (Gallery) (18)
39  Amaya\*
40  St John (-)

# SURVEY – NOMINATIONS

Ranked by the number of reporters' votes.

## Top gastronomic experience

1 Gordon Ramsay (1)
2 Gordon Ramsay at Claridge's (3)
3 Chez Bruce (2)
4 Tom Aikens (4)
5 Le Gavroche (5)
6 Nobu (6)
7 La Trompette (9)
8 The Ivy (8)
9 Pétrus (-)
10 Locanda Locatelli (10)

## Favourite

1 Chez Bruce (2)
2 The Ivy (1)
3 The Wolseley (8)
4 J Sheekey (3)
5 Le Caprice (4)
6 Gordon Ramsay (5)
7 La Trompette (6)
8 Hakkasan (7)
9 Nobu (-)
10 Zuma (10)

## Best for business

1 Bleeding Heart (3)
2 The Don (5)
3 The Wolseley (-)
4 The Square (2)
5 Coq d'Argent (1)
6 The Ivy (7)
7 1 Lombard Street (4)
8 Rhodes 24*
9 Savoy Grill (6)
10 Bank Aldwych (9)

## Best for romance

1 La Poule au Pot (1)
2 Andrew Edmunds (2)
3 Bleeding Heart (3)
4 Chez Bruce (4)
5 The Ivy (6)
6 Le Caprice (5)
7 Julie's (7)
8 Café du Marché (-)
9 Oxo Tower (Bras') (8)
10 Blue Elephant (9)

## Best breakfast/brunch

1  The Wolseley (2)
2  Giraffe (1)
3  Smiths (Ground Floor) (4)
4  Pâtisserie Valerie (-)
5  Simpsons-in-the-Strand (3)
6  Carluccio's Caffè (-)
7  Chelsea Bun Diner (-)
8  Electric Brasserie (9)
9  Bank Aldwych (5)
10  Balans (7)

## Best bar/pub food

1  The Anchor & Hope (2)
2  The Eagle (1)
3  The Engineer (3)
4  The Havelock Tavern (8)
5  Churchill Arms (7)
6  The Cow (9)
7  The Anglesea Arms (4)
8  The Wells (-)
9  Admiral Codrington (3)
10  Earl Spencer (-)

## Most disappointing cooking

1  Oxo Tower (1)
2  The Ivy (2)
3  The Wolseley (5)
4  Gordon Ramsay at Claridge's (3)
5  Quaglino's (6)
6  Tom Aikens (-)
7  Le Pont de la Tour (-)
8  Bluebird (7)
9  Connaught (Angela Hartnett) (-)
10  Sketch (Gallery) (4)

## Most overpriced restaurant

1  Oxo Tower (2)
2  Sketch (Gallery) (1)
3  Nobu (3)
4  The River Café (5)
5  The Ivy (7)
6  Cipriani*
7  Sketch (Lecture Rm) (1)
8  Hakkasan (8)
9  Le Pont de la Tour (6)
10  Gordon Ramsay at Claridge's (-)

# SURVEY – HIGHEST RATINGS

## FOOD                                SERVICE

### £70+

| | FOOD | | SERVICE |
|---|---|---|---|
| 1 | Gordon Ramsay | 1 | Gordon Ramsay |
| 2 | Capital Hotel | 2 | Le Gavroche |
| 3 | Pied à Terre | 3 | Dorchester Grill |
| 4 | Aubergine | 4 | Capital Hotel |
| 5 | Rasoi Vineet Bhatia | 5 | Pétrus |

### £55-£69

| | | | |
|---|---|---|---|
| 1 | Roussillon | 1 | Goring Hotel |
| 2 | 1880 | 2 | The Ledbury |
| 3 | Club Gascon | 3 | Roussillon |
| 4 | Zuma | 4 | Foliage |
| 5 | J Sheekey | 5 | Clarke's |

### £45-£54

| | | | |
|---|---|---|---|
| 1 | Chez Bruce | 1 | Oslo Court |
| 2 | La Trompette | 2 | Lundum's |
| 3 | Morgan M | 3 | Odin's |
| 4 | Assaggi | 4 | Quirinale |
| 5 | Quirinale | 5 | Chez Bruce |

### £35-£44

| | | | |
|---|---|---|---|
| 1 | Tsunami | 1 | Lamberts |
| 2 | Hunan | 2 | Mosaica |
| 3 | Delfina Studio Café | 3 | Vivat Bacchus |
| 4 | Chez Lindsay | 4 | Delfina Studio Café |
| 5 | E&O | 5 | Caraffini |

### £34 or less

| | | | |
|---|---|---|---|
| 1 | Café Japan | 1 | Uli |
| 2 | Rasa | 2 | Mandalay |
| 3 | Jin Kichi | 3 | Vijay |
| 4 | New Tayyab | 4 | Yming |
| 5 | Mirch Masala | 5 | El Rincón Latino |

*for updates visit www.hardens.com*

## AMBIENCE

1 Blakes Hotel
2 Taman gang
3 The Ritz
4 The Lanesborough
5 Hakkasan

1 Les Trois Garçons
2 Belvedere
3 Zuma
4 Toto's
5 The Ivy

1 Archipelago
2 Blue Elephant
3 Odin's
4 Vertigo
5 Lundum's

1 La Poule au Pot
2 Champor-Champor
3 Papageno
4 Pasha
5 Mosaica

1 Gordon's Wine Bar
2 LMNT
3 Andrew Edmunds
4 Annie's
5 Troubadour

## OVERALL

1 Gordon Ramsay
2 Le Gavroche
3 Capital Hotel
4 Pétrus
5 Aubergine

1 Roussillon
2 J Sheekey
3 The Ledbury
4 Foliage
5 Locanda Locatelli

1 Chez Bruce
2 Odin's
3 La Trompette
4 Lundum's
5 Archipelago

1 Mosaica
2 Champor-Champor
3 E&O
4 Delfina Studio Café
5 Chez Lindsay

1 Andrew Edmunds
2 El Rincón Latino
3 Rasa
4 St John N19
5 Shampers

# SURVEY – BEST BY CUISINE

These are the restaurants which received the best average food ratings (excluding establishments with a small or notably local following).

Where the most common types of cuisine are concerned, we present the results in two price-brackets. For less common cuisines, we list the top three, regardless of price.

For further information about restaurants which are particularly notable for their food, see the cuisine lists starting on page 248. These indicate, using an asterisk (*), restaurants which offer exceptional or very good food.

## British, Modern

### £45 and over
1  Chez Bruce
2  1880
3  The Glasshouse
4  Clarke's
5  Notting Hill Brasserie

### Under £45
1  St John
2  Mosaica
3  The Palmerston
4  Lamberts
5  The Anglesea Arms, W6

## French

### £45 and over
1  Gordon Ramsay
2  Capital Hotel
3  Pied à Terre
4  Aubergine
5  Roussillon

### Under £45
1  Racine
2  Le Cercle
3  Le Vacherin
4  Petit Max
5  Café du Marché

## Italian/Mediterranean

### £45 and over
1  Assaggi
2  Quirinale
3  Zafferano
4  Tentazioni
5  Locanda Locatelli

### Under £45
1  Ottolenghi
2  Latium
3  Arancia
4  A Cena
5  The Oak

## Indian

### £45 and over
1  Rasoi Vineet Bhatia
2  Amaya
3  Tamarind
4  Chutney Mary
5  Zaika

### Under £45
1  Rasa
2  New Tayyab
3  Mirch Masala
4  Vijay
5  Lahore Kebab House

## Chinese

### £45 and over
1 Hakkasan
2 Kai Mayfair
3 Ken Lo's Memories
4 Ken Lo's Memories W8
5 Taman gang

### Under £45
1 Hunan
2 Mandarin Kitchen
3 Phoenix Palace
4 Good Earth
5 Yauatcha

## Japanese

### £45 and over
1 Zuma
2 Nobu
3 Tatsuso
4 Sumosan
5 Ubon

### Under £45
1 Café Japan
2 Tsunami
3 Jin Kichi
4 K10
5 Kulu Kulu

## British, Traditional
1 Dorchester Grill
2 Two Brothers
3 St John Bread & Wine

## Vegetarian
1 The Gate
2 Blah! Blah! Blah!
3 Mildred's

## Burgers, etc
1 GBK
2 Wolfe's
3 Lucky Seven

## Pizza
1 Pizza Metro
2 Made in Italy
3 Il Bordello

## Fish & Chips
1 Nautilus
2 Faulkner's
3 Toff's

## Thai
1 Patara
2 Amaranth
3 Churchill Arms

## Fusion
1 Tsunami
2 Nobu
3 Ubon

## Fish & Seafood
1 One-O-One
2 J Sheekey
3 Mandarin Kitchen

## Greek
1 Vrisaki
2 Lemonia
3 The Real Greek

## Spanish
1 Moro
2 Fino
3 Tapas Brindisa

## Turkish
1 Haz
2 Gallipoli
3 Kazan

## Lebanese
1 Beirut Express
2 Ranoush
3 Maroush

# TOP SPECIAL DEALS

*The following menus allow you to eat in the restaurants concerned at a significant discount when compared to their evening à la carte prices.*

*The prices used are calculated in accordance with our usual formula (i.e. three courses with house wine, coffee and tip).*

*Special menus are by their nature susceptible to change – please check that they are still available.*

## Weekday lunch

£60+  The Ritz

£55+  Gordon Ramsay
      Sketch (Lecture Rm)

£50+  Le Gavroche
      Gordon Ramsay at
        Claridge's
      The Greenhouse
      Hakkasan
      L'Oranger
      Pied à Terre
      Savoy Grill
      Umu

£45+  Bibendum
      Capital Hotel
      Lindsay House
      One-O-One

£40+  Boxwood Café
      Dorchester Grill
      The Ivy
      McClements
      Mju
      Nahm
      Orrery
      Pearl
      Pétrus
      Le Soufflé
      Tom Aikens
      Windows on the World

£35+  Aubergine
      Benares
      Brunello
      The Cinnamon Club
      Defune
      Fifteen
      The Lanesborough
      Mirabelle
      Noble Rot
      Oxo Tower (Rest')
      Refuel
      Santini
      Sartoria
      Toto's
      Trader Vics

£30+  The Almeida
      Amaya
      L'Aventure
      Babylon
      Belvedere
      Berkeley Square Café
      Bombay Brasserie
      Le Colombier

Daphne's
Deep
Electric Brasserie
The Glasshouse
Homage
The House
Ikeda
L'Incontro
Kensington Place
Locanda Ottoemezzo
Maggiore's
Montpeliano
Notting Hill Brasserie
Odette's
Patara
Pengelley's
Le Pont de la Tour
  Bar & Grill
La Porte des Indes
Quaglino's
Racine
Tamarind
Zaika

£25+  A Cena
      Bank Aldwych
      Bank Westminster
      Le Bouchon Bordelais
      Boudin Blanc
      Café des Amis du Vin
      Café Fish
      Carpaccio's
      The Criterion Grill
      Dan's
      Le Deuxième
      Eight Over Eight
      Enoteca Turi
      Esenza
      L'Etranger
      Frankie's
      Frederick's
      Gabrielles
      The Greyhound
      The Light House
      Lightship
      Lundum's
      Malmaison
      Mitsukoshi
      Monza
      Pellicano
      La Poule au Pot
      The Quality Chop House
      Quilon
      Sonny's
      Le Suquet
      Veeraswamy

Vivat Bacchus
The Wells
The Wharf

£20+ About Thyme
Al Bustan
The Anglesea Arms
Aviary
Baltic
La Bouchée
Brula
Café du Jardin
Chisou
Circus
Cru
Dover Street
Il Falconiere
Franklins
Garbo's
Glaisters
Greig's
Just Oriental
Ken Lo's Memories
Kwan Thai
The Little Square
Lobster Pot
Michiaki
Mon Plaisir
Orso
Ost. Antica Bologna
Osteria dell' Arancio
The Palmerston
Pasha
Riviera
Sargasso Sea
Singapore Garden
Sophie's Steakhouse
Tomato
Yatra

£15+ The Arches
Cheyne Walk Bras'
Fish Hoek
Inaho
kare kare
Lilly's
Mesclun
Newton's
Pomino
Ragam
Sarkhel's
Wakaba

## Pre/post theatre
## (and early evening)

£60+ The Ritz

£50+ Asia de Cuba
Savoy Grill

£45+ Lindsay House

£35+ Hush
Neal Street
Refuel

£30+ The Almeida
Belvedere
Christopher's

Homage
Le Pont de la Tour
    Bar & Grill
The Portrait
Quaglino's
Racine
Zaika

£25+ Bank Aldwych
Café des Amis du Vin
The Criterion Grill
Daphne's
L'Estaminet
L'Etranger
Frederick's
Gabrielles
Just St James
Luigi's
The Quality Chop House
Redmond's
Veeraswamy

£20+ Baltic
La Bouchée
Café du Jardin
Circus
Le Deuxième
Glaisters
Joe Allen
Maggiore's
The Mall Tavern
Mon Plaisir
Smollensky's
Tuttons

## Sunday lunch

£50+ Dorchester Grill

£45+ Orrery

£40+ Goring Hotel
Mirabelle
Savoy Grill
Smiths (Top Floor)

£35+ Belvedere
Refuel

£30+ Bombay Brasserie
Cheyne Walk Bras'
Odette's
Sargasso Sea
Tamarind
Veeraswamy

£25+ The Abingdon
Maggie Jones's

£20+ The Grapes
Maggiore's
Ziani

£15+ Grenadier

# THE RESTAURANT SCENE

## Boom times roll

This year, we record 142 new openings, eight up on the previous record of 134, noted in 2004. More importantly, perhaps, this is the first time that annual openings have 'broken out' of the narrow range (120-134) which has ruled for the past five years. The number of closings, on the other hand, fell from 82 last year (and a record 113 the year before that) to 67. Openings and closings are listed on pages 20-22.

## Ten years at the top for Ramsay

For the tenth consecutive year, Gordon Ramsay's main restaurant is reporters' top nomination for their 'best meal of the year'. That is certainly a remarkable achievement. But what really makes Gordon's career to date so impressive is that he has geared up on his skills and energy to pull off a much harder trick: the transition from chef to major multiple-restaurateur.

Perhaps surprisingly – in an era when the media tend to hail chefs as supermen – the number of chefs who have what it takes to create a group of consistently successful major restaurants is tiny: in London, only a handful in the last 50 years. In the scale of his empire, however, Ramsay – who has projects on the boil in NYC and Tokyo, as well as nine restaurants in London – looks set to emerge as a *world*-scale restaurateur, of the likes of Jean-Georges Vongerichten or Alain Ducasse.

But despite what the PR machine would have you believe, even Gordon is not, in fact, Superman. The reality is that only two restaurants in his group (*Gordon Ramsay* and – with Marcus Waring's help – *Pétrus*) are really outstanding. The rest are mainly good-to-middling operations made newsworthy by Ramsay's backing, rather than their intrinsic merits. Whether Gordon has much more to 'give' the London restaurant scene in future is therefore, as things stand, rather moot.

## At last, London has restaurant groups which know what they're doing!

The growth of the Ramsay empire over the last dozen years is emblematic of the rise of quality-driven operators at the top of the London restaurant scene.

For much of the '90s, our 'Top 40' (see page 9) of places most-mentioned in the survey was dominated by style-driven operators like Conran and Harvey Nichols, who grabbed headlines with products that were – and, if they still exist, often still are – seriously mediocre. Now, in a very welcome reversal, it's 'quality' not hype which is the hallmark of this same list. This is so whether you look at the three 'groups' most represented in the

Top 40 – Ramsay (5 times), Caprice (3) and Nigel Platts-Martin (3) – or to operators like Alan Yau, Rainer Becker, Namita Panjabi and family or Robert and Robyn Wilson, with two Top 40 names apiece. Each of them is building a portfolio of properties whose popularity looks set to endure.

## Openings of the year

Each year, we select what we see as the ten most notable openings of the past twelve months. This task has been hard this year, as there have been many good openings but relatively few 'stand-outs'. Our selection is:

| | |
|---|---|
| Amaya | Ottolenghi |
| Automat | Ping Pong |
| The Gun | Salt Yard |
| The Ledbury | Sabor |
| Nobu Berkeley | Umu |

## Trends

The following trends seem to us to be apparent in London's restaurant scene at the moment:

• Non-European (and especially Eastern) restaurants continue to account for an ever-greater proportion of first-rank establishments and high-profile openings. Eight of the top 40 establishments are now subcontinental or Asian.

• the 'grazing' trend – for sushi, dim sum, tapas and other small dishes – has intensified.

• Most 'old-fashioned' eat-in/take-away formulas – such as burgers, pizzas and even good old fish 'n' chips – are being given a new 'twist' (by operators new and old).

• From a surprisingly small base, London is at last developing a range of decent Latin American options.

• The division between restaurants and food retail continues to become more blurred. (Recent examples include: baker/cafés such as *Aubaine*; deli/canteens such as *Ottolenghi*; a retail tea shop/brasserie, *Tea Palace*; and a bistro/pâtisserie, *Comptoir Gascon*.)

## Prices

The average price of dinner for one at establishments listed in the guide is £36.82. Prices have on average risen by 4.1% in the past 12 months.

As was the case last year, prices are therefore rising roughly twice as fast as general inflation. At the top end of the market (£50+), the increase of 5.6% approaches three times the rate of consumer inflation generally.

This is the sixth consecutive year in which top-end prices have 'powered ahead'.

# OPENINGS AND CLOSURES

## OPENINGS

Abeno Too
Abingdon Road
Addendum
Albannach
Arturo
As Greek As It Gets
Automat
The Aviary
Awana
Babes 'n' Burgers
Bankside, *EC2*
The Bar & Grill
Bastille
Beauberry House
Beaufort House
Bellamy's
Blue Lagoon, *SW1*
Bombay Bicycle Club, *W11 & NW3*
Brasserie de l'Auberge
Broadway Bar & Grill
The Bull
La Buvette
Chakalaka
China Tang
The Chinese Experience
Chisou
Christopher's In The City
Coco
Comptoir Gascon
Crazy Homies
The Cross Bar
Cube & Star
Dans le Noir
Deep
dim T, *W1*
Epicurean Pizza Lounge
EV
Evo
Fairuz, *W2*
Fiore
Fire & Stone
Firezza
Fish Club
Food@TheMuse
43 South Molton
Frankie's
Fratelli la Bufala
Freemasons Arms
Galvin
The Garden Café
Giardinetto

Glas
Graze
The Green
Greenwich Park
The Greyhound, *SW11*
Grocer on Warwick Café
The Gun
Haché
Hadley House
Hole in the Wall
Homage
Iniga
Isarn
Ishtar
Kisso
Koba
Kurumaya
Laureate
The Ledbury
Leon
Lilly's
Little Earth Cafe
Louvaine
Love India
Luna Rossa
Mamounia
Matilda's
Matriciano
maze
Menier Chocolate Factory
Messanges
Mestizo
Metro
Michiaki
Missouri Grill
Morel
Moti Mahal
Nobu Berkeley
Noura. , *three branches*
Nozomi
Nuovi Sapori
Occo
OQO Bar
Ottolenghi
Le Pain Quotidien
Pengelley's
The Penthouse
The Pig's Ear
Ping Pong
Pomino
Portal
The Princess

## OPENINGS (cont'd)

Pucci Pizza
The Pumphouse
Putney Station
Real Burger World
Relais de Paris
Le Relais de Venise
Rhodes W1
Roast
Rodizio Rico, *N1*
Rowley's, *W1*
Ruby Lounge &
   Sequoia Bar
Sabor
Le Saint Julien
Salt Yard
Sam's Brasserie
San Frediano *(yet again)*
Santa Maria de Buen Ayre
Sarkhel's, *SW14*
Savarona

The Sea Cow, *SW4*
Shanghai Blues
Shikara
Silk
Sketch (Glade)
La Superba
Tapas Brindisa
Taqueria
Tartine, *TW9*
The Tea Palace
Thai on the River
3G
Throgmorton
Tobia
Tugga
W'sens
Whole Hog Canteen
Wizzy
Yelo, *W11*
Yi-Ban, *SW6*

## CLOSURES

Alounak
Amici
Aperitivo, *NW1*
Ashbells
Banners, *N19*
Basil Street Hotel
Belair House
Bersagliera
Blue Pumpkin, *SW15*
La Brasserie Townhouse
Café Delancey
Café Flo
Calzone
Cantina Venegazzú
Centuria
Chelsea Bun Diner, *SW11*
Chez Moi
Coromandel
The Curzon
Darbar
Deca
Dibbens
Dorchester, Oriental
East@West
La Finca, *N1*
Floriana
Garanger Restaurant Bar
Giá

Giardinetto
Heartstone
Hide
Interval
Isola
Mandola
Min's
Monsieur Max
Nicolas Bar à Vins, *SW10*
Nimmos's, *all branches*
Osia
Otto
Parco
Phoenicia
Poissonerie du Pecheur
Poons, *Lisle St*
Putney Bridge
La Rascasse
Retsina
The Rôtisserie
RV2
Sambuca
Scott's, *for the moment*
Seraphin
Le Shop
Shumi
Simply Nico, *all branches*
SoChina

## CLOSURES (cont'd)

La Spiga, *SW3*
Stanley's
sticklebackpink
Tandoori of Chelsea
Thai Break
Thai Canteen
Thierry's
Thyme
Vegia Zena
Zilli 2

# EATING IN LONDON — FAQs

### How should I use this guide?

This guide can be used in many ways. You will often wish to use it to answer practical queries. These tend to be geographical – where can we eat near…? To answer such questions, the Maps (pages 301-319) and Area Overviews (pages 268-300) are the place to start. The latter tell you the key facts about the dozens of restaurants in a particular area in the space of a couple of pages.

But what if you'd like to be more adventurous: seeking out new places purely for interest's sake, rather than their convenience to some other purpose? That is the main point of this brief section – to give you a handy overview of London's dining scene, and also some thoughts as to how you can use the guide to lead you to types of meals you might not otherwise have found (or perhaps even contemplated).

### How does London compare internationally?

London is not Paris, Rome or Madrid. As the capital of a country which, for at least two centuries, has had no particular reputation for its gastronomy, its attractions are rarely indigenous. By-and-large, only tourists look for 'English' restaurants.

Where London does score – and score magnificently – is in the range and quality it offers of other national styles of cooking. Always an entrepot, London is now a culinary melting pot, too: in terms of scale *and* variety, its only obvious competitor is New York.

In one area, London may claim worldwide supremacy. As a paradoxical legacy of empire, it is in the cuisine of the Indian subcontinent. For a combination of variety, quality and innovation, London's 'Indian' (including Pakistani and so on) restaurants are without peer.

### Which is London's best restaurant?

However much we may speak of melting pots and diversity, when people talk about the very best cooking, they tend – rightly or wrongly – to mean the best French cooking. In that sense, the capital's best restaurant is where you can find the capital's best Gallic cooking, and that is clearly *Gordon Ramsay* – the Chelsea flagship of the UK's leading chef. Offering French cooking a whisker behind Ramsay's, there's quite a group of low-key places which – in total contrast – never make the headlines. These comprise the *Capital*, *Pied à Terre* (assuming, post-relaunch, it lives up to its old standards), *Roussillon, Aubergine* and *1880*. Particularly for its 'all-round', if rather 'period', charms, *Le Gavroche* – London's longest-established grand French restaurant – remains of note. For Gallic fish dishes, *Restaurant One-O-One* is still the capital's top place.

Even traditions change, though, and the idea that French is Best is increasingly under attack…

**What's 'in' at the moment?**

The obvious question is: "in with whom?" The all-purpose business-to-media in-place of recent times has been the famous *Ivy*. It may now – for the first time in ten years – no longer be the survey's favourite, but it remains a hard place to book.

Sharing some of the same cachet, but easier to reserve, are siblings *J Sheekey* and *Le Caprice*. *The Wolseley* – launched by Christopher Corbin and Jeremy King who used to own all the above – was hailed on its launch a couple of years ago as the obvious competitor to the Ivy. It has certainly stolen some of the latter's celebrity custom, but has yet to become the total 'wow' which some expected.

Mayfair continues to (re-)emerge as an international in-crowd destination. If that's what you're looking for, *Cipriani* is certainly something of a 'scene'. For those in search of somewhere a little more traditional, new arrival *Bellamy's* is a discreet haven, in a quiet mews. Fresh-out-of-the-wrapper *Automat* seems to be emerging as the NyLon place of the moment.

The fashion (and sometimes Hollywood) crowd remains in thrall to Mourad Mazouz, with his properties *Momo* and *Sketch*. (Despite his efforts, though, the fine dining room at the latter has yet to be taken seriously as a foodie haunt.)

Hip, young-at-heart types, with money to burn, increasingly opt for oriental places. It was *Nobu* which set the trend, but it now has plenty of competition such as *Hakkasan, Taman gang, Roka, Yauatcha* and *Zuma*. As we go to press, *Nobu Berkeley* looks set to make more than a few waves.

For a certain class of 'Euro', and also for A-list film stars, the otherwise incomprehensible allure of Knightsbridge's *San Lorenzo* remains as immutable as ever. In Notting Hill, *The Ledbury* now offers a proper grown-up in-place to complement such younger trustafarian stand-bys as *E&O* and the *Electric*.

**I'm not fussed about fashionable scenes – where can I find a really good meal without spending the earth?**

*J Sheekey* and *Le Caprice* are not that expensive, and, if you want a bit of glamour plus a decent meal in the heart of town, are hard to beat. In Knightsbridge, *Racine* is now well-established as a top quality all-rounder.

The name Nigel Platts-Martin has become a by-word for value amongst those who know about London's restaurant-scene. *Chez Bruce,* his Wandsworth restaurant was the survey's favourite this year. *La Trompette* in Chiswick, *The Glasshouse* in Kew and, now, Notting Hill's *Ledbury* also win raves.

For sheer consistency over years, few restaurants match *Clarke's* in Kensington.

## What if I want the best of British tradition?

Because Britain is a 'pub culture', there are very few traditional restaurants of note (and fewer which can be recommended). *The Dorchester Grill* is currently the grandest of the native flag bearers (though some changes are afoot as this guide goes to press). The venerable *Rules* combines generally good cooking with charming period style. Nearby, the famous *Simpsons-in-the-Strand* has been too variable to recommend in recent years. The City preserves some extraordinary olde-worlde places such as *Sweetings* and *Simpson's Tavern*, and the famous pub *Ye Olde Cheshire Cheese*. Other ancient taverns include the *Grenadier*, the *Queen's Head*, the *Trafalgar Tavern* and the *Windsor Castle*. (For more on modern pubs see below.)

For foodies, Smithfield's *St John* continues to be an inspiration with its exploration of traditional British cooking, including lots of offal: uncompromising food in an uncompromising setting. South Bank gastropub, the *Anchor & Hope* has created a big name – it topped the survey's list of favourite pubs for the first time this year– by offering similar (but perhaps less 'threatening') fare, in a rather similar vein.

For afternoon tea, *The Wolseley* or *The Ritz* are best. Any light meal at *Fortnum's Fountain* is pleasant.

## Isn't London supposed to be a top place for curry?

London is the world's leading Indian restaurant city: the days are long gone when a pint and a curry were seen as the height of culinary adventure. At the top end, names such as *Amaya, Chutney Mary, Vama, Zaika, Tamarind, The Cinnamon Club* and *Rasoi Vineet Bhatia* are 'pushing back the frontiers'.

To eat well on a budget, the capital's inexpensive Indians offer a great deal of choice in almost all areas. Such names as *Rasa, Mirch Masala, New Tayaabs* and the *Lahore Kebab House* stand out, but the number of interesting places is large and growing – see page 263 for a comprehensive list. The very best Indian restaurants are invariably not to be found in the West End, but competent names to look out for include *Chowki, Mela* and *Veeraswamy*.

## What are gastropubs?

Many pubs have re-invented themselves as informal restaurants in recent years. *The Eagle* was the original (1991). For the top ten names, see page 11. The trend goes from strength to strength. There are now almost no affluent suburbs which lack pubs serving food of a quality that even five years ago would have been inconceivable. Outlying examples include *The Ealing Park Tavern, The Earl Spencer* and *St Johns*.

Generally the pub tradition of ordering at the bar is kept, but some of the grander establishments offer full table service and have really become restaurants in all but name.

**Can't we just grab a bowl of pasta?**

Italian cooking remains the 'default' choice for relaxed neighbourhood dining, especially in the more affluent parts of town, and there is an enormous variety of trattorias and pizzerias. In recent years, some excellent high-level Italians have emerged – see the list on page 14. At the mid-level, good Italian newcomers seem to be much more common at the moment than good French ones.

**What about these orientals we've heard so much of?**

Japanese restaurants are finally being accepted in London, as in New York, amongst the city's top dining rooms. *Umu* now has the distinction of offering London's most expensive menu, though it has failed to impress all but a few aficionados of Kyoto cuisine. *Tsunami* in Clapham offers a Japanese-fusion experience similar to that at many 'in'-places, but at a fraction of the cost.

Traditional Chinese restaurants remain a far cry from the Hakkasans and Yauatchas of the world. The very best are not in fact in or near Chinatown. *Hunan* and *Phoenix Palace* are both excellent and on the periphery of the West End. The biggest concentration of very good restaurants is in Bayswater – including *Royal China*, *Four Seasons* and *Mandarin Kitchen*.

Thai cooking is also widespread, but strongest in west London. Fulham's grand *Blue Elephant* has been amazingly consistent over the years, as has Notting Hill's *Churchill Arms* – that curious London formula of Thai-in-a-pub.

**You said diverse: what about other cuisines?**

A major hit of recent years has been the cuisines of North Africa and the Eastern Mediterranean. These cuisines lend themselves well to good budget experiences – the *Tas* chain and *Haz* are among the good, less expensive places.

See the lists on pages 14 and 15 for the top exponents of each type of cuisine by nationality.

**Any suggestions for 'something completely different'?**

How about *Archipelago*, *Champor-Champor*, *LMNT*, the *Lobster Pot*, *Les Trois Garçons*, *Sarastro* or *MVH*?

**Are there any sharp practices I should look out for?**

Yes: the 'blank credit card slip trick'. If you are presented with a credit card slip with a blank line for a gratuity, do **not** assume that a tip is appropriate. Often, 10% or (more usually) 12.5% service has already been included in the sum you are being asked to pay, but the restaurant is hoping that you will inadvertently 'double up'. With 'chip & pin' technology, there is a new variant of this ploy: you are handed the portable credit card terminal, with the option to amend the total for a tip, when service has already been included.

# DIRECTORY

Comments in "double quotation-marks" were made by reporters.

Establishments which we judge to be particularly notable have their NAME IN CAPITALS.

**A Cena TW1**  £40  ❷❷❷
418 Richmond Rd  8288 0108  1–4A
*This "professional yet informal" St Margarets Italian – with its "simple" but "extremely well-cooked" food – is one of the top places to eat around Richmond; lunch in particular is "excellent value". / 10.30 pm; closed Mon & Sun D; booking: max 6, Fri & Sat; set weekday L £25 (FP).*

**Abbaye**  £28  ④④④
102 Old Brompton Rd, SW7  7373 2403  5–2B
55 Charterhouse St, EC1  7253 1612  9–2A
*"A fair attempt at Belgian food" – this "cosy" mini-chain is praised by most reporters for dependable moules/frites (and so on), and some "wonderful" beers. / www.tragusholdings.com; 10.30 pm; no smoking area.*

**The Abbeville SW4**  £33  ❸④❷
67-69 Abbeville Rd  8675 2201  10–2D
*A "heaving" hang-out in the backstreets of Clapham, where "well-executed gastropub fare" comes "fairly priced". / www.theabbeville.co.uk; 10.30 pm; no booking.*

**Abeno WC1**  £33  ❸❷❸
47 Museum St  7405 3211  2–1C
*This "authentic" okonomi-yaki (Japanese omelette) café in Bloomsbury offers a "novel" experience that's customarily well-rated; this year saw the odd "slight disappointment", though – perhaps the strain of opening Abeno Too. / www.abeno.co.uk; 11 pm.*

**Abeno Too WC2**  NEW  £31  ❸❸④
15-18 Gt Newport St  7379 1160  4–3B
*A recent offshoot of Abeno (see also), with similar strengths and weaknesses; it's especially handily located for a Theatreland snack. / 11 pm; no smoking.*

**The Abingdon W8**  £39  ❸❷❷
54 Abingdon Rd  7937 3339  5–2A
*"Lovely" Kensington backstreet bar-cum-restaurant, offering "well-priced and sensible food"; get a booth if you can – they're "great for business or for intimate dining". / 11 pm; no smoking area; set Sun L £28 (FP).*

**Abingdon Road W8**  NEW  £40
11-13 Abingdon Rd  7937 0120  5–1A
*Scheduled for late-2005, a contemporary-style sibling to Barnes's Sonny's – a long-running modern brasserie success story – on the Kensington site formerly occupied by Phoenicia (RIP). (Price given is our guesstimate.)*

**About Thyme SW1**  £36  ⑤④④
82 Wilton Rd  7821 7504  2–4B
*"A hit-and-miss affair, and mostly a miss" – this "clinical" and "overpriced" year-old brasserie has been greeted by Pimlico locals with a chorus of boos. / www.aboutthyme.co.uk; 11 pm; no smoking area; set weekday L £23 (FP).*

### Abu Zaad W12 £16 ❷❸④

29 Uxbridge Rd 8749 5107 7–1C
*"As much a community centre for West London's Syrian population as a restaurant", this "friendly" Middle Eastern café/take-away (near Shepherd's Bush Market) serves up an "extensive" menu at "rock-bottom" prices; "a large range of juices makes up the lack of alcohol". / 11 pm; no Amex; no smoking area.*

### L'Accento Italiano W2 £38 ❸❷❸

16 Garway Rd 7243 2201 6–1B
*"A good, consistent neighbourhood place", in Bayswater, serving an "unpretentious" menu of "well-cooked" Italian fare. / 11.15 pm; closed Sun.*

### Adam Street WC2 £53 ❸❷❷

9 Adam St 7379 8000 4–4D
*"Discreet surroundings", "reliable" cooking and an "interesting" wine list make the "cosy vaults" of this "informal" members' club – open to all at lunch – a "great business venue", just off the Strand. / www.adamstreet.co.uk; L only (open for D to members only), closed Sat L & Sun.*

### Adams Café W12 £25 ❸❷❷

77 Askew Rd 8743 0572 7–1B
*"You get a lovely welcome", at the Bookraa family's homely Shepherd's Bush caff; "a greasy spoon" by day (which does a "splendid breakfast"), it goes Moroccan by moonlight, offering "tasty" tajines and couscous. / 11 pm; D only, closed Sun.*

### Addendum EC3 NEW

1 Seething Ln 7702 2020 9–3D
*Handy for Lloyds, this new City 'fine dining' restaurant is set to open in late-2005; chef Tom Ilic (late of Bonds) has quite a name for robust contemporary cooking – perhaps this will be the venue where he will really begin to shine consistently.*

### Admiral Codrington SW3 £42 ❸④❷

17 Mossop St 7581 0005 5–2C
*This "upmarket" pub has long been a "buzzy" watering hole near Brompton Cross, and offers "enjoyable" (if undemanding) cooking; the dining room's retractable roof enables "outside eating indoors". / www.admiralcodrington.co.uk; 11 pm.*

### The Admiralty
### Somerset House WC2 £54 ❸❸④

Strand 7845 4646 2–2D
*Feedback on this moderately-sized chamber in London's grandest palazzo remains mixed, and even some reporters who proclaim it a "jewel" admit that it can feel "a little arid"; Daniel Groom's cooking is "accomplished", but it can also seem "expensive for what it is". / 10.15 pm; closed Sun D; no smoking area.*

### Afghan Kitchen N1 £19 ❸⑤④

35 Islington Grn 7359 8019 8–3D
*Thanks to the "delicious" cooking – albeit from a "limited menu" – it's always "hard to get a table" at this tiny canteen by Islington Green; it's "cramped", though, and staff "could be friendlier". / 11 pm; closed Mon & Sun; no credit cards.*

**Aglio e Olio SW10**   £28   ❶❷❸
194 Fulham Rd   7351 0070   5–3B
It may be "very noisy" and "canteen"-like, but this Chelsea
trattoria has won many fans with its "reliable" and "down-to-
earth" charms; the menu – with "fabulous" pasta a highlight –
is "reasonably-priced", too. / 11.30 pm.

**Al Bustan SW7**   £38   ❸❸④
68 Old Brompton Rd   7584 5805   5–2B
An "enjoyable Lebanese," in the heart of South Kensington,
with "polite" service and "reasonable" prices; it has a surprisingly
small following among reporters, perhaps because it's
so "cramped". / 10.30 pm; set weekday L £21 (FP).

**Al Duca SW1**   £38   ❸❸④
4-5 Duke of York St   7839 3090   3–3D
"Sound" cooking and a "useful" St James's location help make
this "chic"-looking modern Italian "a handy place to know about";
even so, there's a feeling it "lacks something", especially on the
atmosphere front. / www.alduca-restaurant.co.uk; 11 pm; closed Sun.

**Al Forno SW19**   £28   ❸❷❷
2a King's Rd   8540 5710   10–2B
"Jokey" staff and a "loud" atmosphere set the scene at this old-
fashioned Italian, in Wimbledon Town; the pizzas are "huge" and
not expensive. / 11.30 pm.

**Al Hamra W1**   £45   ❸④④
31-33 Shepherd Mkt   7493 1954   3–4B
This long-established (somewhat "outdated"-looking) Mayfair
Lebanese has some of the best alfresco tables in town (adjacent
to Shepherd Market); prices can seem "surprising", but the
cooking is very "authentic". / www.alhamrarestaurant.com; 11.30 pm.

**Al San Vincenzo W2**   £45   ❷❷❸
30 Connaught St   7262 9623   6–1D
"Now back on form", the Borgonzolo family's tiny Bayswater
establishment offers "a good choice of real Italian specialities",
in a "quiet", "comfortable" and "friendly" setting. / 9.30 pm; closed
Sat L & Sun; no Amex; no smoking.

**Al Sultan W1**   £36   ❸④④
51-52 Hertford St   7408 1155   3–4B
This "professional" and "traditional" Lebanese, near Shepherd
Market, is often compared with the nearby Al Hamra – similarly,
its cuisine is "very good, if not cheap". / www.alsultan.co.uk; 11 pm.

**Al-Waha W2**   £32   ④❸④
75 Westbourne Grove   7229 0806   6–1B
A Bayswater Lebanese, praised for a "genuine" selection of "high-
quality" fare; it once had something of a name locally, in the light
of which it can seem "nothing special" nowadays. / 11.30 pm;
no Amex or Maestro.

**Alastair Little W1**  £62  ❸❸⑤

49 Frith St  7734 5183  4–2A

*"Clean-flavoured" cuisine ("which respects the raw materials")
still wins fans for this seminal Soho spot, who say its "simple"
setting has "a charm of its own"; its appeal eludes doubters,
though, who find "passable" food served at "silly" prices in an
"atmosphere-free" zone.* / 11.30 pm; closed Sat L & Sun.

**Alba EC1**  £39  ❸❷④

107 Whitecross St  7588 1798  9–1B

*A "hidden gem", in the backstreets near the Barbican,
this "authentic" Italian offers "inventive" Piemontese cooking and
a "huge array of wines"; the atmosphere, however, tends to be
of the 'make-your-own' variety.* / 11 pm; closed Sat & Sun.

**Albannach WC2**  NEW  £43  ❸④④

66 Trafalgar Sq  7930 0066  2–2C

*Some "well-crafted" dishes suggest this ambitious modern
Scottish newcomer (with "waiters in kilts" the only overt theming)
could be "really good"; sometimes "amateur" service undercuts
its appeal, though, and the "noisy" downstairs bar is an
unwelcome distraction.* / www.albannach.co.uk; 10 pm; no smoking.

**Ali Baba NW1**  £20  ❷❷⑤

32 Ivor Pl  7723 5805  2–1A

*"You feel like you have been welcomed into an Egyptian family",
when you visit this BYO Marylebone dining room, which offers
"very good" food.* / 11.30 pm; no credit cards.

**All Bar One**  £27  ④④❸

Branches throughout London

*This ubiquitous modern wine bar chain offers a "lively,
if predictable" setting for food that's "fine, if you're out drinking"
(and also "not bad for brunch").* / 10 pm; most City branches closed all
or part of weekend; no smoking area; no booking.

**Alloro W1**  £46  ❷❷❷

19-20 Dover St  7495 4768  3–3C

*"Fantastic Italian cooking", "warm service", and "just the right
balance of formality and glamour" are ingredients which win very
consistent praise for this Mayfair all-rounder.* / 10.30 pm; closed
Sat L & Sun.

**Alma SW18**  £28  ❸④❷

499 Old York Rd  8870 2537  10–2B

*This "lovely" Wandsworth pub serves a "hearty" and "reliable"
menu in its "relaxed" dining annex; rugby days, however, can be
a scrum.* / www.thealma.co.uk; 10.30 pm.

**The Almeida N1**  £47  ❸❷❸

30 Almeida St  7354 4777  8–2D

*"Devoid of the usual Conran condescension", this "comfortable"
Islington venture dispenses "enjoyable" Gallic fare
(from "an abundance of retro trolleys"); it is "not cheap", though,
and critics find it "uninspired".* / www.almeida-restaurant.co.uk; 11 pm;
no smoking area; set weekday L & pre-theatre £33 (FP).

**sign up for the survey at www.hardens.com**

### Alounak W14 £23 ❸④④
10 Russell Gdns 7603 1130 7–1D
*For a "simple, good and cheap" meal, this BYO Olympia-fringe Persian café offers the "best kebabs"; the Bayswater branch is no more.* / 11.30 pm; no Amex.

### Amano Café SE1 £26 ❷❸❷
Victor Wharf, Clink St 7234 0000 9–3C
*A "busy" café, near Borough Market, well worth knowing about for its "great coffee", and "healthy" wraps and sandwiches.* / www.amanocafe.com; 10.30 pm; no smoking; no booking.

### Amaranth SW18 £22 ❶❶❷
346 Garratt Ln 8871 3466 10–2B
*"Absolutely wonderful" Thai food – and at "bargain prices" – wins local adulation for this BYO Wandsworth spot; it has recently added a take-away, and a shop.* / 10.30 pm; D only, closed Sun; no Amex; no smoking area.

### Amato W1 £20 ❸❷❸
14 Old Compton St 7734 5733 4–2A
*"Always consistent, for breakfast or brunch" – this large but sometimes "overlooked" Soho pâtisserie serves "delicious" cakes and "great" coffee.* / www.amato.co.uk; 9.45 pm; no booking.

### Amaya SW1 £50 ❶❸❷
Halkin Arc, 19 Motcomb St 7823 1166 5–1D
*This "exciting" new Belgravia Indian (from the Chutney Mary team) is "one of the year's top openings", offering a "novel" grazing concept that has gone down very well with reporters; service, though, can be "patchy".* / www.realindianfood.com; 11 pm; smoking in bar only; set weekday L £32 (FP).

### Anarkali W6 £28 ❸❸④
303-305 King St 8748 6911 7–2B
*"They try hard", at this "friendly" Hammersmith Indian of three decades' standing; its menu includes the odd "quite original" dish.* / 11.30 pm; no smoking area.

### The Anchor & Hope SE1 £30 ❷❸❸
36 The Cut 7928 9898 9–4A
*"Inventive, original and reasonably-priced" English dishes – in a "hearty" style reminiscent of St John – have made a huge name for this "most sociable of gastropubs", near the Old Vic; "if only you could book…"* / 10.30 pm; closed Mon L & Sun; no Amex; no smoking; no booking.

### ANDREW EDMUNDS W1 £30 ❷❶❶
46 Lexington St 7437 5708 3–2D
*"Cramped and uncomfy", it may be, but this candlelit Soho townhouse has a "special" vibe and remains wildly popular, not least for a "perfect date" – "lovely" staff serve up "homely" food and a "real gem" of a wine list at admirably "sensible" prices; sit on the ground floor if you can.* / 10.30 pm; no Amex; booking: max 6.

### The Anglesea Arms W6 £32 ❶④❷
35 Wingate Rd 8749 1291 7–1B
The "startlingly good" cooking at this "cramped" fixture near
Ravenscourt Park "never disappoints" – for many reporters,
this remains "London's best gastropub"; "you can't book", though,
and service (while "improved") is still "slow". / 10.15 pm; no Amex;
no booking; set weekday L £22 (FP).

### The Anglesea Arms SW7 £35 ④❸❸
15 Sellwood Ter 7373 7960 5–2B
"Buzzing", traditional boozer, leafily located in South Kensington,
whose "cool" terrace has long been a magnet locally;
"top bangers and mash" typifies the not-so-haute menu
aspirations. / 10 pm; no Amex; no smoking area.

### Anglo Asian Tandoori N16 £23 ❷❶❷
60-62 Stoke Newington Church St 7254 3633 1–1C
"Welcoming, unassuming and great value" – this Stoke
Newington curry house is "as consistent as ever"; well, not quite
– "they no longer give flowers to the ladies". / www.angloasian.co.uk;
11.30 pm; no smoking area.

### Annie's £33 ④❶❶
162 Thames Rd, W4 8994 9080 1–3A
36-38 White Hart Ln, SW13 8878 2020 10–1A
"Beautiful decoration that's both cosy and sumptuous" –
plus "extremely welcoming" staff – helps create a "relaxing" vibe
at these west London "gems"; "wonderful brunch" is a highlight
of the "hearty" (and sometimes heavy-handed) cooking. / 10 pm,
Thu-Sat 10.30 pm.

### Antipasto & Pasta SW11 £28 ❸④❸
511 Battersea Park Rd 7223 9765 10–1C
"On half-price nights (Mon, Thu, Sat & Sun), you can't really
go wrong", at this "unchanging" Battersea Italian. / 11.30 pm;
need 4+ to book.

### Antipasto e Pasta SW4 £31 ❸❶❸
31 Abbeville Rd 8675 6260 10–2D
"Cheerful" and "incredibly hospitable", this Clapham trattoria
is praised for its "solid" and "dependable" fare. / 11.30 pm.

### Aperitivo W1 £30 ❸❸❸
41 Beak St 7287 2057 3–2D
A "reliable Soho option", offering "delicious, good-value Italian
tapas" in "slightly cramped" surroundings; the Camden Town
branch is no more. / www.aperitivo-restaurants.com; 11 pm; closed Sun;
no smoking area.

### Apium EC1 £23 ④④④
50-52 Long Ln 7796 4040 9–1B
A "cheap" oriental canteen, that makes a useful-enough pit stop,
near Bart's. / www.apium.co.uk; 10.30 pm; closed Sun; no Amex;
no smoking.

**Apostrophe** £12 ❷❷❸

23 Barrett St, W1   7355 1001   3–1B
20/20 Opt' Store, Tottenham Ct Rd, W1   7436 6688   2–1C
215 Strand, WC2   7427 9890   4–2D
42 Gt Eastern St, EC2   7739 8412   9–1D
3-5 St Bride St, EC4   7353 3704   9–2A

*"Putting Starbucks and Co. to shame", these "funky" coffee shop/pâtisseries are a "real step up from the norm", and are particularly notable for the "tastiest" sandwiches and "excellent" pastries.* / www.apostropheuk.com; L & afternoon tea only, Barrett St 8pm; no smoking; no booking.

**Aquarium E1** £43 ④④④

Ivory Hs, St Katharine-by-the-Tower   7480 6116   11–1A

*The new régime at this "beautifully-located" seafood-specialist (by a dock near Tower Bridge) utterly divides opinion; fans still hail its "top-quality fresh fish", but doubters say the place "would be a joke… if it weren't so expensive".* / www.theaquarium.co.uk; 9.45 pm; closed Sat L; no smoking area.

**Aquasia
Conrad International SW10** £58 ④④④

Chelsea Harbour   7823 3000   5–4B

*"You might be on the Côte d'Azur", if you nab a sunny-day terrace-table at this distant-Chelsea marina-side hotel; the cooking "could do better", though, and the ambience in the dining room itself can be "dead".* / www.conradhotels.com; 10.30 pm; no smoking area.

**Arancia SE16** £25 ❷❷❷

52 Southwark Park Rd   7394 1751   11–2A

*"Very fairly-priced, traditional, rustic Italian food" is just part of the formula that makes this "hidden jewel" – a "front room type place" set "in the middle of nowhere" – a continuing , Bermondsey success story.* / www.arancia-london.co.uk; 11 pm; closed Mon & Sun.

**Archduke Wine Bar SE1** £34 ⑤④❸

Concert Hall Approach, South Bank   7928 9370   2–3D

*This long-established wine bar has an intriguing railway arch location, and it's "useful for a snack", for those visiting South Bank cultural attractions; the food, however, is "not reliably good".* / 11 pm; closed Sat L & Sun; no smoking area.

**The Arches NW6** £34 ④❷❷

7 Fairhazel Gdns   7624 1867   8–2A

*"First-class wines" (including "fantastic bin-ends" at "very low mark-ups") and a "great welcome" make this Swiss Cottage wine bar a popular and convivial stand-by; the "OK" food is rather beside the point.* / 10.30 pm; no Amex; set weekday L £19 (FP).

**Archipelago W1** £49 ❸❶❶

110 Whitfield St   7383 3346   2–1B

*It's not just the "bric-à-brac shop-meets-witch-doctor's hut" décor which makes a visit to this Fitzrovia spot a "total one-off" – the menu is also "bizarre" (locusts, peacock and so on), but "it works" (and at least "you're never short of conversation on a date").* / 10.30 pm; closed Sat L & Sun; no smoking area.

## The Ark W8 £42 ④④④
122 Palace Gardens Ter   7229 4024   6–2B
*The latest incarnation of this Notting Hill Gate survivor divides opinion – to critics, it seems a "flat" place with "disappointing" Italian cuisine, whereas fans say it serves "light" modern dishes in a "cool" and "cosy" setting.* / www.thearkrestaurant.co.uk; 11 pm; closed Mon L & Sun.

## Arkansas Café E1 £23 ❸❸❸
107b Commercial St   7377 6999   9–1D
*"Great burgers, grilled by Bubba the chef, in the hustling setting of Spitalfields Market" have made this "authentic" American BBQ joint something of a local institution.* / L only, closed Sat; no Amex; no smoking area.

## Armadillo E8 £34 ❷❶❷
41 Broadway Mkt   7249 3633   1–2D
*"Not just great food, but great food the likes of which you've never tasted before" – this "genuine" and "unique" Hackney South American offers an experience which satisfies almost all reporters.* / www.armadillorestaurant.co.uk; 10.30 pm; closed Mon.

## Artigiano NW3 £43 ④❸❸
12a Belsize Ter   7794 4288   8–2A
*A "pleasant enough" modern Italian, in Belsize Park; the "pricey" food is only "OK", though, and service "goes wobbly at times of stress".* / www.etruscarestaurants.com; 11 pm; closed Mon L.

## L'Artista NW11 £25 ④❷❷
917 Finchley Rd   8731 7501   1–1B
*Near Golder's Green station, this "always-manic", "neighbourhood" veteran serves "OK" pizza and pasta at "very reasonable" prices.* / 11.30 pm; no smoking area.

## L'Artiste Musclé W1 £31 ④④④
1 Shepherd Mkt   7493 6150   3–4B
*This cramped Shepherd Market bistro is known for its "ooh la la" Frenchness, and its "simple", "cheap and cheerful" nosh – it continues to misfire from time to time.* / 10.30 pm.

## Arturo W2 NEW £40 ❷❷❸
23 Connaught St   7706 3388   6–1D
*"Very good" Italian cooking is making this small, smart Bayswater newcomer quite a hit locally; its set lunch menu is particularly worth seeking out.* / www.arturorestaurant.co.uk; 10.30 pm; no smoking area.

## As Greek As It Gets SW5 NEW £20 ❶④⑤
233 Earl's Court Rd   7244 7777   5–2A
*The menu is "limited, and difficult to navigate", but "the food is great", at this Earl's Court chain-prototype (from the man who brought you Shish); the premises, however, afflicted by traffic noise, signally lack charm.* / www.asgreekasitgets.com; 11.30 pm; no smoking area.

### Asia de Cuba
**St Martin's Lane WC2**       £72       ④④❸
45 St Martin's Ln   7300 5500   4–4C
"Fantastic" fusion cooking is sometimes found at this "futuristic"
Covent Garden design-hotel dining room – it's a shame that
"ludicrous" prices and "distinctly average" service too often take
the edge off the experience. / www.asiadecuba-restaurant.com; midnight,
Sat 1 am; no smoking area; set pre-theatre £51 (FP).

### Ask! Pizza       £25       ④❸❸
Branches throughout London
The "dependable" charms of this "bright and cheerful" pizza
chain make it "a contender for the PizzaExpress crown";
foodwise, though, its rival – now under the same ownership – re-
opened a clear lead this year. / www.askcentral.co.uk; 11 pm;
some branches have smoking restrictions; some booking restrictions apply.

### Assaggi W2       £53       ❶❶❸
39 Chepstow Pl   7792 5501   6–1B
"Simple dishes from supreme ingredients", served by "passionate
and attentive" staff, make this "stripped-down" and "ordinary"-
looking Bayswater dining room – over a pub – once again the
survey's "best Italian"; it can be "ludicrously hard to get a table".
/ 11 pm; closed Sun; no Amex.

### Les Associés N8       £33       ❸❷❸
172 Park Rd   8348 8944   1–1C
A reputation for "always-reliable" cooking in a "charming" setting
has long preceded this "front room-style" Gallic hide-away,
in Crouch End; this year, however, quite a few reporters noted
"unlucky" experiences. / 11 pm; Tue–Sat D only, closed Mon & Sun D;
no smoking area.

### Atlantic Bar & Grill W1       £52       ⑤⑤④
20 Glasshouse St   7734 4888   3–3D
"A definite no-no" – this potentially "lovely" Art Deco
bar/restaurant is slated by all and sundry for its "indifferent"
cooking, its "surly" service and its "silly" prices.
/ www.atlanticbarandgrill.com; midnight; D only.

### The Atlas SW6       £29       ❷❸❷
16 Seagrave Rd   7385 9129   5–3A
"Good" (sometimes "outstanding") Mediterranean grub, in "large
portions", has won a big fan club for this "hard-to-find" boozer,
near Earl's Court II; it can get "horribly noisy".
/ www.theatlaspub.co.uk; 11 pm; no Amex; no booking.

### Atrium SW1       £40       ⑤⑤④
4 Millbank   7233 0032   2–4C
The restaurant in the lobby of Parliament's media centre
is included primarily for completeness – a thoroughly mediocre
place, its only interest is its proximity to the levers of power.
/ www.atrium.com; 9.30 pm; no smoking.

**Aubaine SW3** £40 ④⑤❷

260-262a Brompton Rd   7052 0100   5–2C
*"Go for the excellent cakes and coffee"*, but *"avoid"* the
sometimes *"terrible"* main meals at this *"posey lunch and brunch
place"*, near Brompton Cross; it suffers from service that's
*"beyond haphazard"*. / www.aubaine.co.uk; 10.30 pm; no smoking.

**Auberge** £32 ⑤⑤④

6-8 St Christopher's Pl, W1   7486 5557   3–1B
1 Sandell St, SE1   7633 0610   9–4A
31 Tooley St, SE1   7407 5267   9–4C
56 Mark Ln, EC3   7480 6789   9–3D
*Moules/frites is the basic 'offer' of this small chain; to fans it's
"an acceptable stand-by" – to doubters, so "deeply uninspired"
as to have "no redeeming features".* / 10.30 pm; Sandell St closed
Sun & EC3 closed weekends; no smoking area, SE1 branches.

**AUBERGINE SW10** £90 ❶❷❸

11 Park Wk   7352 3449   5–3B
*"Exquisite"* cooking (by William Drabble), *"outstanding"* service
and *"a refreshing lack of pretension"* feature in many reports
on this *"discreet"* Chelsea *"haven"*; it's hardly inexpensive,
of course, and the atmosphere can sometimes seem rather
*"hushed"*. / 11 pm; closed Sat L & Sun; set weekday L £38 (FP).

**Aurora W1** £38 ❸❸❶

49 Lexington St   7494 0514   3–2D
A *"romantic"*, *"cosy"* (*"cramped"*) Soho bistro, which *"feels like
a secret hide-away"*; the food and service are *"good, but nothing
to shout about"*. / 10.30 pm; closed Sun; no Amex.

**Aurora**
**Great Eastern Hotel EC2** £61 ❷❷❸

40 Liverpool St   7618 7000   9–2D
Chef Allan Pickett has seriously bucked-up the cooking
at Conran's *"spacious"* and *"impressive"* (*"if rather cold"*) City
dining room; some reporters still find it *"horrendously overpriced"*,
but perhaps that's just part of being a *"power scene"*.
/ www.great-eastern-hotel.co.uk; 10 pm; closed Sat & Sun; booking: max 8.

**Automat W1** [NEW] £38 ❸❸❷

33 Dover St   7499 3033   3–3C
There is nothing especially high-tech about this straightforward
new American brasserie in Mayfair, but it had already established
a strong local following on our early visit (June 2005); it looks
nondescript from the street, but the interior is striking,
and surprisingly spacious. / Rated on Editors' visit; 1 am; no smoking area.

**L'Aventure NW8** £49 ❸❸❷

3 Blenheim Ter   7624 6232   8–3A
*"You could be in France"* (*"apart from the prices"*, of course),
at this *"enchanting"* St John's Wood fixture (whose *"ultra-
romantic"* terrace is a particular summer attraction); this year's
reports, however, were more mixed than usual. / 11 pm; closed
Sat L & Sun; set weekday L £30 (FP).

### The Avenue SW1 £47 ④④④
7-9 St James's St   7321 2111   3–4D
*"Hard to fault, but hard to love" – this "cavernous" and rather "corporate" spot is hailed by reporters as "a great place for a business lunch"; by St James's standards, it's quite "reasonably priced", too.* / www.egami.co.uk; midnight, Fri & Sat 12.30 am, Sun 10 pm; closed Sat L.

### The Aviary SW20 NEW £34 ❸❷❸
193 Worple Rd   8947 2212   10–2A
*"At last, a good Raynes Park local", serving "surprisingly good" cooking in an agreeable, "modern" setting.* / www.the-aviary.co.uk; 10.30 pm; closed Mon; no Amex; no smoking; set weekday L £22 (FP).

### Awana SW3 NEW £40
85 Sloane Ave   awaiting tel   5–2C
*Scheduled to open in late-2005, this Knightsbridge newcomer promises 'authentic Malaysian cuisine done in a modern way'; if it's anything like the Mango Tree (same owner), expect a slick and professional operation, with styling that feels a little 'corporate'.*

### Axis WC2 £45 ❸❷④
1 Aldwych   7300 0300   2–2D
*"Spacious" tables, "high standards" of service, and "quality" cooking make this "sleek" Covent Garden basement "a business favourite" (and it's also useful pre-theatre); if its Vorticist décor were not "far too cold", it might enjoy an even wider following.* / www.onealdwych.com; 10.45 pm, Sat 11.30 pm; closed Sat L & Sun.

### Aziz SW6 £39 ❸❷❶
24-32 Vanston Pl   7386 0086   5–4A
*Since last year's revamp, the pros and cons at this "hidden gem", near Fulham Broadway, have swapped about – "good service and décor" now help create a "great evening ambience", but the modern Middle Eastern-inspired cooking is "no longer especially exciting".* / 11 pm.

### Azou W6 £28 ❸❷❸
375 King St   8563 7266   7–2B
*"Lovely couscous" is a highlight of the "competent" fare that's served at this notably welcoming Hammersmith North African.* / 11 pm; no Amex.

### Babes 'n' Burgers W11 NEW £22 ❸⑤④
275 Portobello Rd   7727 4163   6–1A
*"Great with kids in tow", this rather "home-made" Notting Hill newcomer – almost under the Westway – offers "cheap" organic burgers (and juices and so on), plus a play room at the back; shame the service can be so "crummy".* / 11 pm, Sun 8 pm; no Amex; no smoking; no booking, Sat L & Sun L.

### Babur Brasserie SE23 £30 ❷❶❷
119 Brockley Rise   8291 2400   1–4D
*"Special themes add interest" to the menu at this "bustly" Brockley Indian whose "very welcoming" staff and "excellent" cooking have made it a "south east London favourite"; the restaurant re-opens after a three-month revamp in late-2005.* / www.babur-brasserie.com; 11.15 pm; closed Fri L; no smoking area.

### Babylon
### Kensington Roof Gardens W8 £56 ④④❷
99 Kensington High St 7368 3993 5–1A
"You pay for the view" – and your stroll through the "wonderful", "romantic" rooftop gardens – when you visit Richard Branson's "fantastically-situated", ninth-floor Kensington venture; the food is "unimpressive", though, and service is "not great" either.
/ www.roofgardens.com; 11 pm; closed Sun D; no smoking in dining room; set weekday L £31 (FP).

### Back to Basics W1 £40 ❶❷④
21a Foley St 7436 2181 2–1B
"Just fabulous fresh fish" – that's the formula that wins rave reviews for this "noisy and cramped" Fitzrovia "treasure"; "booking is a must" (ideally for an early table, as "the food goes very quickly") – for a "perfect summer lunch, sit outside".
/ www.backtobasics.uk.com; 10.30 pm; closed Sun.

### Baker & Spice £35 ❸⑤④
54-56 Elizabeth St, SW1 7730 3033 2–4A
47 Denyer St, SW3 7589 4734 5–2D
75 Salusbury Rd, NW6 7604 3636 1–2B
"Mouth-watering displays" of pastries, sandwiches and light dishes make it "impossible to choose what to eat", at these "Eurotrash/rich kids'" cafés; you may have to slum it, though, at a "fun communal table", and prices are "daylight robbery".
/ www.bakerandspice.com; 7 pm, Sun 5 pm; SW1 closed Sun; no Amex; SW1 no smoking; no bookings.

### Balans £34 ⑤❸❸
34 Old Compton St, W1 7439 3309 4–2A **NEW**
60 Old Compton St, W1 7439 2183 4–3A
239 Old Brompton Rd, SW5 7244 8838 5–3A
214 Chiswick High Rd, W4 8742 1435 7–2A **NEW**
187 Kensington High St, W8 7376 0115 5–1A
Though avowedly "gay-friendly", these "camp and energetic" diners have become institutions of universal appeal – especially for brunch; the cooking, however, is "very uneven" nowadays.
/ www.balans.co.uk; varies from midnight to 24 hours; no smoking area; some booking restrictions apply.

### Balham Kitchen & Bar SW12 £39 ④④❷
15-19 Bedford Hill 8675 6900 10–2C
Locals say Nick 'Soho House' Jones's "brilliant and buzzy" hang-out is "a great boost for SW12", and a particularly handy option for a "trendy" brunch; the occasional critic, though, gripes of lacklustre service and of "overpriced and average" food.
/ www.balhamkitchen.com; 11 pm; no smoking area.

### Baltic SE1 £38 ❸❸❷
74 Blackfriars Rd 7928 1111 9–4A
A "groovy, cavernous and moodily-lit" setting, "unexpectedly tasty food" and "a vast range of fantastic vodka cocktails" have made this unlikely Polish bar/restaurant Borough's coolest destination; it can get "very noisy". / www.balticrestaurant.co.uk; 11 pm; set weekday L & pre-theatre £24 (FP).

**Bam-Bou W1**  £41  ❷❸❶

1 Percy St  7323 9130  2–1C
*"Dark and mysterious" décor helps lend a "beautiful and
romantic" air to this "confusingly rambling" Fitzrovia townhouse,
which serves "delicately-flavoured" Vietnamese cuisine; there are
also "great cocktails" in the "evocative" bar.* / www.bam-bou.co.uk;
11 pm; closed Sat L & Sun; booking: max 8.

**The Banana Leaf Canteen SW11**  £26  ❸❸❸

75-79 Battersea Rise  7228 2828  10–2C
*"The queues speak for themselves", at this "consistent" and
"reasonably-priced" Thai canteen, in Battersea.* / 11 pm; no smoking
area; need 6+ to book.

**Bangkok SW7**  £31  ❷❷⑤

9 Bute St  7584 8529  5–2B
*"Good food, terrible décor" – that's the formula which has long
sustained the UK's oldest Thai, near South Kensington tube.*
/ 10.45 pm; closed Sun; no Amex.

**Bank Aldwych WC2**  £49  ④④④

1 Kingsway  7379 9797  2–2D
*This "cavernous" and "noisy" '90s-mega-brasserie "lacks sparkle,
but is still OK"; its business-friendly location ensures it's often
"full of suits", and it's also handy for breakfast, brunch and pre-
theatre.* / www.bankrestaurants.com; 11 pm; closed Sun; set weekday L &
pre-theatre £29 (FP).

**Bank Westminster
St James Court Hotel SW1**  £46  ④❸❸

45 Buckingham Gate  7379 9797  2–4B
*"Unexciting but blameless", this large brasserie is "one of the few
good options in the area" (near Victoria Street), especially for
business.* / www.bankrestaurants.com; 10.30 pm; closed Sat & Sun;
set weekday L £28 (FP), set D £31 (FP).

**Bankside**  £29  ④❸❸

32 Southwark Bridge Rd, SE1  7633 0011  9–4B
1 Angel Ct, EC2  0845 226 0011  9–2C  **NEW**
*"A good South Bank stand-by", this basement near Tate Modern
offers a "varied-enough" menu at competitive prices; there's now
a City branch, too.* / www.banksiderestaurants.co.uk; SE1 10.30 pm,
EC2 10 pm; SE1 closed Sat L & Sun, EC2 closed Sat & Sun; no smoking area.

**Banners N8**  £30  ❸❷❶

21 Park Rd  8348 2930  1–1C
*"Book in advance for weekend breakfast", which is the star turn
at this "funky" and "chaotic" Crouch End phenomenon; the said
meal comprises "a massive range of dishes, from Continental
to American, cooked to perfection".* / 11.30 pm; no Amex.

**The Bar & Grill EC1**  **NEW**  £42  ❸❸④

2-3 West Smithfield  0870 4422 541  9–2A
*This Farringdon newcomer (from the people who run the national
'Living Room' chain) feels "a bit too posh" for its burgers 'n'
steaks formula; despite "good" culinary standards, it has yet
to gather much of a following among reporters.*
/ www.barandgrill.co.uk; 11.15 pm; closed Sun.

**Bar Bourse EC4** £45 ④④④

67 Queen St 7248 2200 9–3C

*A "small but friendly" basement, near Mansion House; it's rated by a few reporters as a "good City lunching rendezvous" (even if "the service always seems to tail off during the meal"). / L only, closed Sat & Sun.*

**Bar Capitale** £31 ❷❷④

The Concourse, 1 Poultry, EC2 7248 3117 9–2C
Bucklersbury Hs, 14 Walbrook, EC4 7236 2030 9–3C

*"Modestly-priced but tasty pizzas" make these "very buzzy" diners useful City stand-bys (in the evening, as well as for lunch). / www.mithrasbars.co.uk; 9 pm; closed Sat & Sun; EC2 no smoking area.*

**Bar du Musee SE10** £40 ⑤④❷

17 Nelson Rd 8858 4710 1–3D

*This impressively laid out Greenwich bar/restaurant "looks so nice" – especially the "great garden" – that it's a shame it "always seems to get something wrong"; the cooking is "all style over substance", and often "badly served". / www.greenwich-inc.com; 10 pm; no Amex.*

**Bar Estrela SW8** £20 ❸④❷

111-115 South Lambeth Rd 7793 1051 10–1D

*This "authentic and good-value" café remains a linchpin of Vauxhall's 'Little Portugal'; dining at the roadside tables "can be very enjoyable", too ("but don't expect to rush"). / 11 pm; no smoking area.*

**Bar Italia W1** £12 ④❷❶

22 Frith St 7437 4520 4–2A

*"Amazing coffee at all hours" fuels "the late-night buzz", at this "entertaining" Soho institution; "when Italian footie is on the box, to call the atmosphere 'dramatic' would be an understatement..." / open 24 hours, Sun 3 am; no booking.*

**Bar Mezé** £28 ❷❸④

462 Muswell Hill Broadway, N10 8442 2661 8–1C
64 Northcote Rd, SW11 7228 5010 10–2C

*"Good-quality, simple food" is the attraction of this self-explanatory Cypriot mini-chain, which attracts only upbeat reports. / www.barmeze.com; N10 11 pm, SW11 10.30 pm; no smoking area.*

**Barcelona Tapas** £26 ④❸❸

481 Lordship Ln, SE22 8693 5111 1–4D
1a Bell Ln, E1 7247 7014 9–2D
1 Beaufort Hs, St Botolph St, EC3 7377 5111 9–2D
24 Lime St, EC3 7929 2389 9–2D **NEW**
13 Well Ct, EC4 7329 5111 9–2B

*"There's always a great ambience and a friendly welcome", at these "reliable tapas stand-bys" – in "the hidden backstreets of the City", and also in leafy Dulwich. / 10.30 pm; City branches closed Sat & Sun.*

**The Barnsbury N1**  £34  ❸❸❷
209-211 Liverpool Rd  7607 5519  8–2D
"Lovely" and "relaxed" Islington gastropub, which offers a "great choice" of "well-cooked" dishes. / www.thebarnsbury.co.uk; 10 pm; no smoking area.

**Base**  £36  ❸❸④
61 Beauchamp Pl, SW3  7584 2777  5–1C  NEW
195 Baker St, NW1  7486 7000  2–1A
71 Hampstead High St, NW3  7431 2224  8–2A
"Anything from a casual snack to a full-on dining experience" is well catered for at this "bright", modern "bistro-style" outfit in Hampstead; the newer Marylebone and Knightsbridge branches have yet to attract commentary. / www.basefoods.com; 10.45 pm, SW3 7 pm; NW1 closed Sun; NW3 closed Mon D; no smoking area.

**Basilico**  £28  ❸④④
690 Fulham Rd, SW6  0800 028 3531  10–1B
26 Penton St, N1  0800 093 4224  8–3D  NEW
515 Finchley Rd, NW3  0800 316 2656  1–1B
175 Lavender Hill, SW11  0800 389 9770  10–2C
178 Upper Richmond Rd, SW14  0800 096 8202  10–2B
Thin-crust pizza "like no other" has long sustained the lofty reputation of this pizza delivery chain; ratings were down a bit this year though. / www.basilico.co.uk; 11pm; no Amex; no smoking; no booking.

**Bastille N1**  NEW  £32  ❸④❸
100 St Paul's Rd  7704 2345  1–1C
The former Canonbury site of Centuria (RIP) has now been relaunched in a somewhat unusual, Gallic-gastropub format; an early reporter praises its "decent, fairly-priced grub" and "relaxed" style. / 10.30 pm; closed weekday L.

**Beach Blanket Babylon W11**  £44  ⑤⑤❶
45 Ledbury Rd  7229 2907  6–1B
"Any lover will be impressed", by the "amazing" Gothic interior of this "lovely" Notting Hill bar/restaurant; it's a notably "complacent" operation, though, serving "average and very expensive" food in its "dark candlelit cellar".
/ www.beachblanketbabylon.uk.com; midnight; no Amex.

**Beauberry House**  NEW
**Belair Park SE21**  £45
Gallery Rd, Dulwich Village  8299 9788  1–4C
This Grade I Georgian house (formerly Belair House, RIP) is scheduled to relaunch in late-2005; the introduction of a 'Japanese fusion' menu should certainly cause quite a stir, near Dulwich Park – the cooking will have to 'fight', though, if it's to measure up to the architectural distinction of the building!
/ 10.30 pm; closed Sun D.

**Beaufort House SW3** NEW £33 ④❷❷

354 King's Rd 7352 2828 5–3C

*A handy location and windows that open to the street help make this pretty corner newcomer an ideal refuge for Chelsea cruisers; the food – heavy on "brunch treats" (and salads) – is rather incidental, though, and by night the place is mainly a bar.* / L only, bar menu available at D; no smoking.

**Bedlington Café W4** £21 ❸④④

24 Fauconberg Rd 8994 1965 7–2A

*After a brief flirtation with the name 'Thai Valley', this once-celebrated greasy spoon in Chiswick is back to its old title – the virtues of its 'moonlight' guise as a "cheap and cheerful" BYO Thai canteen remain pretty much unchanged.* / 10 pm; closed Sun L; no credit cards; no smoking.

**Beirut Express W2** £22 ❶④④

112-114 Edgware Rd 7724 2700 6–1D

*"Great shwarmas", "the best falafel wraps" and "awesome fresh juices" help make this "fab little Lebanese" a top "cheap and cheerful" choice.* / www.maroush.com; 1 am; no credit cards.

**Beiteddine SW1** £38 ❸❷④

8 Harriet St 7235 3969 5–1D

*A 'flat' ambience holds back this long-established Lebanese, which – for somewhere just off Sloane Street – languishes in curious obscurity; fans say its "classic" dishes can be "heavenly".* / midnight.

**Belgo** £30 ④④❸

50 Earlham St, WC2 7813 2233 4–2C

72 Chalk Farm Rd, NW1 7267 0718 8–2B

*"Amazing beers" are the undisputed draw of these "crammed" and "buzzy" Belgian-theme venues; critics find them "pricey" and plain "not nice!", but the ratings revived (a bit) this year, and fans insist that – if you "stick to the basics" – you get "great moules/frites".* / www.belgo-restaurants.com; 11.30 pm, Mon-Thu 11 pm; WC2 no smoking area.

**Bellamy's W1** NEW £55 ❸❸❸

18-18a Bruton Pl 7491 2727 3–2B

*Ex-Annabel's manager Gavin Rankin has helped create an instant "buzz" at this "discreet" Gallic brasserie-style newcomer, on the Mayfair mews site formerly occupied by Caviar Kaspia (RIP); its "assured" cooking is "expensive" for what it is, though, and some tables are "squashed".* / 10.15 pm; closed Sat L & Sun.

**The Belsize NW3** £34 ④❷❷

29 Belsize Ln 7794 4910 8–2A

*"Not just an Identikit gastropub" – this north London boozer is a "cool" place with "real character"; its menu "combines pub fare with more adventurous dishes", at prices some find "inflated".* / 11 pm.

## Belvedere W8 £55 ❸❷❶

Holland Pk, off Abbotsbury Rd 7602 1238 7–1D
*Given its "idyllic" location and "beautiful" Art Deco style, it is easy to assume that this Holland Park destination will be of most interest for its "romantic" charms; this is probably true, but reports on Billy Reid's MPW-inspired cuisine are improving, and service is "attentive".* / www.whitestarline.org.uk; 10 pm; closed Sun D; set weekday L & pre-theatre £32 (FP), set Sun L £35 (FP).

## Ben's Thai W9 £24 ❷④❸

93 Warrington Cr 7266 3134 8–4A
*"Consistently good, fresh and authentic" Thai grub makes this dining room – above a palatial Victorian pub – an ever-popular Maida Vale stand-by.* / 10 pm; D only; no Amex; no smoking area.

## Benares W1 £55 ❷❷❸

12 Berkeley Hs, Berkeley Sq 7629 8886 3–3B
*Ex-Tamarind chef Atul Kochar's "stylish" (if slightly "soulless") Mayfair two-year-old is slowly growing in stature; his "elegant, if expensive" nouvelle Indian cuisine won more applause this year, as did the the "attentive" service.* / www.benaresrestaurant.com; 10.30 pm; closed Sat L & Sun L; no smoking; set weekday L £39 (FP).

## Bengal Clipper SE1 £29 ❸❸❷

Shad Thames 7357 9001 9–4D
*"An Indian restaurant with a pianist" is a bit of a rarity, and the latter adds to the stylish impression made by this large South Bank subcontinental; the cooking is "reliable" too – service a little less so.* / www.bengalclipper.co.uk; 11.30 pm.

## Benihana £50 ④④④

37 Sackville St, W1 7494 2525 3–3D
77 King's Rd, SW3 7376 7799 5–3D
100 Avenue Rd, NW3 7586 9508 8–2A
*"A good floor-show for the kids" and "value-for-money special deals" lead some reporters to recommend this "sanitised" teppan-yaki chain; others, though, see it as "a concept that's passed its sell-by date".* / www.benihana.co.uk; 10.30 pm; smoking restricted during cooking.

## Bentley's W1 £60

11-15 Swallow St 7734 4756 3–3D
*This "classic" (staid) Mayfair seafood parlour changed hands just as this guide was going to press; Richard Corrigan (in partnership with Searcy's) is promising to inject "much more rock 'n' roll" when it re-opens in late-2005 – hopefully that doesn't necessitate trashing its characterful, early-20th-century interior.* / 11.30 pm.

## Benugo £12 ❷④④

14 Curzon St, W1 7629 6246 3–4B
23-25 Gt Portland St, W1 7631 5052 3–1C
V&A Museum, SW7 7581 2159 5–2C **NEW**
116 St John St, EC1 7253 3499 9–1A
82 City Rd, EC1 7253 1295 9–1C
*"Freshly-prepared sandwiches", "great coffee" and "excellent soups" help make these quality cafés "ideal for a quick lunch"; service, though, "can wilt under pressure".* / www.benugo.com; L & afternoon tea only; W1 & EC1 branches closed Sat & Sun; W1 & EC1 branches, no credit cards.

### Beotys WC2 £45 ④❸❸
79 St Martin's Ln 7836 8768 4–3B
This "old-fashioned" Franco-Greek Theatrelander is still
a "safe haven" for some (generally more mature) reporters; given
its location, it continues to inspire astonishingly little feedback,
though, and there is the odd "dreadful" report. / 11.30 pm; closed
Sun; no smoking area.

### Berkeley Square Café W1 £55 ❸❷④
7 Davies St 7629 6993 3–3B
"You can impress without being intimidating", say fans of this
"understated" Mayfair venture, which offers "simple food,
incredibly well-prepared"; doubters just find it "nothing special".
/ www.berkeleysquarecafe.com; 10 pm; closed Sat D & Sun; set D £32 (FP), set
weekday L £32 (FP).

### Bermondsey Kitchen SE1 £32 ④❸❸
194 Bermondsey St 7407 5719 9–4D
This simple venture generally lives up to its name as a
"good neighbourhood haunt", offering food that's "well-sourced,
and well-prepared"; one or two reporters, though, find it "hit-and-
miss". / www.bermondseykitchen.co.uk; 10.30 pm; closed Sun D; no Amex;
no smoking area.

### Bertorelli's £38 ⑤④④
11-13 Frith St, W1 7494 3491 4–2A
19-23 Charlotte St, W1 7636 4174 2–1C
44a Floral St, WC2 7836 3969 4–2D
15 Mincing Ln, EC3 7283 3028 9–3D **NEW**
1 Plough Pl, EC4 7842 0510 9–2A **NEW**
This Italian chain may "look good at first sight", but its cuisine
is "fantastically dull" and its atmosphere "substandard".
/ www.santeonline.co.uk; 9.30 pm-midnight; WC2 & Charlotte St closed Sun;
no smoking area.

### Bevis Marks EC3 £45 ❷❷❸
4 Heneage Ln 7283 2220 9–2D
"Interesting, because it's so distinctive" – this "hidden oasis",
attached to a City synagogue, offers some "excellent" kosher
dishes, in an "airy" and "historic" setting.
/ www.bevismarkstherestaurant.com; 7.15 pm; closed Fri D, Sat & Sun;
no smoking.

### Bibendum SW3 £66 ❸❷❷
81 Fulham Rd 7581 5817 5–2C
"Classy" styling helps maintain the allure of this airy modern
classic, in Brompton Cross's landmark Michelin Building;
the "epic" wine list is arguably a greater attraction than the slick
cuisine, though, and both come with "a big price tag".
/ www.bibendum.co.uk; 11.30 pm; booking: max 12; set weekday L £47 (FP).

### Bibendum Oyster Bar SW3 £40 ❸❸❸
81 Fulham Rd 7589 1480 5–2C
"For a quick and delicious snack", a trip to this stylish café in the
foyer of Brompton Cross's Michelin building – which offers
"fantastic, fresh, simply-prepared seafood" (all cold) – is a
popular treat; the minority which finds the place "nothing
special", however, was more vocal this year. / www.bibendum.co.uk;
10.30 pm; no booking.

### Big Easy SW3 £40 ④④❸
332-334 King's Rd   7352 4071   5–3C
*This "loud" American joint is a "fun" place, serving "chunky"
portions of "decent" burgers, ribs and seafood; "they only get
away with the prices because it's Chelsea", though.*
/ www.bigeasy.uk.com; 11.20 pm, Fri & Sat 12.20 am; no smoking area.

### Bistro 1 £18 ④❸④
75 Beak St, W1   7287 1840   3–2D
33 Southampton St, WC2   7379 7585   4–3D
*"It's cheap, it's nice, and the waiters are always happy", at these
"buzzy" budget bistros, which are popular with most (if not quite
all) reporters.* / www.bistro1.co.uk; 11.30 pm.

### Bistro Aix N8 £40 ❸④❸
54 Topsfield Pde   8340 6346   8–1C
*A Crouch End bistro whose "classic French cuisine" is, say its
fans, "worth crossing postcodes for"; there are doubters, though,
who find it "overpriced" and "pretentious".* / www.bistroaix.co.uk;
11 pm; closed Mon; no smoking area; set D £26 (FP).

### Bistrot 190 SW7 £48 ④⑤❸
190 Queen's Gate   7584 6601   5–1B
*A "lively" brasserie of long standing, handily located for the Albert
Hall; service is "slow" and "negligent", but some reporters say
the food is "much improved" of late.* / www.gorehotel.com; midnight;
no smoking area.

### Bistrothèque E2 £36 ❸❷❷
23-27 Wadeson St   8983 7900   1–2D
*"Hard to find, but a gem when you do!" – this "interesting"
Bethnal Green warehouse-conversion has won quite a following
with its "original" menu.* / 10.30 pm.

### Black & Blue £38 ❸❸④
90-92 Wigmore St, W1   7486 1912   3–1A
105 Gloucester Rd, SW7   7244 7666   5–2B
215-217 Kensington Church St, W8   7727 0004   6–2B
205-207 Haverstock Hill, NW3   7443 7744   8–2A
1-2 Rochester Walk, SE1   awaiting tel   9–4C   NEW
*"Yummy burgers" and "well-sourced steaks" win applause for this
growing chain of "smart" (if "bland") diners; its "artery-clogging"
English breakfasts also get the thumbs-up.* / 11 pm, Fri & Sat
11.30 pm; no Amex; no smoking area; no booking.

### Blah! Blah! Blah! W12 £25 ❷❸④
78 Goldhawk Rd   8746 1337   7–1C
*"Imaginative" fare has long made it worth braving the
"uninspiring" frontage and "noisy" interior of this BYO veggie,
near Goldhawk Road tube; this year's reports were a fraction less
rapturous than usual, though.* / 11 pm; closed Sun; no credit cards.

### Blakes Hotel SW7 £101 ④❸❶
33 Roland Gdns   7370 6701   5–2B
*If you're "hell bent on a luxurious romantic experience",
this "sexy", if "dated", South Kensington basement is happy
to oblige; prices for its "oriental-inspired" cuisine are, however,
"simply outrageous".* / www.blakeshotels.com; 11.30 pm.

### Blandford Street W1 £41 ④❸④
5-7 Blandford St 7486 9696 2–1A
*"Charming and committed"* ownership notwithstanding,
this Marylebone restaurant has often seemed *"to put the bland
into Blandford"*; let's hope a recent total revamp injects a little va-
va-voom! / www.blandford-street.co.uk; 10.30 pm; closed Sat L & Sun L;
no smoking area.

### El Blasõn SW3 £45 ④❸④
8-9 Blacklands Ter 7823 7383 5–2D
This *"plush"* and rather old-fashioned Spaniard occupies a *"quiet
and secluded"* Chelsea backstreet location; for its tiny fan club,
the decent food and *"friendly"* staff make it a *"gem"*. / 11 pm;
closed Sun; no smoking area.

### BLEEDING HEART EC1 £45 ❷❷❶
Bleeding Heart Yd, Greville St 7242 8238 9–2A
*"All occasions are covered"* – from a smoochy dinner to a client
lunch – at this *"superb"* and seriously popular all-rounder,
off Holborn; a semi-subterranean *"warren"* of a place,
it comprises a tavern, wine bar and restaurant, where *"helpful"*
staff serve up *"old-school Gallic cuisine"* (and *"a good range
of wines"*). / www.bleedingheart.co.uk; 10.30 pm; closed Sat & Sun.

### BLUE ELEPHANT SW6 £47 ❷❷❶
3-6 Fulham Broadway 7385 6595 5–4A
*"Getting lost in the foliage"* brings on a *"holiday mood"*, at this
*"wonderful"*, *"OTT"* Fulham *"old favourite"* (which comes
complete with *"waterfalls, streams and Koi carp"*); the Thai food,
if not the main point, is *"simply delicious"* (and the *"Sunday
buffet is recommended"*). / www.blueelephant.com; midnight; closed Sat L;
set always available £30 (FP).

### Blue Jade SW1 £28 ④❶④
44 Hugh St 7828 0321 2–4B
*"Friendly"* service boosts the appeal of this Thai *"stalwart"*,
hidden-away in Pimlico; the food is *"reliable"*, if possibly *"a bit
expensive for what it is"*. / 11 pm; closed Sat L & Sun.

### Blue Kangaroo SW6 £29 ④❸❷
555 King's Rd 7371 7622 5–4B
*"It's not fine dining, but that doesn't matter"*, at this Fulham
yearling, where the prime attraction is the soft-play zone in the
basement – *"that parents can sit over a bottle of vino whilst the
kids run wild safely downstairs is priceless!"*
/ www.thebluekangaroo.co.uk; 7.30 pm; no smoking.

### Blue Lagoon £29 ❸❸④
23 Haymarket, SW1 7930 7800 4–4A NEW
284 Kensington High St, W14 7603 1231 7–1D
*"Not bad-value"* food has made this Kensington Thai a useful
option before a trip to the nearby Odeon; its new branch,
in Haymarket, offers an even wider selection of post-dinner
entertainments... / www.blue-lagoon.co.uk; 11.30 pm; no smoking area.

**The Blue Pumpkin SW17**  £28  ④④❸

16-18 Ritherdon Rd  8767 2660  10–2C

*Now established in Tooting Bec, this simple local brasserie is handy "for anything from brunch to after-dinner drinks"; the Putney original is no more.* / www.bluepumpkin.co.uk; 10.30 pm; smoking in bar only.

**Bluebird SW3**  £50  ⑤⑤⑤

350 King's Rd  7559 1000  5–3C

*Conran's cavernous Chelsea landmark "fails on every level" – given its food ("average", but "outrageously pricey"), its surroundings ("clinical") and its service ("incredibly bad"), it's "amazing that it's still trading".* / www.conran.com; 11 pm.

**Bluebird Café SW3**  £37  ⑤⑤④

350 King's Rd  7559 1155  5–3C

*It's "good for watching the world go by", but the pavement café at Conran's prominent Chelsea landmark otherwise offers an experience that's "bland" and "vastly overpriced".* / www.conran.com; 10 pm; closed Sun D; no booking.

**Bluebird Club & Dining Rooms SW3** £53  ❸❸❸

Beaufort St  7559 1129  5–3C

*Tom has "worked wonders", say fans of the revamp Conran Jr has given to Sir Tel's Chelsea club dining room (now open to the public); Mark Broadbent's cooking is generally "very impressive", too (though the odd "average" result is not unknown).* / www.conran.com; 10.45 pm; closed weekday L.

**Blueprint Café
Design Museum SE1**  £47  ④④❷

28 Shad Thames, Butler's Wharf  7378 7031  9–4D

*You get "excellent views of Tower Bridge" (they even give you binoculars) from Conran's "bright and airy" first-floor South Bank fixture; "everything else is secondary", though... to an extent some reporters find "really shocking".* / www.conran.com; 10.45 pm; closed Sun D.

**Bodean's**  £32  ❸④④

10 Poland St, W1  7287 7575  3–1D
169 Clapham High St, SW4  7622 4248  10–2D

*"If you like ribs and meat, this is the place" – an American mini-chain which "faithfully imports that strip-mall ambience"; it's liked by most reporters, but ratings are depressed by the vocal few who find it a total turn-off.* / www.bodeansbbq.com; 11 pm.

**Bohème Kitchen & Bar W1**  £38  ④④❷

19 Old Compton St  7734 5656  4–2A

*This "trendy" bar/bistro has a more "laid-back" vibe than neighbouring Café Bohème; it makes a "decent Soho rendezvous", with food that's "more edible than at many such places".* / www.bohemekitchen.co.uk; 11.45 pm.

**Boiled Egg & Soldiers SW11**  £20  ④④④

63 Northcote Rd  7223 4894  10–2C

*"Great if you've got kids, less so with a hangover" – this "cramped" caff, in the heart of Wandsworth's 'Nappy Valley', is known for "fantastic fry-ups"; standards, though, "are slipping".* / 6.30 pm, Sun 4 pm; L & afternoon tea only; only Maestro; no booking.

### Boisdale SW1                    £46    ④④❷
13-15 Eccleston St   7730 6922   2–4B
This "reassuringly un-PC" Caledonian fixture in Belgravia
specialises in "red meat, whisky, cigars and jazz" (plus an
"encyclopaedic" wine list); it's a great shame that too many
"insipid" dishes and often-"sloppy" service are beginning
to diminish its appeal. / www.boisdale.co.uk; 10.30 pm; closed
Sat L & Sun.

### Boisdale of Bishopsgate EC2    £47    ④❸❸
202 Bishopsgate   7283 1763   9–2D
"The City's best hamburger" helps make the bar of this
Caledonian-themed venture a popular spot for informal business;
for more serious matters, the (somewhat "charmless") basement,
with its "widely-spaced tables" (and "especially the booths") has
its uses. / www.boisdale.uk.com; 9 pm; closed Sat & Sun.

### The Bollo House W4             £32    ④④❸
13-15 Bollo Ln   8994 6037   7–2A
Even some reporters who find this Chiswick-fringe gastropub
"mediocre", praise it as a "useful" destination, in a thin area.
/ www.thebollo.co.uk; 10 pm.

### Bombay Bicycle Club            £35    ❷❷❸
128 Holland Park Ave, W11   7243 1106   6–2A   NEW
3a Downshill Hill, NW3   7435 3544   8–2A   NEW
95 Nightingale Ln, SW12   8673 6217   10–2C
The mass roll-out "hasn't affected quality", at the original
Wandsworth branch – long popular for its "light" and
"interesting" Indian dishes – of this growing chain; reports on its
new West Hampstead and Holland Park siblings (and the take-
aways) are similarly upbeat. / www.bombaybicycleclub.co.uk; 11 pm;
D only ex NW3 Sun open L & D.

### Bombay Brasserie SW7           £55    ❷❸❷
Courtfield Close, Gloucester Rd   7370 4040   5–2B
"My boss from Mumbai takes me here" – one endorsement
of the ever-more "reliable" standards at this grand South
Kensington subcontinental, where the large conservatory,
in particular, has "a great ambience, reminiscent of the Raj".
/ www.bombaybrasserielondon.com; 11.30 pm; D only; no smoking area;
set weekday L & Sun L £30 (FP).

### Bombay Palace W2               £38    ❶❶❸
50 Connaught St   7723 8855   6–1D
"High-quality" cooking and "the highest standards of service"
make this grand (if "slightly clinical") subcontinental, just north
of Hyde Park, well worth seeking out; it remains too little-known.
/ www.bombay-palace.co.uk; 11.30 pm; no smoking area.

### Bonds
Threadneedles Hotel EC2           £65    ❸④④
5 Threadneedle St   7657 8088   9–2C
Fans say Barry Tonks's "interesting" – if "over-fancy" – cuisine
makes it "worth persevering" with this boutique hotel dining room
in the City, even if it is rather "pricey" and "pretentious", and has
lacklustre service. / www.theetoncollection.com; 9.50 pm; closed Sat & Sun.

### Il Bordello E1 £36 ❷①❷

75-81 Wapping High St   7481 9950   11–1A

*Wapping's "perfect neighbourhood joint" is "always full, always buzzing"; its "beaming" staff deliver "massive" portions of "well-priced and genuine Italian fare", which includes some "memorable" pizza. / www.ilbordello.com; 11 pm; closed Sat L.*

### La Bouchée SW7 £39 ④④❷

56 Old Brompton Rd   7589 1929   5–2B

*This "charming", "cramped" and "authentic" Gallic bistro in South Kensington is a "cosy" choice, tailor-made for romance – the "boring" food is unlikely to distract you from your dining-companion. / 11 pm; no Amex; set weekday L & pre-theatre £24 (FP).*

### Le Bouchon Bordelais SW11 £47 ⑤④④

5-9 Battersea Rise   7738 0307   10–2C

*It's hard to avoid the conclusion that this veteran Battersea bistro – which draws too much flak for "unfocussed" service and "clueless" cooking – is now "past its prime". / www.lebouchon.co.uk; 11 pm; no smoking area; set weekday L £26 (FP).*

### Boudin Blanc W1 £43 ❸❸❷

5 Trebeck St   7499 3292   3–4B

*"Cosy inside, and just as good outside on a balmy summer evening" – this rustic Shepherd Market restaurant makes a "romantic" destination for some "straightforward" Gallic fare; it's "cramped and noisy", though, and "not cheap". / www.boudinblanc.co.uk; 11 pm; set weekday L £26 (FP).*

### Boulevard WC2 £30 ④④❸

40 Wellington St   7240 2992   4–3D

*"Decent food" at "good-value" prices (for Covent Garden) has long made this "easy-going" brasserie of more interest than its tourist-trap neighbours; this year, however, it took more flak for being "formulaic and boring". / www.boulevardbrasserie.co.uk; midnight; no smoking area.*

### Boxwood Café
### The Berkeley SW1 £57 ❸❸④

Wilton Pl   7235 1010   5–1D

*Critics of this "dull" and "pricey" Knightsbridge basement – which is nothing like a café – find it "below expectations for a Ramsay establishment"; it also has its fans, though, for whom it offers a "fun", luxury take on fast food, not least the "ultimate" burger (made of veal and foie gras). / www.gordonramsay.com; 11 pm; no smoking; booking: max 8; set weekday L £40 (FP), set brunch £37 (FP).*

### The Brackenbury W6 £37 ❷❷❷

129-131 Brackenbury Rd   8748 0107   7–1C

*A "short but imaginative" menu and "friendly" staff help make this "cosy" spot in a Hammersmith backstreet a "perfect neighbourhood restaurant"; two years into her proprietorship, Lisa Inglis "has improved standards considerably". / 10.45 pm; closed Sat L & Sun D; no smoking.*

**Bradley's NW3**                                    £42            ④④④
25 Winchester Rd   7722 3457   8–2A
*"Tucked-away in Swiss Cottage", this neighbourhood spot is still putting in a "hit-and-miss" performance; to fans, it's a "classy" destination with "first-rate" food – critics say it has become "a shadow of its former self", and charges "unjustifiable" prices.* / 11 pm; closed Mon, Sat L & Sun D.

**Brady's SW18**                                    £22            ❷❷❸
513 Old York Rd   8877 9599   10–2B
*As ever, "superb fresh fish and great chips" ensure a huge local following for Mr Brady's "lively" and "comfortable" Wandsworth bistro.* / 10.30 pm; D only, closed Sun; no credit cards; no booking.

**Brahms SW1**                                      £20            ④❸④
147 Lupus St   7233 9828   5–3D
*The setting may be "noisy" and "careworn", but this "friendly" Pimlico bistro has quite a name for its "inexpensive but satisfying" fare; sceptics, though, say it's "very cheap, and you can see why".* / 10.45 pm; closed Sat L; no smoking area.

**La Brasserie SW3**                                £40            ④④❸
272 Brompton Rd   7581 3089   5–2C
*The "timeless" Parisian charms of this "bustling" Brompton Cross veteran have long made it a "very good stand-by", especially for breakfast or lunch; standards this year, however, were even more up-and-down than usual.* / www.la-brasserie.co.uk; 11 pm; no booking, Sat L & Sun L.

**Brasserie de l'Auberge SW10** NEW  £39            ❸❸④
268 Fulham Rd   7352 1859   5–3B
*A brave new attempt at the authentic Gallic brasserie experience, from pub operator Massive (best known for the 'Tup' chain); the food is variable-to-good, but the setting, on a busy distant-Chelsea corner, is far from ideal.* / 10.30 pm; no smoking area; set always available £25 (FP).

**Brasserie Rocque EC2**                            £32            ⑤④④
37 Broadgate Circle   7638 7919   9–2D
*A "great setting" helps make this "uninspired" City brasserie "good for business near Broadgate" – otherwise, "give it a miss".* / 10 pm; closed Sat & Sun; no booking at D.

**Brasserie Roux
Sofitel St James SW1**                              £45            ❸❸④
8 Pall Mall   7968 2900   2–3C
*An "airy" spot, near Trafalgar Square, serving "simple" but "well-executed" dishes; the atmosphere might seem a bit "business-like" for social gatherings (but the pre-theatre menu is "excellent value").* / www.sofitelstjames.com; 11.30 pm; no smoking area.

**Brasserie St Quentin SW3**                        £43            ❸❷❸
243 Brompton Rd   7589 8005   5–2C
*"Classic French dishes" in a "comfy", "traditional" setting still draw a "refined" following to this Knightsbridge stalwart; although it's been totally eclipsed by its neighbour, Racine, in recent years, diehard fans insist it's "much better".* / www.brasseriestquentin.co.uk; 10.30 pm.

**Bread & Roses SW4**  £27  ④❸❷

68 Clapham Manor Street  7498 1779  10–1D
A "family-friendly" approach (at weekends) features in reports
on this "independent", co-op-run pub, near Clapham Common;
"the food is of no great significance", but it comes in "hearty"
portions. / www.breadandrosespub.com; 9.30 pm; no Amex; no smoking area;
no booking.


**Brian Turner**
**Millennium Hotel W1**  £56  ④④④

44 Grosvenor Sq  7596 3444  3–2A
TV-chef Turner deserves a better advertisement than this "fairly
luxurious" (but somewhat "depressing") modern dining room
in Mayfair; fans praise it for "the best of British food done well" –
doubters just find the cooking "uninspiring". / 10.30 pm; closed
Sat L & Sun; no smoking area.


**Brick Lane Beigel Bake E1**  £4  ❶❸④

159 Brick Ln  7729 0616  1–2D
"A great mix of people, from clubbers to taxi drivers" joins the
permanent queue for "the best beigels in the world", at this
"wondrous" East End veteran; "could anything be cheaper?"
/ open 24 hours; no credit cards; no smoking; no booking.


**The Bridge SW13**  £35  ④❷❸

204 Castelnau  8563 9811  7–2C
It feels more "ordinary" than when it first opened, but this
"comfortable" gastropub, just south of Hammersmith Bridge, still
makes a "relaxing" venue, especially for lunch; it has
a "delightful" garden. / www.thebridgeinbarnes.co.uk; 10.30 pm; smoking
in bar only.


**Brilliant UB2**  £33  ❷❷④

72-76 Western Rd  8574 1928  1–3A
"Bollywood on the screens" and "large parties of locals" set the
scene at this famous Punjabi (in the middle of suburban Southall);
it offers an authentically "different" menu, executed to a
"consistently good" standard. / www.brilliantrestaurant.com; 11 pm;
closed Mon, Sat L & Sun L; no smoking area; booking: weekends only.


**Brinkley's SW10**  £32  ④❸❷

47 Hollywood Rd  7351 1683  5–3B
"The food is not always great, but the wine list is impressive and
good value", at this "fun" Chelsea bar/restaurant; even some
of the locals, though, can find its following a bit "strident".
/ www.brinkleys.com; 11.30 pm; closed weekday L; no smoking in bar.


**(The Court)**
**British Museum WC1**  £36  ⑤④❷

Gt Russell St  7323 8990  2–1C
The "inspiring" location offers some compensation for the
"drearily average" food at the Great Court's mezzanine
restaurant. / www.digbytrout.co.uk; 5 pm; Thu & Fri 9 pm; L only, Thu-Fri
open L & D; no Amex; no smoking.

**Broadway Bar & Grill SW1** NEW £32 ❸❸❸
11 Haymarket 7976 1313 4–4A
*This prominent Theatreland site was home to the ambitious but
short-lived Osia (RIP); under the same owner, it's now a useful,
if uninspired, grand American diner; the hidden-away rear bar
remains the star attraction. / Rated on Editors' visit; 11 pm;
no smoking area.*

**La Brocca NW6** £29 ❸❷❷
273 West End Ln 7433 1989 1–1B
*A "lively" and "cramped" West Hampstead "favourite" –
"consistently good pizza and pasta" help ensure that it's "always
packed" ("even on a Monday night"). / 11 pm; booking: max 8.*

**Browns** £34 ⑤④④
47 Maddox St, W1 7491 4565 3–2C
82-84 St Martin's Ln, WC2 7497 5050 4–3B
Islington Grn, N1 7226 2555 8–3D
Butler's Wharf, Shad Thames, SE1 7378 1700 9–4D
3-5 Kew Grn, TW9 8948 4838 1–3A
Hertsmere Rd, E14 7987 9777 11–1C
8 Old Jewry, EC2 7606 6677 9–2C
*This potentially "convivial" English brasserie chain "just manages
to get worse and worse", and many reporters think its "tired"
formula is "mediocrity defined". / www.browns-restaurants.com;
10 pm-11 pm; EC2 closed Sat & Sun; W1 L only; no smoking area.*

**Brula TW1** £36 ❷❶❷
43 Crown Rd 8892 0602 1–4A
*"You could have been transported to the suburbs of Paris", at this
"great local favourite" in St Margarets; it offers "super", "above-
bistro" cooking and "friendly" service, in a cosy (if "slightly
curious") room. / 10.30 pm; no Amex; set weekday L £23 (FP).*

**Brunello**
**Baglioni Hotel SW7** £71 ④④④
60 Hyde Park Gate 7368 5700 5–1B
*A year-old Kensington design-hotel dining room – in "decadent
modern style" – where the cooking is "OK... good even",
and complemented by an "impressive" Italian wine list; sadly,
however, many reporters' enduring memory is of the "ludicrous"
prices. / www.baglionihotellondon.com; 10.30 pm; set weekday L £38 (FP).*

**Bu San N7** £21 ❷❸⑤
43 Holloway Rd 7607 8264 8–2D
*No one cares about the "simply awful" décor of this family-run
Korean near Highbury & Islington tube – it offers "great cheap
food" that's "unusual" and "full of flavour". / 11 pm; closed
Sat L & Sun L; no Amex.*

**Buchan's SW11** £36 ❸❷❷
62-64 Battersea Bridge Rd 7228 0888 5–4C
*"Lively and fun", this Scottish-themed bar/restaurant, in Battersea
won more praise this year for its "reliable" fare.
/ www.buchansrestaurant.com; 10.45 pm.*

### The Builder's Arms SW3     £31    ④④❶
13 Britten St   7349 9040   5–2C
"A lovely, cosy ambience" that's "ideal for boozy weekend
lunches" helps make this "tucked-away" Chelsea fixture
"the ultimate gastropub", for its many fans; increasingly, though,
the cooking is "nothing special". / 9.45 pm; no Amex; no smoking area;
no booking.

### The Bull N6   NEW     £39
13 North Hill   0845 456 5033   1–1C
A new Highgate pub-cum-dining room, from the people behind
'House' in Islington; we were not able to fit in a visit before this
guide went to press, but early reviews have tended to judge its
cooking as good but uneven. / www.inthebull.biz; 10.30 pm; closed
Mon L; no Amex; no smoking.

### Buona Sera     £28    ❸❸❷
289a King's Rd, SW3   7352 8827   5–3C
22 Northcote Rd, SW11   7228 9925   10–2C
"Surprisingly good food, and surprisingly good value" maintain the
appeal of these "buzzy" budget Italians; the "fun" and "novel"
Chelsea branch (with 'double-decker' seating) has a particularly
"cosy" atmosphere. / midnight; SW3 closed Mon; SW11 no Amex.

### The Burlington W4     £36    ❸❸④
I Station Pde, Burlington Ln   8995 3344   1–3A
This "relaxed", "out-of-the-way" Chiswick yearling (an offshoot
of Redmond's) "has potential", with cooking rated somewhere
between "not bad" and "excellent" this year; the ambience can
lag, though – "more people should try it". / www.theburlington.org.uk;
10 pm; closed Mon L & Sat L; no smoking area.

### Burnt Chair TW9     £40    ❸❷④
5 Duke St   8940 9488   1–4A
"Simple cooking, but very impressive wine" – that's the deal
at this small outfit, near Richmond Green, whose owner
is "usually on hand to give recommendations". / www.burntchair.com;
II pm; closed Mon, Sat L & Sun; no Amex; no smoking.

### Busaba Eathai     £27    ❷❸❷
106-110 Wardour St, W1   7255 8686   3–2D
8-13 Bird St, W1   7518 8080   3–1A   NEW
22 Store St, WC1   7299 7900   2–1C
"A cheap eat that makes you feel you are somewhere special" –
Alan Yau's "communal" Thais seem like a "posher Wagamama";
they serve "tasty" dishes at "very good-value" prices in "stylish",
low-lit surroundings. / II pm, Fri & Sat 11.30 pm; no smoking;
no booking W1.

### Busabong SW10     £34    ❸❷④
la Langton St   7352 7414   5–3B
An "extremely friendly" Thai, near World's End, serving
"very reliable" grub at "good-value" prices. / www.busabong.co.uk;
11.15 pm; closed Sun L.

### Bush Bar & Grill W12 £39 ④④❸
45a Goldhawk Rd   8746 2111   7–1C
*Hidden off a grotty Shepherd's Bush highway, this "buzzy" bar/restaurant ("convenient to the BBC") is "a bit of a TV/new media scene"; "even if it's a relief in this part of town, it's not all it's cracked up to be", though.* / www.bushbar.co.uk; 11.30 pm; closed Sun D.

### Bush Garden Café W12 £12 ❷❸❷
59 Goldhawk Rd   8743 6372   7–1C
*In the grotty environs of Goldhawk Road tube, this "charming, neighbourhood café" – with a small garden – makes an unexpected find; it serves "good coffee", nice cakes and "lovely breakfasts".* / 5 pm; L only; no smoking.

### Butlers Wharf Chop House SE1 £50 ⑤④④
36e Shad Thames   7403 3403   9–4D
*"Eat in the bar, from the excellent-value menu", best to enjoy the "beautiful views of Tower Bridge" from this Conran river-sider; the alternative is the restaurant proper, where "poor English food" is served by "disinterested" staff.* / www.conran.com; 10.45 pm; closed Sun D.

### La Buvette TW9 NEW £32 ❷❷❷
6 Church Walk   8940 6264   1–4A
*On the "bland" Richmond scene, this new Brula-sibling – "a small bistro, set in a churchyard in the heart of the town" – has been "a most welcome arrival"; it delivers "simple, but well-executed" Gallic cooking at good prices.* / 10.30 pm; no Amex; no smoking.

### Cactus Blue SW3 £35 ④④❸
86 Fulham Rd   7823 7858   5–2C
*The food is "actually OK", say fans of this stylish Chelsea Tex/Mex; it's always seemed more a bar than a restaurant, though, and an "inappropriately loud" DJ certainly does nothing to aid digestion.* / 11 pm; closed weekday L; no smoking area.

### Café 209 SW6 £18 ❸❸❶
209 Munster Rd   7385 3625   10–1B
*"Owner Joy is one hell of a character", at this quirky Fulham Thai BYO; thanks to its "tasty", "cheap" chow, it gets "cramped beyond belief", but it's still "such fun".* / 10.30 pm; D only, closed Sun; no credit cards.

### Café Bagatelle
### Wallace Collection W1 £39 ⑤④❶
Manchester Sq   7563 9505   3–1A
*"A haven of tranquillity, near Oxford Street", this glazed museum courtyard is a "lovely" location – "pity the menu's so uninspiring".* / www.wallacecollection.org; L only; no smoking.

### Café Bohème W1 £34 ④❸❶
13 Old Compton St   7734 0623   4–2A
*"Watching the Soho crowds go by" adds to the "great" (rather Rive Gauche) atmosphere that makes this "convivial" brasserie a "long-standing favourite"; the food is not remarkable, but is generally "well-executed".* / www.cafeboheme.co.uk; 2.45 am, Sun 11.30 pm; no smoking area; booking: max 7.

### Café Crêperie de Hampstead £19 ❸⑤④
2 Exhibition Rd, SW7   7589 8947   5–2C
77 Hampstead High St, NW3   no tel   8–2A
*"Good-value" crêpes make this micro-chain (of which the original
branch is simply a stall) a consistently popular destination;
the "cramped" South Kensington outlet is so small, though,
that it's difficult to see why its service is so poor.*
/ www.hampsteadcreperie.com; 10.30 pm; NW3 no credit cards;
SW7 no smoking.

### Café de Maya NW3 £22 ❸❷④
38 Primrose Hill Rd   7209 0672   8–3B
*"Run by a lovely family", this Primrose Hill oriental offers
"consistent" Thai/Malay food.* / 11 pm; D only, closed Mon; no Amex;
no smoking area.

### Café des Amis du Vin WC2 £44
11-14 Hanover Pl   7379 3444   4–2D
*This Covent Garden stalwart, by the ROH, got a new owner and
a make-over in 2005, and initial signs give some hope that its
"average" standards are on the up; the "fine array of cheese"
in the basement wine bar has mercifully survived.*
/ www.cafedesamis.co.uk; 11.30 pm; closed Sun D; set weekday L &
pre-theatre £29 (FP).

### Café du Jardin WC2 £39 ④❸④
28 Wellington St   7836 8769   4–3D
*"Great before a show, but I'm not sure I'd want to spend the
evening there" – a pretty representative comment on this
"dependable" Covent Garden stand-by, which is especially well-
known for its lunch and pre- and post-theatre deals.*
/ www.cafedujardin.com; midnight; set weekday L & pre-theatre £23 (FP).

### Café du Marché EC1 £40 ❷❷❶
22 Charterhouse Sq   7608 1609   9–1B
*Many regulars are "never disappointed" with this "little corner
of France", in a former Clerkenwell warehouse; it serves "honest,
affordable fare of high quality", and – though "superb for
a relaxed business lunch" – is most popular for romance.* / 10 pm;
closed Sat L & Sun; no Amex.

### Café Emm W1 £24 ④④❸
17 Frith St   7437 0723   4–2A
*It's certainly "no Michelin-winner", but for a "reliable" re-fuel this
ever-busy Soho stand-by delivers "huge portions of exactly what
it says on the menu, at the best prices".* / www.cafeemm.com;
10.30 pm, Fri & Sat 11.30 pm; no Amex; no booking after 6.30 pm.

### Café Fish W1 £38 ④④⑤
36-40 Rupert St   7287 8989   4–3A
*This Theatreland fish-bistro is "useful pre-theatre", and some
reporters tip it as a "dependable" stand-by at any time;
the setting can seem "too canteen-like" though, and service
is "increasingly erratic".* / www.santeonline.co.uk; 11 pm, Sun 9 pm;
no smoking area; set weekday L & set D £25 (FP).

### Café in the Crypt
### St Martin's in the Fields WC2          £23          ④⑤❸
Duncannon St   7839 4342   2–2C
*"For a quick stop in the hectic heart of town", some reporters tip
this "noisy" self-service cafeteria in a "delightful" crypt; the food
"looks better than it is", but is at least "cheap". / www.smitf.org;
7.30 pm, Thu-Sat 10 pm; no Amex; no smoking area; no booking.*

### Café Japan NW11          £27          ❶❷④
626 Finchley Rd   8455 6854   1–1B
*"The freshest sushi and sashimi in town" is the highlight of the
"great Japanese food" served (at "super prices") at this
"cheerfully busy" Golder's Green café; no one minds that it's
"a bit of a dive". / 10 pm; closed Mon & Tue; no Amex; no smoking.*

### Café Laville W2          £28          ④❸❷
453 Edgware Rd   7706 2620   8–4A
*Views "don't get much better" than that from this Little Venice
café, above the Grand Union Canal – an outstanding "sunny
morning" breakfast destination. / www.cafelaville.co.uk; 10.30 pm;
no Amex; no smoking area.*

### Café Lazeez          £36          ❸④❸
21 Dean St, W1   7434 9393   4–2A
93-95 Old Brompton Rd, SW7   7581 9993   5–2C
*In the mid-'90s, this modern chain produced some of London's
first nouvelle Indian food, and its "light" cuisine remains quite
"interesting"; of late, however, some reporters fear that it has
"lost its way". / www.cafelazeez.com; 10.45 pm-midnight; W1 closed Sun;
no smoking area.*

### Café Med          £36          ④④❸
320 Goldhawk Rd, W6   8741 1994   7–1B
21 Loudon Rd, NW8   7625 1222   8–3A
370 St John's St, EC1   7278 1199   8–3D
*The "buzzy" but "relaxing" branches of this Med-inspired chain –
notably NW8 with its "lovely terrace" – make handy stand-bys;
their cooking, however, is often no more than "adequate".
/ 11.30 pm.*

### Café Mozart N6          £25          ❸❷❶
17 Swains Ln   8348 1384   8–1B
*With its "great outside tables", this "old-fashioned" Viennese café
is "brilliant for breakfast", for Sachertorte and coffee, or for
a "hearty mittel European dish" from the main menu; it's "always
busy". / 10 pm; no Amex; no smoking; no booking at L.*

### Café Pacifico WC2          £30          ⑤④④
5 Langley St   7379 7728   4–2C
*"Noisy dump" is a term of affection one fan uses for this
"cheesy" Mexican cantina in Covent Garden; some reporters
do still tip it as a "fun" venue – others say it's "just plain bad".
/ www.cafepacifico_laperla.com; 11.45 pm; no booking.*

**Café Pasta** £29 ④④④
Branches throughout London
*The brand which PizzaExpress bought… and then did practically
nothing with; it induces almost no feedback from reporters these
days, but is occasionally acclaimed as a "decent" stand-by.*
*/ www.pizzaexpress.co.uk; 11 pm-midnight; no smoking areas.*

**Café Portugal SW8** £24 ❸❷❸
5a-6a Victoria Hs, South Lambeth Rd   7587 1962   10–1D
*"The best Portuguese cooking in 'Little Portugal'" is to be found
at this "cheap and excellent" Vauxhall café. / www.cafeportugal.com;
11 pm; no smoking area.*

**Café Rouge** £27 ⑤⑤④
Branches throughout London
*Despite the odd claim of "massive improvements", reporters are
still damning about this dismal faux-Gallic bistro chain – "after
15 years in business, you'd have thought they could have sorted
the food out by now". / www.caferouge.co.uk; 11 pm, City branches earlier;
most City branches closed all or part of weekend.*

**Café Spice Namaste E1** £37 ❷❷❸
16 Prescot St   7488 9242   11–1A
*It may have "an unprepossessing location", near Tower Bridge,
but the "sensationally different" Parsi cooking at Cyrus Todiwala's
"brightly decorated" (going-on "garish") subcontinental remains
well worth seeking out. / www.cafespice.co.uk; 10.45 pm; closed
Sat L & Sun.*

**Caffè Caldesi W1** £43 ❸④④
118 Marylebone Ln   7935 1144   2–1A
*Marylebone sibling to Caldesi, with a "lovely ground-floor
deli/wine bar, and a serious restaurant above"; fans say it's
"very good indeed" all-round, but – like its parent – doubters find
it "average", and "not cheap". / www.caldesi.com; 10.30 pm.*

**Caffè Nero** £10 ④④④
Branches throughout London
*"Just the best coffee" – "strong", "rich" and "aromatic" –
underpins the wide appeal of this "relaxed" Italian chain, even if
its pastries and panini are no more than "passable". / 7 pm-11 pm,
City branches earlier; most City branches closed all or part of weekend;
no credit cards; no booking.*

**Caffè Uno** £31 ⑤⑤⑤
Branches throughout London
*Some reporters do still view this "basic" pizza/pasta chain as a
"useful pit stop"; rather too many doubters, though, "only want
them included in the guide as a warning of how terrible they are".
/ www.caffeuno.co.uk; 11 pm; some branches have no smoking areas.*

**La Cage Imaginaire NW3** £34 ④❷❷
16 Flask Walk   7794 6674   8–1A
*A "cute" and "cosy" Gallic restaurant, in a quiet Hampstead lane;
its "old-fashioned" cooking can be a bit "bland", though,
and "extras bump up the bill". / 11 pm, Sat 11.30 pm; closed Mon L;
no smoking area.*

### Calabash
### Africa Centre WC2 £23 ④④⑤
38 King St 7836 1976 4–3C
*It can be "a bizarre and very un-London experience" to visit the
dowdy basement, under Covent Garden's Africa Centre;
its "quirky" pan-African menu is realised to an "OK" standard.
/ 10.30 pm; closed Sat L & Sun; no Amex.*

### Caldesi W1 £50 ❸④④
15-17 Marylebone Ln 7935 9226 3–1A
*This Tuscan trattoria, north of Oxford Street, has been going for
two decades now, and is hailed by fans as a "true Italian" with
"varied" cooking; it's "very pricey" though, and – as ever –
some reporters feel it's "nothing special". / www.caldesi.com; 11 pm;
closed Sat L & Sun; no smoking area.*

### Cambio de Tercio SW5 £45 ❷❸❸
163 Old Brompton Rd 7244 8970 5–2B
*Cooking with "passion and imagination" is returning this "buzzy"
Earl's Court fixture – sometimes regarded as London's leading
Spanish restaurant – to its previous eminence; service, though,
can be "erratic". / www.cambiodetercio.com; 11.30 pm.*

### Camden Brasserie NW1 £35 ④❸④
9-11 Jamestown Rd 7482 2114 8–3B
*For its fans, this is a "good reliable spot", whose (pretty static)
menu includes "the best steak and chips in town"; ratings,
however, have continued to drift since it shifted premises last
year, supporting the view that "the move did nothing for a rather
tired formula". / 11 pm.*

### Camerino W1 £42 ❷❷❸
16 Percy St 7637 9900 2–1C
*"Unpretentious and very enjoyable", this year-old Italian,
off Tottenham Court Road, offers "well-conceived" dishes and
"interesting" wines in a "simple but pleasing" setting;
the "characterful" staff are "helpful", too.
/ www.camerinorestaurant.com; 11 pm; closed Sat L & Sun.*

### Cantaloupe EC2 £35 ❸④❸
35-42 Charlotte Rd 7613 4411 9–1D
*"Noisy, but a good overall experience" – this "chilled", industrial-
look Shoreditch bar offers tapas-style dishes "suited to sharing".
/ www.cantaloupe.co.uk; 10.30 pm; bar menu only Sat L & Sun.*

### Cantina del Ponte SE1 £38 ⑤⑤⑤
36c Shad Thames 7403 5403 9–4D
*"Gorgeous views of Tower Bridge" don't make up for the
"formulaic c\*\*p" dispensed – year in, year-out – at this ghastly
Conran group Italian. / www.conran.com; 10.45 pm.*

### Cantina Italia N1 £30 ❸❸❸
19 Canonbury Ln 7226 9791 8–2D
*There's a "great buzz" – that's to say it's really "cramped and
noisy" – at this popular Islington spot, which is praised by locals
for its "authentic" and "interesting" menu. / 11 pm, Fri & Sat
11.30 pm; closed weekday L; no Amex; no smoking area.*

**Cantina Vinopolis**
**Vinopolis SE1**                                £44        ④④❸
1 Bank End   7940 8333   9–3C
*"A huge variety of wines by the glass" is the main draw to this
"impressively-housed" brasserie, in the arches of the South Bank's
wine museum; the food is just "for soaking up the alcohol".*
/ www.vinopolis.co.uk; 10.30 pm; closed Sun D; no smoking.

**Il Cantuccio di Pulcinella SW11**        £26        ❷❶❸
143 St John's Hill   7924 5588   10–2C
*"Excellent antipasti" and "custom-made wood-fire pizzas" are
highlights of the "consistently good-quality food" at this
Wandsworth yearling; owners and staff are "real characters", too.*
/ www.ilcantucciodipulcinella.co.uk; 11 pm; closed Tue; no Amex.

**Canyon TW10**                                  £45        ⑤⑤❸
Riverside   8948 2944   1–4A
*"A triumph of location over substance" it may be, but this
California-style riversider, near Richmond Bridge, can still make
"an excellent place for weekend brunch"; the food can, however,
be "dreadful", and service "terrible".* / www.hertfordgroup.co.uk;
10.30 pm; no smoking area.

**CAPITAL HOTEL SW3**                        £79        ❶❷❸
22-24 Basil St   7589 5171   5–1D
*The "real subtlety" of Eric Chavot's "wonderful" Gallic cuisine
makes him "a match for any of the celebrity chefs"; service –
in this "quiet" and "formal" small dining room, by Harrods –
is often "excellent", too.* / www.capitalhotel.co.uk; 11 pm; no smoking;
set weekday L £49 (FP).

**LE CAPRICE SW1**                              £50        ❷❶❶
Arlington Hs, Arlington St   7629 2239   3–4C
*"Slick... but not showy" – this "perennial favourite", "'80s time-
warp" brasserie, behind the Ritz, is still "a place to impress",
thanks to its "assured" service, "always-buzzing" atmosphere
and "honest" food.* / midnight.

**Caraffini SW1**                                  £44        ❷❶❷
61-63 Lower Sloane St   7259 0235   5–2D
*"Staff always have a smile for you", at this "jovial" Italian,
near Sloane Square; "for straightforward food in a buzzy
atmosphere, it's hard to beat".* / www.caraffini.co.uk; 11.30 pm;
closed Sun.

**Caravaggio EC3**                              £48        ⑤⑤⑤
107-112 Leadenhall St   7626 6206   9–2D
*This "pleased-with-itself" City Italian has long been "outrageously
expensive"; nowadays, however, "there are many better
alternatives nearby" and patience with its "small portions" and
"poor service" is wearing thin.* / www.estruscarestaurants.com; 10 pm;
closed Sat & Sun.

**Carluccio's Caffè**    £28    ④④❸

8 Market Pl, W1    7636 2228    3–1C
St Christopher's Pl, W1    7935 5927    3–1A
236 Fulham Road, SW10    7376 5960    5–3B
1-7 Old Brompton Rd, SW7    7581 8101    5–2C    **NEW**
5-6 The Grn, W5    8566 4458    1–3A
305-307 Upper St, N1    7359 8167    8–3D
32 Rosslyn Hill, NW3    7794 2184    8–2A    **NEW**
60 St John's Wood High St, NW8    7449 0404    8–3A    **NEW**
Putney Wharf, Brewhouse St, SW15    8789 0591    10–2B
2 Nash Court, E14    7719 1749    11–1C    **NEW**
12 West Smithfield, EC1    7329 5904    9–2A

*"I thought it was brilliant when it opened, now it's not so good" –
ratings on Antonio and Priscilla Carluccio's burgeoning chain
of "bright", "busy" and "very noisy" Italian deli-cafés have slipped
from pretty good to very average over the years; ("great kids'
menu", though). / www.carluccios.com; 11 pm; no smoking area; no booking
weekday L.*

**Carnevale EC1**    £32    ❸❷④

135 Whitecross St    7250 3452    9–1B
*"Veggie food that's never dull" sustains the appeal of this "lovely"
(but "crowded") little café, in a backstreet near the Barbican.
/ www.carnevalerestaurant.co.uk; 10.30 pm; closed Sat L & Sun; no Amex.*

**Carpaccio's SW3**    £48    ④④❷

4 Sydney St    7352 3433    5–2C
*Fans find this "fun" Chelsea Italian "a great place to eat well and
party"; it strikes some reporters as "overpriced", though,
especially in the light of the sometimes "dull" food and
"unfriendly" service. / www.carpaccio.uk.com; 11.30 pm; closed Sun;
set weekday L £29 (FP).*

**Casale Franco N1**    £39    ④❸❷

rear of 134-137 Upper St    7226 8994    8–3D
*A "genuine Italian feel" has long won fans for this family-run
fixture, tucked away down an Islington alley; pizza is a highlight,
but prices generally are "on the expensive side". / 11 pm, Sun 9 pm;
closed Mon & weekday L; no smoking area; need 6+ to book.*

**The Castle W11**    £29    ❸④❸

100 Holland Park Ave    7313 9301    6–2A
*In thinly-provided Holland Park, this groovily dolled-up gastropub
makes "a great place to hang with friends", and serves affordable
modern pub grub. / 9 pm; no Amex; need 6+ to book.*

**The Castle SW11**    £26    ❸❸❸

115 Battersea High St    7228 8181    10–1C
*A hidden-away Battersea boozer, with "plenty of bright space,
a conservatory and a garden"; it also offers "good modern pub
cuisine" (including "excellent burgers"). / www.thecastle.co.uk;
9.45 pm; no Amex.*

**Cat & Mutton E8**    £31    ④④❸

76 Broadway Mkt    7254 5599    1–2D
*Fans find this "lovely", year-old gastropub "a really good addition
to the flourishing Broadway Market scene"; it can seem "noisy"
and "smoky", though, and service can be "haphazard".
/ www.catandmutton.co.uk; 10 pm; closed Mon L & Sun D.*

### Cây Tre EC1 £26 ❶❷④
301 Old St 7729 8662 9–1B
*"Brilliant" and "reasonably priced" food wins acclaim for this year-old Hoxton Vietnamese, where service is "pleasant" and the décor is in "simple café-style". / 11 pm.*

### Cecconi's W1
5a Burlington Gdns 7434 1500 3–3C
*Now a sibling to the Electric Brasserie (et al), this grand Mayfair Italian is set for a relaunch in late-2005; a more informal all-day formula is planned, with a section devoted to cichetti (Venetian tapas). / 11 pm.*

### Cellar Gascon EC1 £41 ❷❸❷
59 West Smithfield Rd 7796 0600 9–2B
*"A tremendous variety of SW French wine" ("stuff they don't usually send here") and "quality" tapas – as at Club Gascon – make this "busy" Clerkenwell outfit "perfect for a light bite". / midnight; closed Sat L & Sun.*

### Le Cercle SW1 £38 ❶❷❷
1 Wilbraham Pl 7901 9999 5–2D
*"Perfect execution" of an "excellent French-tapas concept" (plus "many wines by the glass") has won instant acclaim for this year-old Belgravia-fringe sibling to Club Gascon; the ambience is "stylish and sophisticated", too, … "for what's essentially a basement". / 10.45 pm; closed Mon & Sun; smoking in bar only.*

### Chada £29 ❸❷④
16-17 Picton Pl, W1 7935 8212 3–1A
208-210 Battersea Park Rd, SW11 7622 2209 10–1C
*"Always empty, but the food is outstanding" – that's how most locals see this long-established Battersea Thai (and even those who find it "tired", say the cooking's "still OK"); as usual, the W1 branch induced little feedback (but such as there was is very good). / 11 pm; closed Sun, SW11 D only; no smoking area.*

### Chai Pani W1 £31 ❸❷④
64 Seymour St 7258 2000 2–2A
*From its inception, this year-old Marble Arch Rajasthani has seemed oddly "quaint", and its "unusual" veggie menu has yet to win it much of a following. / 10 pm; no smoking area.*

### Chakalaka SW15 NEW £40 ❸❸④
136 Upper Richmond Rd 8789 5696 10–2B
*"A very original menu" – featuring a "great selection of South African meat" and game, in "large" portions – is the draw to this "fun" and "loud" newcomer, near East Putney tube. / www.chakalakarestaurant.co.uk; 11 pm; no Amex; no smoking area.*

### Chamberlain's EC3 £59 ④④④
23-25 Leadenhall Mkt 7648 8690 9–2D
*It may have an "attractive" setting and offer "excellent fresh fish", but this "cramped" Leadenhall Market fixture also strikes some reporters as "ridiculously overpriced" ("even by City standards"). / www.chamberlains.org; 9.30 pm; closed Sat & Sun; no smoking area; set D £21 (FP).*

### Chamomile NW3 £15 ❸❷④

45 England's Ln 7586 4580 8–2B
*"Obliging and cheerful"*, this Belsize Park café/pâtisserie
is especially popular as a breakfast/brunch spot. / 5.45 pm; L only;
no Amex; no smoking area; no booking.

### Champor-Champor SE1 £39 ❶❷❶

62 Weston St 7403 4600 9–4C
An *"incredible"* oriental-fusion menu – *"with delicate, well-judged
flavours that can't be matched anywhere else in town"* – helps
make it a *"wonderful"* and *"stimulating"* experience to visit this
*"cave of Eastern exotica"*, tucked-away behind London Bridge
station. / www.champor-champor.com; 10.15 pm; closed L (unless receive
a booking for 6+), closed Sun; booking: max 12.

### The Chancery EC4 £44 ❷❷④

9 Cursitor St 7831 4000 9–2A
This *"small but perfectly-formed"* yearling has been a big hit with
the Chancery Lane business/legal crowd, thanks to its *"great-
value"*, *"beautifully-presented"* food, and its *"always-attentive"*
service; it can, however, seem *"devoid of atmosphere"*.
/ www.thechancery.co.uk; 9 pm; closed Sat & Sun; no smoking area.

### The Chapel NW1 £30 ④❸④

48 Chapel St 7402 9220 6–1D
Near Edgware Road tube, this early-wave gastropub still serves
dependable food in an *"unpretentious"* (and sometimes *"smoky"*)
setting. / 10 pm.

### Chapter Two SE3 £36 ❸❸❸

43-45 Montpelier Vale 8333 2666 1–4D
*"Good"* and *"reasonably-priced"* cuisine and *"friendly"* service
again lead many Blackheath residents to hail this *"relaxing"*
brasserie as *"a great local"*; it inspired a few *"lacklustre"* reports
this year, though. / www.chaptersrestaurant.co.uk; 10.30 pm, Fri & Sat
11.30 pm; no smoking in dining room; booking: max 10.

### Charlotte's Place W5 £41 ❸❷❸

16 St Matthew's Rd 8567 7541 1–3A
*"A real gem, by Ealing Common"*, praised for offering
a *"good overall experience"* – the ground floor is in contemporary
style, upstairs it's *"eccentric, like the '70s"*. / www.charlottes.co.uk;
10.30 pm; closed weekday L & Sun D; no Amex.

### Chelsea Bun Diner SW10 £23 ❸❸④

9a Lamont Rd 7352 3635 5–3B
*"A wonderful place for a lazy, full-works breakfast"* –
this *"cramped"* World's End diner remains west London's most
famous hangover recovery point (with an *"overwhelming choice"*
of *"interesting"* breakfast menus). / www.chelseabunrestaurant.co.uk;
11 pm; no Amex; no booking, Sat & Sun.

### Chelsea Kitchen SW3 £14 ④❸❸

98 King's Rd 7589 1330 5–2D
*"If you want cheap"* – near Sloane Square – this *"friendly"* '50s-
survivor is *"the place to go"*; dishes may be *"basic"* but they're
*"very filling"*, and, anyway, *"who's complaining, at these prices?"*
/ 11.45 pm; no smoking area.

### Cheyne Walk Brasserie SW3  £56  ③④②
50 Cheyne Walk   7376 8787   5–3C
*"Impressively cool, retro-modern" décor has helped make this
Chelsea two-year-old – where many of the Gallic dishes are
prepared on a large open grill – popular with some reporters;
"the effect can wear off when the bill arrives", though,
and service is surprisingly "unprofessional".*
/ www.cheynewalkbrasserie.com; midnight; closed Mon L & Sun D;
set weekday L £19 (FP), set brunch £34 (FP).

### CHEZ BRUCE SW17  £50  ❶❶②
2 Bellevue Rd   8672 0114   10–2C
*Bruce Poole's "perfect neighbourhood spot", by Wandsworth
Common, has finally edged out The Ivy as reporters' No 1
London-wide favourite; "time and time again", it delivers "terrific"
cuisine, "exceptional" service and a "staggering" wine list, and all
at eminently "reasonable" prices.* / 10.30 pm, Sun 10 pm; no smoking;
booking: max 6 at D.

### Chez Gérard  £40  ④④④
Thistle Hotel, Buckingham Palace Rd, SW1   7868 6249   2–4B
31 Dover St, W1   7499 8171   3–3C
8 Charlotte St, W1   7636 4975   2–1C
119 Chancery Ln, WC2   7405 0290   2–2D
45 East Ter, Covent Garden, WC2   7379 0666   4–3D
9 Belvedere Rd, SE1   7202 8470   2–3D
64 Bishopsgate, EC2   7588 1200   9–2D
14 Trinity Sq, EC3   7480 5500   9–3D
1 Watling St, EC4   7213 0540   9–2B
*Fans still hail this well-known chain as a "formulaic, but reliable"
option serving "the best steak/frites in town"; for its many
detractors, though, it's just "very mediocre" nowadays, and the
sagging ratings suggest that new owners Paramount risk inducing
"terminal decline".* / www.santeonline.co.uk; 10 pm-11.30 pm;
City branches closed all or part of weekend; no smoking area.

### (Deli)
### Chez Kristof W6  £18  ②❸❸
111-115 Hammersmith Grove   8741 1177   7–1C
*Next to the Hammersmith restaurant of the same name,
this trendy communal-table deli is a good option for a "simple,
but well-cooked" snack, and great for brunch-plus-papers.*
/ www.chezkristof.co.uk.

### Chez Kristof W6  £39  ❸❸②
111-115 Hammersmith Grove   8741 1177   7–1C
*This "very decent neighbourhood place" – on the Hammersmith
site of Maquis (RIP) – serves "hearty", if slightly "hit-and-miss"
Gallic country fare in "simple" but "convivial" surroundings;
there's also a very nice terrace for sunny days.*
/ www.chezkristof.co.uk; 11 pm.

### Chez Liline N4  £34  ②②④
101 Stroud Green Rd   7263 6550   8–1D
*"You're mad", if you let yourself be put off by the "awful location"
of this Finsbury Park fixture, as it offers "outstanding fish, with a
unique Mauritian flavour"; last year's revamp, however, has been
double-edged – "it's made the place more popular, but they can't
cope".* / 10.30 pm; closed Sun L; no smoking area.

### Chez Lindsay TW10 £35 ❷❷❸
11 Hill Rise 8948 7473 1–4A
*Some reporters feel "as if in Brittany", when they visit this "cosy"
and "friendly" bistro, near Richmond Bridge; the "excellent
seafood and crêpes" are just as you'd hope, and there's also
an interesting list of ciders. / 10.45 pm; no Amex.*

### Chez Marcelle W14 £23 ❶❷⑤
34 Blythe Rd 7603 3241 7–1D
*"Stuff yourself with delicious food, and still get change from £20"
– that's the proposition at the "charming" Marcelle's "excellent"
Olympia Lebanese; it is pretty "basic", though. / 10.30 pm; closed
Mon, Tue-Thu D only; no credit cards; no smoking area.*

### Chiang Mai W1 £30 ❷④⑤
48 Frith St 7437 7444 4–2A
*This "authentic northern Thai", in Soho, generated few reports
this year; loyal fans, though, insist you "can still enjoy excellent
food" here, and "without spending a fortune". / 11 pm; closed Sun L.*

### Chimes SW1 £26 ⑤④④
26 Churton St 7821 7456 2–4B
*The "predictable" charms of this very '70s Pimlico pie-house –
especially the "great" cider selection – win it support in some
quarters; remarkably, however, the food is "getting worse".
/ www.chimes-of-pimlico.co.uk; 10.15 pm.*

### China Tang NEW
### Dorchester Hotel W1
53 Park Ln 7629 9988 3–3A
*Mayfair's former Dorchester Club is being relaunched, in Art
Deco style, around the publication date of this guide; the aim –
in conjunction with Hong Kong design supremo and club owner,
David Tang – is, it would seem, to create London's leading
Cantonese restaurant.*

### The Chinese Experience W1 NEW £32 ❷❷❸
118-120 Shaftesbury Ave 7437 0377 4–3A
*"A great new Chinese, in hideous Shaftesbury Avenue!", where
the "most welcoming" staff deliver "very competent" cooking
(including "excellent dim sum") in "clean and modern" café-style
surroundings. / 11 pm.*

### Chisou W1 NEW £38 ❷❷⑤
4 Princes St 7629 3931 3–1C
*"Delicious" sushi and sashimi – plus an "interesting" range
of other "quality" dishes – win high praise for this low-key ("no-
ambience") Japanese, near Hanover Square. / 10.15 pm; closed Sun;
set weekday L £23 (FP).*

### Chor Bizarre W1 £42 ❸❸❷
16 Albemarle St 7629 9802 3–3C
*"It's expensive, but you get what you pay for", at this "high-
quality", but little-known Mayfair Indian, where
a "very interesting" menu is served in a room wittily decorated
with subcontinental bric-à-brac. / www.chorbizarre.com; 11 pm; closed
Sun L; no smoking area.*

**Chowki W1**  £24  ❷❸❸

2-3 Denman St   7439 1330   3–2D

*"Regularly-changing regional menus"* which are *"always reliable, and good value-for-money"* help make this *"pleasant"* and *"bustly"* modern Indian, near Piccadilly Circus, a very handy West End stand-by. / www.chowki.com; 11.30 pm; no smoking area.

**Choys SW3**  £33  ④❷❸

172 King's Rd   7352 9085   5–3C

*"An institution"* for Chelsea locals – this *"efficient"* and *"friendly"* Chinese has been around *"forever"*, but is *"still reliable"*. / 11 pm; no smoking area.

**Christopher's WC2**  £53  ④④④

18 Wellington St   7240 4222   4–3D

*Christopher Gilmour's grand surf 'n' turf American occupies a "lovely building" in Covent Garden; even some of its fans, though, concede that it "does nothing outstandingly well", and critics just find it a thoroughly "average" place, with "outrageous" prices.* / www.christophersgrill.com; 11.30 pm; closed Sun D; booking: max 12; set pre-theatre & brunch £31 (FP).

**Christopher's In The City EC3** NEW £53

20 Creechurch Ln   7623 3999   9–2D

*This new sibling to the grand Covent Garden surf 'n' turf American is slated to open in early autumn 2005; its east-City location doesn't seem an 'obvious' one, so it will be interesting to see how it fares.*

**Chuen Cheng Ku W1**  £26  ❸❸❸

17 Wardour St   7437 1398   4–3A

*"Fun and frequent trolleys"* serve *"authentic (and delicious) Hong Kong-style dim sum"*, at this vast and gaudy Chinatown landmark; if it has attractions as a dinner destination, nobody mentions them. / 11.45 pm; no smoking area.

**Churchill Arms W8**  £17  ❷④❷

119 Kensington Church St   7792 1246   6–2B

*"Fantastic, basic Thai food at unbeatable prices"*, served in a *"traditional pub"* setting, has become a *"classic combination"* at this well-known Kensington hostelry (with conservatory dining annex) – it's *"always packed"*. / 10 pm; closed Sun D; no smoking area.

**Chutney Mary SW10**  £52  ❷❷❷

535 King's Rd   7351 3113   5–4B

*Having taken on a "sleek" new look a couple of years ago, this "professional"Chelsea/Fulham-fringe Indian offers a "deservedly popular" all-round formula, which includes "consistently very good" and "subtly-spiced" cuisine.* / www.realindianfood.com; 10.30 pm; closed weekday L; no smoking area; booking: max 12; set brunch £31 (FP).

**Chutneys NW1**  £23  ❸④④

124 Drummond St   7388 0604   8–4C

*"The great-value lunch buffet"* is the stand-out reason to visit this simple 'Little India' vegetarian, near Euston. / 10.45 pm; no Amex; no smoking at L; need 5+ to book.

### Ciao Bella WC1 £29 ❸❷❷
90 Lamb's Conduit St 7242 4119 2–1D
It looks like "just another pizza/pasta place", but this "great local Italian" has a following stretching far beyond the Bloomsbury set; those in the know, however, suggest avoiding both the pizza and the basement. / 11.30 pm.

### Cibo W14 £42 ❷❷❸
3 Russell Gdns 7371 6271 7–1D
"Big plates" (literally) of "great" Italian cooking win nothing but praise for this "charming" – if sometimes "noisy" – Olympia fixture; despite apparently being a favourite of Michael Winner, it has unaccountably fallen from fame in recent years.
/ www.ciborestaurant.com; 11 pm; closed Sat L & Sun D.

### Cicada EC1 £34 ❷❸❷
132-136 St John St 7608 1550 9–1B
This always "buzzy" bar/restaurant – Will Ricker's original venture – remains a "funky" Clerkenwell linchpin, serving "delicious", "Asian-fusion" dishes. / www.cicada.nu; 10.45 pm; closed Sat L & Sun; no smoking area.

### Cigala WC1 £41 ❸❸④
54 Lamb's Conduit St 7405 1717 2–1D
"Authentic" Spanish cuisine and "interesting" wines have won a foodie following for this Bloomsbury corner spot; the "variable" cooking "could be much better", though – some reporters fear they simply "try too hard". / www.cigala.co.uk; 10.45 pm.

### Cinnamon Cay SW11 £36 ❷❷❸
87 Lavender Hill 7801 0932 10–1C
"Outstanding cooking at reasonable prices" makes this Battersea Antipodean "everything a neighbourhood restaurant should be"... and arguably more. / www.cinnamoncay.co.uk; 10.30 pm; closed Sun.

### THE CINNAMON CLUB SW1 £55 ❷❸❸
Gt Smith St 7222 2555 2–4C
This "top-notch" Indian – with its "innovative" and "unusual" modern cuisine – draws a crowd rich with "media-types, politicos and luvvies" to its swish premises (a converted library, near Westminster Abbey). / www.cinnamonclub.com; 10.45 pm; closed Sat L & Sun; no smoking area; set weekday L & set D £36 (FP).

### Cipriani W1 £67 ⑤⑤④
25 Davies Street 7399 0500 3–2B
"Great people-watching" ("you can check out trends in plastic surgery") is the only justification for visiting this year-old Mayfair outpost of Venice's Harry's Bar – otherwise it's an "arrogant" operation, where "average" cooking is dished up at "criminal" prices. / www.cipriani.com; 11.45 pm; booking: max 6.

### Circus W1 £49 ❸❸❸
1 Upper James St 7534 4000 3–2D
This minimalist, '90s media-canteen in Soho is generally hailed as a "calm and sophisticated" venue (with a "lively bar"); its cooking rarely scales dizzying heights, but usually hits the mark. / www.egami.co.uk; midnight; closed Sat L & Sun; set weekday L & pre-theatre £21 (FP).

**City Miyama EC4**   £43   **❶❷**⑤
17 Godliman St   7489 1937   9–3B
*"The quality of the sushi more than makes up for the total lack of ambience", at this "excellent" City Japanese; there's also a good teppan-yaki.* / 9.30 pm; closed Sat D & Sun.

**CLARKE'S W8**   £62   **❶❶❸**
124 Kensington Church St   7221 9225   6–2B
*"First-rate" ingredients, "simply" but "beautifully" prepared, are a hallmark of Sally Clarke's "phenomenally consistent" Kensington fixture (whose dinner menu offers zero choice); its setting is "romantic" to some, but "dull" to others (especially downstairs).* / www.sallyclarke.com; 10 pm; closed Mon D & Sun; no smoking; booking: max 14.

**The Clerkenwell Dining Room EC1**   £46   ④**❸**④
69-73 St John St   7253 9000   9–1B
*This "modern" but "unpretentious" Farringdon restaurant has won quite a name for its "first-class" food; "standards have slipped" this year, though, and there are some reports of "average" dishes in "stingy" portions.* / www.theclerkenwell.com; 11.30 pm; closed Sat L & Sun D.

**Club Gascon EC1**   £56   **❶❷❷**
57 West Smithfield   7796 0600   9–2B
*"Foie-gras-tastic" food combinations (served tapas-style) and a "knockout" wine list – both rooted in SW France – create some "stunning" gastronomic experiences at this "slightly cramped" City-fringe fixture; aficionados tip the tasting menu as the way to go.* / 10 pm; closed Sat L & Sun.

**Club Mangia
The Punch Tavern EC4**   £19   **❸❸❸**
99 Fleet St   7353 6658   9–2A
*An historic tavern where contemporary dishes are served buffet-style; fans say it's a "novel" and "well-priced" formula, and praise the "good", un-City-like ambience.* / 11 pm; closed Sat & Sun; no smoking area at L.

**Coach & Horses EC1**   £33   **❷❸❸**
26-28 Ray St   7278 8990   9–1A
*"Simple but excellent traditional fare" and a "genuine" approach again wins high praise for this "unpretentious" pub, near The Guardian.* / www.thecoachandhorses.com; 9.30 pm; closed Sat L & Sun D.

**Coco EC1**   **NEW**   £34   ④**❷❷**
70 Exmouth Mkt   7833 3332   9–1A
*"A simple and enjoyable new Caribbean restaurant", on the former Clerkenwell site of Don Pedro (RIP); service is "charming", and "lots of veggie options and gentle reggae music add to the appeal".* / 10.30 pm; no Amex; no smoking area.

**for updates visit www.hardens.com**

**Cocoon W1**  £52  ❸④❷

65 Regent St  7494 7600  3–3D

*This "happening" and "very now" newcomer occupies the first-floor West End site that once was Odéon (long RIP); though the Pan-Asian dishes are "quite good", they can seem a bit "over-trendy", and staff "find it hard to keep up".*
/ www.cocoon-restaurants.com; 11.45 pm; closed Sat L & Sun L; smoking in bar only.

**The Collection SW3**  £54  ④④❸

264 Brompton Rd  7225 1212  5–2C

*"The bar is buzzing most nights", at this supposedly glamorous Brompton Cross fixture; its mezzanine restaurant is dropping off the radar as a place to eat, though, due to its perennially "overpriced" and "disappointing" Asian-fusion fare.*
/ www.the-collection.co.uk; 11.30 pm; D only.

**Le Colombier SW3**  £44  ❸❷❷

145 Dovehouse St  7351 1155  5–2C

*A new chef is injecting a bit of (much-needed) 'élan' into the cooking at Didier Garnier's "elegant" and "personal" bourgeois restaurant, on a quiet Chelsea corner, which is on the verge of becoming a "great all-rounder"; a superb terrace is a feature.*
/ 10.30 pm; set weekday L £31 (FP).

**Como Lario SW1**  £41  ❸❸❸

22 Holbein Pl  7730 2954  5–2D

*"Friendly" ("if hectic") service underpins the appeal of this "traditional" Italian "favourite", near Sloane Square; under a new chef, the food "has improved" of late.* / www.comolario.uk.com; 11.30 pm; closed Sun; no smoking area.

**Comptoir Gascon EC1**  NEW  £26

63 Charterhouse St  7608 0851  9–1A

*As this guide goes to press, this elegant traiteur-pâtisserie, by Smithfield Market, is set to add a 'bistro' function to its attractions – unlike Club Gascon, there will be no 'tapas' dishes, just a limited range of substantial dishes (at, we are told, reasonable prices).*

**(Angela Hartnett's Menu)**
**The Connaught W1**  £78  ❸❸❸

Carlos Pl  7592 1222  3–3B

*Many reporters still find it a "very classy" experience to visit this "sumptuous" bastion of old Mayfair (reformatted three years ago by Gordon Ramsay); the overall verdict on Angela Hartnett's cooking remains distinctly middling, though, and the setting "lacks the character it had of old".* / www.angelahartnett.co.uk; 11 pm; no smoking; booking: max 8; set always available £50 (FP).

**The Contented Vine SW1**  £35  ④❸④

17 Sussex St  7834 0044  5–3D

*This "ordinary"-looking wine bar is hailed as a "fun local" in a "frighteningly thin area" (Pimlico); its cooking is not art, but is "honest".* / www.contentedvine.com; 10.30 pm.

### Il Convivio SW1 £42 ❷❶❸
143 Ebury St   7730 4099   2–4A
"Really improved" over the past couple of years, this "attractive" Belgravia Italian wins praise for the "high-quality" realisation of its "interesting" menu, and its "stylish presentation and service". / www.etruscarestaurants.com; 10.30 pm; closed Sun.

### Coopers Arms SW3 £28 ❸❷❷
87 Flood St   7376 3120   5–3C
"A quiet Chelsea backstreet" is home to this "excellent" pub, which numbers "good" food and "unfailingly helpful" staff among its attractions; "get there early". / www.drinkatthecoopers.co.uk; 9.30 pm; closed Sun D; no booking, Sun.

### La Copita W12 £25 ❸④④
63 Askew Rd   8743 1289   7–1B
"Flavourful" and "cheap" tapas help make this "very simple" Shepherd's Bush shop-conversion a good budget choice (especially in a group). / 10 pm; closed Mon & Sun L.

### Coq d'Argent EC3 £53 ④④❸
1 Poultry   7395 5000   9–2C
Not many sites in the heart of the City have "fantastic gardens" and "wonderful views" – with these 'natural' advantages, it's all too predictable that this sixth-floor Conran establishment should charge "sky-high" prices for a "dull" overall experience. / www.conran.com; 10 pm; closed Sat L & Sun D.

### Cork & Bottle WC2 £28 ⑤④❶
44-46 Cranbourn St   7734 7807   4–3B
"A godsend in the hustle and bustle of Leicester Square" – this "cramped" basement remains a "humming" West End "haunt"; nothing to do with the "tired" salads-and-so-on selection, though – it's Don Hewitson's "amazing" wine list people come for. / www.donhewitson.com; 10.45 pm; no smoking area; no booking after 6.30 pm.

### Corney & Barrow £32 ④❸❷
Branches throughout London
"A great buzz" – especially at the strikingly large Broadgate branch – is the mainstay of this modern City wine bar chain; the food is "mediocre, as a rule". / www.corney-barrow.co.uk; 10.30 pm; closed Sat & Sun; no smoking areas.

### Costa's Grill W8 £19 ④❷❸
12-14 Hillgate St   7229 3794   6–2B
"Unchanged in the 30 years I've been going", this "friendly" taverna, just off Notting Hill Gate, offers "good basic Greek food"; its "lovely" garden is a particular summer attraction. / 10.30 pm; closed Sun (closed 2 weeks in Aug); no credit cards; no smoking area.

### Cotto W14 £30 ❷❷④
44 Blythe Rd   7602 9333   7–1D
"Shame about the obscure location", say fans of James Kirby's Olympia local, which offers "outstanding" but "affordable" contemporary cuisine; the "chilly" décor does little to help the cause, though. / 10.30 pm; closed Sat L & Sun.

**Cottons NW1**   £38   ❸④❷

55 Chalk Farm Rd   7485 8388   8–2B
*"Great old reggae music"* and *"the biggest range of rums ever"*
fuel the fun at this *"friendly"* Camden Town Caribbean;
its cooking has improved over the years, with *"delicious"* seafood
a highlight. / www.cottons-restaurant.co.uk; 11 pm; closed weekday L;
no Amex; no smoking area.

**The County Hall Restaurant
London Marriott Hotel SE1**   £51   ⑤④④

Queens Walk   7902 8000   2–3D
You get *"super views of the London Eye"* from this Thames-side
hotel dining room; the limited commentary on the cuisine,
however, puts it somewhere between *"average"* and *"poor"*.
/ www.marriott.com/lonch; 10.30 pm; no smoking at breakfast; need 8+
to book.

**The Cow W2**   £36   ❷④❷

89 Westbourne Park Rd   7221 0021   6–1B
*"Great oysters and Guinness"* are the classic choice at Tom
Conran's *"trendy"* but *"unpretentious"* Irish bar, on the fringe
of Notting Hill (where service is *"at best unhurried"*); the *"cosy"*
– less commented-on – upstairs room serves *"more elaborate"*
fare. / 10.30 pm; no Amex.

**Crazy Bear W1**   £45   ❸❸❶

26 Whitfield St   7631 0088   2–1C
The *"funkiest"* décor – *"especially the loos!"* – helps make a visit
to this Fitzrovia yearling an *"enjoyable"* occasion, for most
reporters; surprisingly good-quality oriental fare comes as a
*"bonus"*. / www.crazybeargroup.co.uk; 10.30 pm; closed Sat L & Sun.

**Crazy Homies W2**   NEW   £35   ❸❷❷

127 Westbourne Park Rd   7727 6771   6–1B
*"Good Mexican food (by London standards)"* has won applause –
if from a modestly-sized fan club – for the snacks at Tom
Conran's small new bar, on the fringe of Notting Hill. / 10.30 pm;
closed weekday L; no Amex.

**Cristini**   £36   ❸❷④

13 Seymour Pl, W2   7724 3446   2–2A
28 Sussex Pl, W2   7706 7900   6–1D
*"Young and friendly"* staff serve up *"authentic"* and *"good-value"*
dishes at this Italian duo – in rather cramped bistro premises
near Marble Arch, and in a little more comfort near Lancaster
Gate. / www.cristini.co.uk; 10.30 pm; Seymour Pl, Sat-Mon D only; Sussex
Pl closed Sun; Seymour Pl, no smoking area.

**The Criterion Grill W1**   £51   ⑤⑤❷

224 Piccadilly   7930 0488   3–3D
It still has a *"stunning"* neo-Byzantine interior, but this *"once-fine"*
Piccadilly Circus restaurant *"continues its slide downhill"* –
it offers *"uninteresting food, badly served"*. / www.whitestarline.org.uk;
11.15 pm; closed Sun; set weekday L & pre-theatre £29 (FP).

### Crivelli's Garden
### National Gallery WC2     £34     ④⑤④

Trafalgar Sq   7747 2439   4–4B

*Some reporters feel this gallery café (with great views over
Trafalgar Square) is "pretty good for a museum"; its food is far
from outstanding, though, and service can be "diabolically slow".*
/ 7.45 pm; L only, except Wed open L & D; no smoking.

### The Cross Bar SW3   NEW    £35     ❸❸④

99 Fulham Rd   7225 2244   5–2C

*Given its trendy Brompton Cross location, it's hard not to find this
relaunch of the Crescent (under the same owners) a bit lacking
in style; the headline attraction, however – the diverse and
affordable wine list – is as strong as ever (and the food seems
to have been pepped up).* / Rated on Editors' visit; 10 pm.

### Cross Keys SW3     £42     ❸④❷

1 Lawrence St   7349 9111   5–3C

*A "light, bright conservatory" helps make this Old Chelsea
gastropub a "refreshing" destination; the nosh it serves
is generally "good", too.* / www.thexkeys.co.uk; 11 pm.

### The Crown E3     £37     ❷④❷

223 Grove Rd   8981 9998   1–2D

*"Always decent" food (all organic) and a "great" atmosphere
make this vast gastropub, overlooking Victoria Park, a classic
"relaxed" East End destination.* / www.singhboulton.co.uk; 10.30 pm;
closed Mon L; no Amex; no smoking in dining room.

### Crown & Goose NW1     £27     ❸❷❷

100 Arlington Rd   7485 8008   8–3B

*"The atmosphere's buzzing" and prices are "cheap" at this long-
standing Camden Town gastropub; the food can be "great",
too, but it "all depends on who's cooking".* / 10 pm; no Amex.

### The Crown & Sceptre W12     £27     ❸④❷

57 Melina Rd   8746 0060   7–1B

*Simple but "quality" gastropub fare – with "great burgers"
a highlight – wins consistent praise for this relatively un-mucked-
about-with Fullers pub, in a Shepherds Bush backwater.* / 9.45 pm;
no Amex; no smoking area.

### Cru N1     £42     ④④❸

2-4 Rufus St   7729 5252   9–1C

*It's a shame that standards continue to drift at this nice-looking
Hoxton restaurant-cum-wine bar – the "fantastic" list of vino
is now the only undoubted attraction.* / www.cru.uk.com; 11 pm; closed
Mon; set weekday L £23 (FP).

## Crussh £9 ❸❷④

4 Millbank, SW1   7233 0032   2–4C
1 Curzon St, W1   7629 2554   3–3B
BBC Media Village, Wood Ln, W12   8746 7916   6–2A
27 Kensington High St, W8   7376 9786   5–1A
One Canada Sq, E14   7513 0076   11–1C
Unit 21 Jubilee Pl, E14   7519 6427   11–1C
48 Cornhill, EC3   7626 2175   9–2C
Reuters Refresh, 85 Fleet St, EC4   7427 9888   9–2A

"A welcome lunchtime alternative to the ubiquitous mass-made sandwich" – this "healthy" chain is widely praised for "excellent organic soups" and "outstanding, refreshing smoothies".
/ www.crussh.com; 4.30 pm-7 pm; some branches closed all or part of weekend; no credit cards; no smoking.

## Cuba Libre N1 £31 ④④④

72 Upper St   7354 9998   8–3D

"Average food, but a fun night out" – the formula's the same as ever as this "funky" Islington Cuban veteran, where the cocktails come "highly recommended". / 11 pm, Fri & Sat midnight; no Amex; booking: max 12.

## Cube & Star N1 NEW £39 ❸❸❷

39a Hoxton Sq   7739 8824   9–1D

Decorated entirely by vast backlit photographs – on the ceiling, too – this lofty Hoxton newcomer (on the site of the Shoreditch Electricity Showrooms, RIP) certainly makes an initial impression; it was very early days when we visited in May 2005, but the Latin American dishes, and the service, showed some promise. / Rated on Editors' visit; www.thecubeandstar.co.uk; 10.30 pm; no smoking.

## Curryleaf £27 ④④④

18 Charlotte St, W1   7436 7402   2–1C
20 City Rd, EC1   7374 4842   9–1C

A fairly traditional subcontinental mini-chain of recent vintage; muted survey commentary suggests its branches make tolerable stand-bys. / www.curryleaf.co.uk; 11 pm; EC1 closed Sun; no smoking area.

## CVO Firevault W1 £45 ④④❶

36 Gt Titchfield St   7636 2091   3–1C

Part of a high-tech fireplace shop, this Fitzrovia basement – "lit only with candles" – is tipped as an "extremely romantic" place to eat; critics, however, find it "gimmicky" and "too pricey". / www.cvo.co.uk; 10.30 pm; closed Sun.

## Da Mario SW7 £30 ❸❸❸

15 Gloucester Rd   7584 9078   5–1B

"Cheerful" and "buzzy", this Kensington veteran maintains its reputation for "great pizza and pasta"; it's one of the few places handy for the Albert Hall. / www.damario.co.uk; 11.30 pm.

## Dalchini SW19 £29 ❸❷④

147 Arthur Rd   8947 5966   10–2B

Haka Chinese cooking – "a sort of cross between the best of China and of India" – is the speciality at this "friendly" Wimbledon Park offshoot of Sarkhel's; "it's a strange mix of cuisines, but excellent when it works". / www.dalchini.com; 10.30 pm, Fri & Sat 11 pm; closed Mon; no Amex; no smoking.

**Dan's SW3** £43 ④❷❷

119 Sydney St 7352 2718 5–3C
*"Improved food" is winning warmer vibes for this old-time
Chelsea townhouse; it's the "sweet garden", though, which
remains the star attraction. / 10.30 pm; closed Sun D; set weekday L
£25 (FP).*

**Dans le Noir EC1** NEW

29 Clerkenwell Grn awaiting tel 9–1A
*Already well-established in Paris, Zurich and Berlin, this 'novelty'
dining concept – where you eat in total darkness – may, or may
not, storm London when it opens its doors in Clerkenwell, in late-
2005. / www.danslenoir.com.*

**Daphne NW1** £23 ❸❷❷

83 Bayham St 7267 7322 8–3C
*"Always the same menu and staff" help induce a sense of well-
being at this "comforting" and "cosy" Camden Town Greek,
which serves "good-value", "straightforward" dishes. / 11.30 pm;
closed Sun; no Amex.*

**Daphne's SW3** £50 ④❸❷

110-112 Draycott Ave 7589 4257 5–2C
*The glamour-days of this Brompton Cross Italian now seem rather
behind it; though tipped for "for a relaxed lunch" or romance,
otherwise it's just an "average" Chelsea "stand-by" nowadays –
all the more surprising, when you know it's part of the Caprice
group. / www.daphnes-restaurant.co.uk; 11.30 pm; booking: max 12;
set weekday L £33 (FP), pre-theatre £25 (FP).*

**Daquise SW7** £25 ④④④

20 Thurloe St 7589 6117 5–2C
*"An intriguing, if shabby, outpost of Poland" – this "quirky" South
Kensington "stalwart" still wins fans with its "basic", "heart-
warming" and cheap scoff; it's also known for "good pastries"
and afternoon tea. / 11 pm; no Amex; no smoking area.*

**De Cecco SW6** £35 ❸❷❸

189 New King's Rd 7736 1145 10–1B
*This "always fun" Italian local, near Parson's Green, remains
"justifiably" crowded, thanks to its "consistently good and fresh
food", and its "great" staff. / www.dececcorestaurant.com; 11 pm; closed
Sun D.*

**Deep SW6** NEW £50 ❸④⑤

The Boulevard, Imperial Wharf 7736 3337 5–4B
*Christian Sandefeldt's brave (but foolhardy?) new fish specialist
espouses a laudable 'sustainable stocks' policy; like us, though,
early reporters have found it "pricey for what you get", and its
location – a kookily-minimalist unit in a dead new development –
is no great incentive to trek to the back end of beyond
(past Chelsea Harbour). / www.deeplondon.co.uk; 11 pm; closed Mon;
smoking in bar only; set weekday L £31 (FP).*

**Defune W1**　　　　　　　　£60　　　❷④⑤
34 George St　7935 8311　3–1A
*"Forget the Nobu-style impostors – this is the real thing",
says one (Japanese) reporter about this Marylebone joint, which
has long been renowned for its "authentic" sushi and other
dishes; the prices, though, can still seem "an insult", especially
given its Spartan setting.* / 10.45 pm; set weekday L £36 (FP).

**Del Buongustaio SW15**　　　£35　　　⑤⑤⑤
283 Putney Bridge Rd　8780 9361　10–2B
*A once-fêted Putney Italian, which nowadays incites few reports –
too many of these say that it's "lost all its flair".*
/ www.delbuongustaio.com; 11 pm; closed Sun; no Amex.

**Delfina Studio Café SE1**　　　£36　　　❶❶❷
50 Bermondsey St　7357 0244　9–4D
*"Great space, great experience" – this "light and airy"
Bermondsey art gallery is universally hailed for its "amazingly
interesting" food and its "smiley", "professional" staff; "pity it's
only open for lunch" (except Fridays).* / www.delfina.org.uk; 10 pm;
L only, except Fri when open L&D, closed Sat & Sun.

**Delfino W1**　　　　　　　　£32　　　❸④④
121a Mount St　7499 1256　3–3B
*A handy Mayfair pizzeria (opposite the Connaught) that's
"unpretentious", "functional" and "good-value".* / www.finos.co.uk;
11 pm; closed Sat L & Sun.

**La Delizia SW3**　　　　　　£28　　　❷④❸
63-65 Chelsea Manor St　7376 4111　5–3C
*"Fantastic" pizzas ("with a very thin base") win praise for this
"small", "friendly" and "crowded" Chelsea survivor.* / 11.30 pm;
no Amex.

**Demera W12**　　　　　　　£23　　　❷④④
129 Askew Rd　8762 0234　7–1B
*No awards for style (or speed) will be heaped on this Shepherd's
Bush café; its spicy and filling Ethiopian grub, however, offers
"good value", and "it's fun watching the coffee-roasting ritual".*
/ 10.30 pm; no credit cards.

**The Depot SW14**　　　　　£36　　　⑤⑤❷
Tideway Yd, Mortlake High St　8878 9462　10–1A
*"Full of itself, and for no reason other than that it's always
packed" – this "child-friendly" Barnes brasserie trades
shamelessly on its "marvellous" riverside location, and serves
"dreadful", "bland" food.* / 10.30 pm; no smoking area.

**Destino W1**　　　　　　　£41　　　④④❶
25 Swallow St　7437 9895　3–3D
*This year-old Latin American, with its "amazing" '20s tiled décor,
could hardly be more central (a stone's throw from Piccadilly
Circus); it generates remarkably little feedback, not helped by iffy
service and middling food – "super cocktails" in the bar are the
best bet.* / www.destinolondon.com; 11 pm; closed Sun L.

## Le Deuxième WC2 £42 ④❸④

65a Long Acre 7379 0033 4–2D
*"Handy for the Royal Opera House"*, this *"crowded"* venue
makes *"a good stand-by"*, pre- or post-show; the food
is *"not especially memorable, but decent enough in an area
swarming with chains"*. / www.ledeuxieme.com; midnight; set weekday L
£26 (FP), pre-theatre £24 (FP).

## Devonshire House W4 £39 ❸❷❸

126 Devonshire Rd 8987 2626 7–2A
*"Consistently good"* cooking and *"interesting"* wines win strong
local support for this slightly *"sombre"* gastropub, five minutes'
walk from Chiswick High Road. / www.thedevonshirehouse.co.uk;
10.30 pm; closed Mon.

## Dexter's Grill SW17 £27 ④❸❸

20 Bellevue Rd 8767 1858 10–2C
*"Gutsy"* burgers are the top tip at this *"kid-friendly"* hang-out
by Wandsworth Common – the sole London remnant of Tootsies'
spin-off chain. / www.tootsies.co.uk; 11 pm; no smoking area.

## Deya W1 £41 ❶❷④

34 Portman Sq 7224 0028 2–2A
*"A surprise, just north of Oxford Street"* – this *"nice-despite-
being-part-of-an-hotel"* Indian delivers *"impressively subtle"*
cooking from a *"very innovative"* menu; despite Michael Caine's
backing, however, it remains almost unknown.
/ www.deya-restaurant.co.uk; 10.45 pm; closed Sat L & Sun.

## dim T £26 ④④❸

32 Charlotte St, W1 7637 1122 2–1C **NEW**
3 Heath St, NW3 7435 0024 8–2A
*"Cool"* interiors draw a *"buzzy"* crowd to these *"casual"* dim sum
cafés; for a *"cheap and cheerful"* meal, the *"interesting"* menu
provides lots to go at, but some dishes are *"only average"*. / 11 pm,
NW3 Sat 11.30 pm; W1 no smoking area; NW3 no booking 7.30 pm -
9.30 pm.

## Dish Dash SW12 £31 ❷❷❷

11-13 Bedford Hill 8673 5555 10–2C
There's *"always a party atmosphere"*, at this Balham Persian,
where *"delicious mezze"* and *"fab kebabs"* are the menu stars.
/ www.dish-dash.com; 11 pm.

## Ditto SW18 £38 ❸❷❷

55-57 East Hill 8877 0110 10–2B
*"Things have improved a lot"*, under the new régime at this
*"pleasant"*, *"relaxed"* and *"easy"* Wandsworth local; *"very good"*
service is a particular highlight, and the menu – if still *"fairly
standard"* – is *"well-executed"*. / www.doditto.co.uk; 11 pm; no Amex;
no smoking area.

## Diverso W1 £50 ④❸④

85 Piccadilly 7491 2222 3–4C
This rather 'retro' grand Italian, opposite the Ritz, divides
reporters – some praise the *"lovely food and romantic
atmosphere"*, but almost as many complain that it's *"staid"*,
*"unexciting"* and *"really poor"*. / 11.30 pm; closed Sun L.

**Diwana Bhel-Poori House NW1**    £19    ❸④⑤
121-123 Drummond St   7387 5556   8–4C
*"Are standards slipping?"*, at this veteran veggie curry house,
near Euston; the ratings suggest slight decline, but *"rock-bottom
prices"* (in particular the *"outstanding lunchtime buffet"*) and
*"truly authentic"* south Indian food still win enthusiastic support.
/ www.diwanarestaurant.com; 11.30 pm; no smoking.

**$ EC1**    £30    ④❷④
2 Exmouth Mkt   7278 0077   9–1A
*Stick to the "great burgers" and you won't go too far wrong
at this would-be hip Clerkenwell pub-conversion; the top
attraction, though, is the louche basement bar.*
/ www.grillsandmartinis.co.uk; 11 pm; no Amex.

**The Don EC4**    £47    ❷❷❷
20 St Swithin's Ln   7626 2606   9–3C
*"A hidden gem"*, *"right in the heart of the City"*, this *"efficient
and friendly"* Gallic restaurant is as close as the Square Mile gets
to a *"perfect"* business destination – either the *"cosy"* cellar
bistro, or the more formal ground-floor; the wine list is *"brilliant"*,
too. / www.thedonrestaurant.com; 10 pm; closed Sat & Sun.

**don Fernando's TW9**    £29    ❸❷❷
27f The Quadrant   8948 6447   1–4A
*"Justifiably a Richmond institution"*, this *"very lively"* joint serves
a wide selection of *"good-value"*, *"traditional"* tapas; *"now they've
expanded, you can even get a seat"*. / www.donfernando.co.uk; 11 pm;
no smoking area; no booking.

**Don Pepe NW8**    £30    ❸❶❷
99 Frampton St   7262 3834   8–4A
*"Good food"*, *"genuine, caring service"* and a *"really Spanish feel"*
ensure that the UK's longest-established tapas bar, near Lord's,
is still worth a visit. / 11.45 pm; closed Sun.

**(Grill Room)
Dorchester Hotel W1**    £73    ❸❶❷
53 Park Ln   7629 8888   3–3A
*For British "tradition at its finest"*, this *"luxurious"*, Spanish
Baronial dining room has been hard to beat in recent years;
a new chef (Olivier Couillaud, from La Trompette) was appointed
in mid-2005 – let's hope he keeps the best of the old as well
as installing a little of the new. / www.dorchesterhotel.com; 11 pm;
set weekday L £44 (FP), set Sun L £52 (FP).

**Dove W6**    £27    ④❸❶
19 Upper Mall   8748 5405   7–2B
*It's the "unspoilt" interior and "great" riverside location that
'make' a visit to this ancient Hammersmith tavern; the standard
pub menu is "a bit duller than it should be", but the place
is hugely popular nonetheless; no kids.* / 9 pm; closed Sun D;
no booking.

### Dover Street Restaurant & Bar W1  £63  ⑤⑤❸
8-10 Dover St   7491 7509   3–3C
*The food, as ever, scores "nul points", but the music is "second to none" – it "packs 'em in nightly" – at this "cheesy but fun" dine 'n' dance basement, in Mayfair. / www.doverst.co.uk; 2 am; closed Sat L & Sun; no jeans or trainers; set weekday L £24 (FP).*

### The Drapers Arms N1  £36  ❸④❸
44 Barnsbury St   7619 0348   8–3D
*"Competent" cooking and "charming" décor still figure in most reports on this Georgian tavern, "leafily located" in Barnsbury; compared with the standards after its 2001 relaunch, though, it's fallen back significantly, and some locals wonder if it's "beginning to lose the plot". / www.thedrapersarms.co.uk; 10.30 pm; closed Sun D; no smoking; booking: max 8.*

### Drones SW1  £47  ④❸④
1 Pont St   7235 9555   5–1D
*"Comfortable, reliable and competent" – that's how most reporters see Marco Pierre White's "discreet" Belgravia outpost; perhaps that's another way of saying it's "a bit dull" (and its ratings perceptibly declined this year). / www.whitestarline.org.uk; 10.45 pm; closed Sat L & Sun D.*

### Drunken Monkey E1  £22  ❸❸❸
222 Shoreditch High St   7392 9606   9–1D
*"Funky", "loud" and "lively" former boozer in Clerkenwell; its "average but cheap dim sum" helps make it a useful stand-by. / www.thedrunkenmonkey.info; 10.45 pm; closed Sat L.*

### Duke of Cambridge SW11  £36  ④④❸
228 Battersea Bridge Rd   7223 5662   10–1C
*"They need to guard against complacency" at this attractive Battersea boozer, which has a pleasant terrace and is a popular re-fuelling stop after a trip to the Park. / www.geronimo-inns.co.uk; 9.45 pm; no Amex.*

### The Duke of Cambridge N1  £37  ❷❸❸
30 St Peter's St   7359 3066   1–2C
*"North London trendies predominate, but you do get great organic food" – "all the way down to the Cola!" – at this "airy" and "lively" gastropub favourite, on the fringe of Islington. / www.singhboulton.co.uk; 10.30 pm; no Amex; no smoking area.*

### E&O W11  £40  ❶❷❶
14 Blenheim Cr   7229 5454   6–1A
*"Cracking" – "I mean, wow!" – fusion tapas are the lead attraction at Will Ricker's "oh-so-trendy" Notting Hill celeb-haunt; the service – "without W11 attitude" – is "charming", too. / www.eando.nu; 10.45 pm; booking: max 6.*

### The Eagle EC1  £25  ❸④❷
159 Farringdon Rd   7837 1353   9–1A
*Still always "packed", this Clerkenwell boozer – which, in 1992, was London's first gastropub – is still hailed as "the original and best" by legions of reporters; overall, however, this year's ratings support those who say it's "resting on its laurels". / 10.30 pm; closed Sun D; no Amex; no booking.*

**Eagle Bar Diner W1**  £26  ❸④❷
3-5 Rathbone Pl  7637 1418  4–1A
*"Good American-style burgers" (plus "excellent cocktails" and
"amazing shakes") have helped make quite a hit of this "funky"
and "always-busy" bar/diner, just a few yards from Oxford Street.*
/ www.eaglebardiner.com; midnight, Mon 10.45 pm; closed Sun D; no Amex;
need 6+ to book.

**Ealing Park Tavern W5**  £32  ❸❷❷
222 South Ealing Rd  8758 1879  1–3A
*"Too popular, but deservedly so" – though its ratings slipped
a fraction this year, this South Ealing gastropub still wins all-round
praise for its "friendly" and "vibrant" atmosphere, and its "tasty"
grub.* / 10.15 pm; closed Mon L; no smoking in dining room; booking: max 10.

**Earl Spencer SW18**  £30  ❸④❸
260-262 Merton Rd  8870 9244  10–2B
*"Arrive early", to nab a table at this large gastropub on an "ugly"
bit of road in Southfields, as its "great-value pub food" has made
it a smash hit locally; however, like its sibling (the Havelock Arms),
it risks getting "smug".* / www.theearlspencer.co.uk; 10 pm; no booking.

**The Easton WC1**  £28  ❸④❸
22 Easton St  7278 7608  9–1A
*"Straightforward" cooking and a "friendly vibe" win fans for this
airy gastropub, near Clerkenwell's trendy Exmouth Market.*
/ www.theeaston.co.uk; 10.30 pm; closed Sat L; no Amex.

**Eat**  £11  ❸❸⑤
Branches throughout London
*"The best soups" ("changing daily") are a mainstay of this
popular "Pret-alternative" – fans insist it "beats the hell out of its
competitor", but, as ever, its rival is better-rated by reporters
overall.* / www.eatcafe.co.uk; 5 pm-6 pm; most City branches closed all or part
of weekend; no credit cards; no smoking; no booking.

**Eat & Two Veg W1**  £29  ⑤④❸
50 Marylebone High St  7258 8595  2–1A
*It's sad that the mould-breaking styling of this "fresh and funky"
Marylebone veggie is let down by food with "all the inspiration
of an NHS cafeteria"; breakfast, however, can be "really good";
(a Bayswater sibling came and went this year).*
/ www.eatandtwoveg.com; 11 pm; no smoking area.

**The Ebury SW1**  £46  ④④❸
11 Pimlico Rd  7730 6784  5–2D
*Tom Etridge's "buzzy" and "hip" bar-cum-restaurant was initially
a great hit with Pimlico folk; it's sad that some reporters –
bemoaning "shrunken" portions and "the loss of the flavour and
charm the dishes once had" – now dismiss the place as a plain
"rip-off".* / www.theebury.co.uk; 10.30 pm.

**Ebury Street Wine Bar SW1**  £40  ④❸❸
139 Ebury St  7730 5447  2–4A
*"Dated but civilised", this Belgravia fixture has long been
a popular destination, with a "cosy" and "lively" atmosphere;
for some reporters, though, its declining food standards make
it "no longer worth a visit".* / 10.15 pm; May-Aug closed Sun L;
no smoking.

**ECapital W1** £34 ❸❷④

8 Gerrard St 7434 3838 4–3A

*"Choose carefully, and you can have an exceptional meal", at this Shanghai-cuisine Chinatown spot; even fans concede that "there are also misses", though, and the place never quite seems to have lived up to its potential. / 11.30 pm.*

**Eco** £29 ❷④❸

162 Clapham High St, SW4 7978 1108 10–2D
4 Market Row, Brixton Mkt, SW9 7738 3021 10–2D

*"Huge pizzas with every imaginable topping" still draw crowds to the "bustling" ("too loud") and "cramped" Clapham branch of this odd duo; its (lunch-only) Brixton Market sibling also gets the thumbs-up – you may need to queue. / SW4 11 pm, Fri & Sat 11.30 pm, SW9 5 pm; SW9 L only, closed Wed & Sun; SW9 no booking.*

**Ed's Easy Diner** £23 ④❸❷

12 Moor St, W1 7439 1955 4–2A
Trocadero, 19 Rupert St, W1 7287 1951 3–3D
15 Gt Newport St, WC2 7836 0271 4–3B **NEW**
362 King's Rd, SW3 7352 1956 5–3B
O2 Centre, 255 Finchley Rd, NW3 7431 1958 8–2A

*"Step back into '50s America", at these "buzzy", "Happy Days"-style diners; to some, the food is only "OK", but fans wax lyrical about the "juicy" patties, the "chunky" chips and the shakes "to die for". / 10.30 pm-midnight; no Amex; no smoking, except O2 Centre, no smoking area; no booking.*

**Eddalino W1** £48 ❸❷④

10 Wigmore St 7637 0789 3–1B

*A traditional Italian, near the Wigmore Hall; it's "a bit pricey", but – with its "keen" staff and its "well-served and prepared staple dishes" – arguably deserves to be better known. / www.eddalino.com; 10.30 pm; closed Sun; no smoking area.*

**Edera W11** £40 ④❷④

148 Holland Park Ave 7221 6090 6–2A

*A Holland Park Italian, sometimes tipped as "a gem"; its food can be "over-elaborate", though, and risks being "too dear for a 'local', and not good enough for a 'destination'". / www.atozrestaurants.com; 11 pm.*

**Edokko WC1** £30 ❷❷❸

50 Red Lion St 7242 3490 2–1D

*This "Japanese lunchtime favourite", just by Gray's Inn, is a "traditional" and "charming" establishment, attracting uniform praise for its "authentic" and "affordable" cuisine. / 10 pm; closed Sat & Sun; no Amex.*

**Efes** £27 ④❸❸

1) 80 Gt Titchfield St, W1 7636 1953 2–1B
2) 175-177 Gt Portland St, W1 7436 0600 2–1B

*"Not the place for a quiet dinner" – these Turkish restaurants of long standing in Marylebone (apparently now under separate ownership) still offer a "cheap" and quite "cheerful" experience. / 11.30 pm; Gt Titchfield St closed Sun, Gt Portland St closed Fri-Sun D; no smoking area.*

### Eight Over Eight SW3 £44 ❶❷❸

392 King's Rd   7349 9934   5–3B
*"It's not quite as exhaustingly trendy as its big sister E&O",*
*but Will Ricker's Chelsea outpost offers a similar blend*
*of "amazing" Asian fusion dishes in a "chic" setting that's "always*
*humming". / www.eightovereight.nu; 10.15 pm; closed Sun L; set weekday L*
*£26 (FP).*

### 1802
### Museum In Docklands E14 £36 ❸④❷

1 West India Quay, Hertsmere Rd   0870 444 3886   11–1C
*This large Searcy's-run wine bar is the best of a striking row*
*of largely alfresco (and mainly chain) operations, with views*
*of Canary Wharf; an "unexpected pleasure", it has a "spacious"*
*and "relaxing" setting, and offers "good lunchtime value".*
*/ www.searcys.co.uk; 10 pm; closed Sun D; no smoking area; no booking at D.*

### 1880
### The Bentley Hotel SW7 £67 ❶❷❸

27-33 Harrington Gdns   7244 5555   5–2B
*Andrew Turner's "technically brilliant" cooking is "among the*
*capital's best", and his "fantastic 9-course grazing menus" offer*
*an "enjoyable, educational and truly memorable gastronomic*
*experience"; the setting – in a South Kensington basement –*
*is "opulent" going on "OTT". / www.thebentley-hotel.com; 10 pm; D only,*
*closed Sun; no smoking; booking: max 8.*

### Ekachai EC2 £25 ❷❸④

9-10 The Arcade, Liverpool St   7626 1155   9–2D
*This "useful" Malaysian/Thai canteen near Liverpool Street serves*
*"tasty and plentiful" scoff; "there's a big queue every lunchtime"*
*("but turnover is fast"). / 10 pm; closed Sat & Sun; no smoking area;*
*book only at D.*

### El Rincón Latino SW4 £28 ❸❶❶

148 Clapham Manor St   7622 0599   10–2D
*"You're teleported to Spain", at this "treasure" of a tapas bar,*
*off Clapham High Street – staff are "so welcoming" and its*
*"fresh-tasting" dishes offer "good value". / 11.30 pm.*

### Electric Brasserie W11 £45 ❸④❷

191 Portobello Rd   7908 9696   6–1A
*"The place to be seen on lazy weekends", this "really buzzy" and*
*"funky" Notting Hill in-crowd brasserie is especially popular as a*
*brunch destination… and for a "fantastic" burger at any time.*
*/ www.the-electric.co.uk; 10.45 pm; set weekday L £30 (FP).*

### Elena's L'Etoile W1 £49 ❸❷❷

30 Charlotte St   7636 7189   2–1C
*This "old-fashioned" Fitzrovia "stalwart" draws a large following,*
*thanks to its "elegantly faded" charm and "cosseting" service*
*(still presided over by octogenarian Elena Salvoni); the traditional*
*Gallic fare can be "hit-and-miss", but "the experience usually*
*transcends the food". / www.simplyrestaurants.com; 10.30 pm; closed*
*Sat L & Sun.*

### Elephant Royale
### Locke's Wharf E14          £34     ❸❷❷

Westferry Rd   7987 7999   11–2C

A "lovely" riverside location, with gorgeous views of Greenwich,
is the high-point at this Isle of Dogs Thai (whose interior strikes
some reporters as a bit "Basildon-esque"); the food is "tasty",
if "pricey" for what it is. / www.elephantroyale.com; 10.30 pm;
no smoking area.

### Elistano SW3          £37     ④❸❸

25-27 Elystan St   7584 5248   5–2C

For most reporters, this "buzzing" backstreet Italian remains
a "top Chelsea secret", thanks to its "good value" and its
"100% reliability"; ever-declining ratings, however, support those
who insist it's "going downhill". / 10.45 pm.

### The Elk in the Woods N1          £33     ④④❷

39 Camden Pas   7226 3535   8–3D

"A useful refuge from the chain-hell of Upper Street",
this "trendy" Islington restaurant offers "solid" (somewhat
"bland") nosh in a "cosy", 'retro-modern' setting.
/ www.the-elk-in-the-woods.co.uk; 11 pm; no Amex.

### Embassy W1          £50     ④④⑤

29 Old Burlington St   7851 0956   3–3C

"Too many footballers and their wives" add to the "loud" and
"frantic" vibe at this Mayfair nightclub dining room; most (if not
all) reporters feel that chef Gary Hollihead "always delivers",
but at prices that can seem "unjustifiable".
/ www.embassylondon.com; 11.30 pm; closed Mon, Sat L & Sun.

### Emile's SW15          £30     ❷❷❷

96-98 Felsham Rd   8789 3323   10–2B

Now thoroughly "back on form", this rambling Putney bistro
is "a lovely place for supper with friends" – "welcoming" and
"very relaxed", it offers "great food at bargain prices".
/ emiles-restaurant.co.uk; 11 pm; D only, closed Sun; no Amex.

### The Endurance W1          £30     ④④④

90 Berwick St   7437 2944   3–2D

"It's not trying as hard as when it opened", but this so-untrendy-
it's-almost-trendy gastropub, in the sleaziest part of Soho, can still
be a handy central stand-by. / L only; no Amex.

### The Engineer NW1          £40     ❸④❸

65 Gloucester Ave   7722 0950   8–3B

"Lovely" but "too popular", this "casual" Primrose Hill gastropub
(which benefits from "the best garden") "trades on its reputation"
a bit these days; that said, the food "seems to have improved"
of late. / www.the-engineer.com; 11 pm; no Amex.

### Enoteca Turi SW15          £45     ❷❷❸

28 Putney High St   8785 4449   10–2B

It's the "very interesting and educational" Italian wine list which
has made a big name for the Turi family's simple venture
by Putney Bridge, but the "genuine" cooking is "consistently
good", too. / 11 pm; closed Sun; no smoking area; set weekday L £28 (FP).

**The Enterprise SW3**     £39     ④❸❷

35 Walton St   7584 3148   5–2C
*"A great, busy bar" fuels the "fun" at this "lively" Chelsea pub-conversion "stalwart"; its comfort food is generally "tasty", if not much more.* / www.christophersgrill.com; 10.30 pm; no booking, except weekday L.


**Epicurean Pizza Lounge EC1** NEW   £34

10 Clerkenwell Grn   7490 5577   9–1A
*Only half-launched as this guide goes to press, this smart Clerkenwell newcomer is already being praised in the press for its exotic pizzas; when the main dining room opens – not scheduled until early-2006 – this might become quite a place.* / 10.45 pm; no smoking area.


**Eriki NW3**     £30     ❷❸❸

4-6 Northways Pde, Finchley Rd   7722 0606   8–2A
*"Not your usual Indian" – this "upscale" Swiss Cottage subcontinental, with its "original" cooking and "excellent" décor, makes quite a "find"; service is generally good, too, but the occasional "snotty" reception is not unknown.* / www.eriki.co.uk; 11.15 pm; closed Sat L.


**Esarn Kheaw W12**     £27     ❶❸④

314 Uxbridge Rd   8743 8930   7–1B
*Thanks to its "wow" cooking, this little-known Shepherds Bush spot remains – for its few adherents – "the one true Thai".* / www.esarnkheaw.co.uk; 11 pm; closed Sat L & Sun L.


**L'Escargot W1**     £45     ❸❷❸

48 Greek St   7437 2679   4–2A
*The "complex" cuisine in the "romantic" upstairs Picasso Room of this Soho veteran (formula price £60) scored well this year, but the "traditional" fare in the "elegant" main brasserie also won consistent praise; chef Jeff Galvin, however, left post-survey to set up on his own account.* / www.whitestarline.org.uk; 11.30 pm; closed Sat L & Sun (Picasso Room also closed Mon).


**Esenza W11**     £43     ❸④④

210 Kensington Park Rd   7792 1066   6–1A
*"OK, but could do better" – a "cramped" Notting Hill Italian yearling, which has yet live up to its stablemates (Osteria Basilico and Mediterraneo).* / 11.30 pm; set weekday L £26 (FP).


**Est Est Est**     £29

29 Chiswick High Rd, W4   8747 8777   7–2B
57-58 Upper St, N1   7359 9198   8–3D
27-29 Bellevue Rd, SW17   8672 3122   10–2C
38 High St, SW19   8947 7700   1–4A
*After a rocky time in recent years, this "bright" and "bustling" (but, too often, "dire") pizza-and-more chain was acquired, by the 'Living Room' people, in the spring of 2005; given their 'revitalisation' plans, we've left it un-rated.* / 11 pm; no smoking areas.

### L'Estaminet WC2 £46 ④❸❸
14 Garrick St 7379 1432 4–3C
*"Particularly good-value"* pre-theatre deals and an *"extensive cheeseboard"* are top attractions at this *"predictable"* Gallic stalwart, in Covent Garden; otherwise, however, it can seem *"ordinary"*. / 11 pm; closed Sat L & Sun; set pre-theatre £26 (FP).

### L'Etranger SW7 £61 ❷❸❸
36 Gloucester Rd 7584 1118 5–1B
Jerome Tauvron's *"imaginative"* and *"prettily-presented"* Franco-Japanese cuisine is winning more consistent acclaim for this *"understated"* South Kensington two-year-old, which is also noted for its *"outstanding"* wine list. / www.etranger.co.uk; 11 pm; closed Sat L & Sun; set weekday L & pre-theatre £27 (FP).

### EV SE1 NEW £28 ④❷❷
97-99 Isabella St 7620 6191 9–4A
This *"interesting bar/restaurant/shop"* – an offshoot of Tas – is housed in a set of railway arches and makes an *"unusual"* South Bank destination (and a *"great party venue)"*; initially at least, its Turkish fare has been rather *"bland"*. / 11.30 pm; no smoking.

### The Evangelist EC4 £29 ④❸❸
33 Black Friars Ln 7213 0740 9–3A
A style-bar stand-by in a City back lane, which serves reasonably satisfactory *"gastropub-type"* food. / www.massivepub.com; 9 pm; closed Sat & Sun.

### Evo SW4 NEW £25 ④❸④
57 Abbeville Rd 8673 2791 10–2D
A good lunchtime eat-all-you-can deal is the most notable feature of this new Chinese café, in the backstreets of Clapham. / 11 pm; Mon-Wed closed L; no smoking area.

### Exmouth Grill EC1 £34 ④④④
55-57 Exmouth Mkt 7837 0009 9–1A
The initial promise of this *"trying-to-be-cool"* Clerkenwell yearling looks unfulfilled; fans praise it as a *"friendly"* place with *"plain but good"* cooking – it generated little feedback, though, and doubters just find it *"lacklustre"*. / www.exmouthgrill.com; 10 pm; closed Mon, Thu L & Sun.

### Exotika WC2 £20 ❸❷⑤
7 Villiers St 7930 6133 4–4D
It may be too *"stark"* and *"minimalist"*, but this small diner, by Charing Cross, is *"handy all the same"*, as it offers *"a wide range"* of *"basic"* and *"healthy"* dishes, all at affordable prices. / www.exotika.co.uk; 11 pm; no smoking.

### Eyre Brothers EC2 £47 ❷❸④
70 Leonard St 7613 5346 9–1D
*"Fine dining in an area usually more focussed on cool"* – that's how one reporter sees this Shoreditch modern Iberian, whose *"well-spaced"* quarters are popular, not least for business; atmosphere, however, can be *"surprisingly lacking"*. / www.eyrebrothers.co.uk; 10.45 pm; closed Sat L & Sun D; no smoking area.

**Fairuz** £39 ❷❸④
3 Blandford St, W1   7486 8108   2–1A
27 Westbourne Grove, W2   7243 8444   6–1C **NEW**
"Mezze with myriad flavours and textures", and "obliging" staff
help make this "homely" Marylebone outfit a "favourite"
Lebanese; its new Bayswater sibling is of less interest. / W1
11.30 pm, W2 midnight.

**Fakhreldine W1** £49 ❸❸❸
85 Piccadilly   7493 3424   3–4C
"Friendly" staff add to the upbeat vibe of this "buzzy", first-floor
Mayfair Lebanese, recently rejuvenated, which enjoys "fine views"
of Green Park; the food's "not cheap", but "very good".
/ www.fakhreldine.co.uk; midnight.

**Il Falconiere SW7** £35 ④④④
84 Old Brompton Rd   7589 2401   5–2B
The set-price menu at this long-established trattoria offers
"very good value, for South Kensington"; otherwise,
it's unremarkable. / www.ilfalconiere.co.uk; 11.30 pm; closed Sun;
set weekday L £21 (FP).

**La Famiglia SW10** £45 ❸❸❸
7 Langton St   7351 0761   5–3B
"Still one of the buzziest Italians in London", this age-old World's
End trattoria exerts a curiously timeless appeal, even if it is
"too noisy", and certainly "not cheap" – key selling points include
"characterful" staff and a "magical" garden.
/ www.lafamiglialondon.com; 11.45 pm; no smoking area.

**The Farm SW6** £41 ❸④❸
18 Farm Ln   7381 3331   5–3A
"Tasty" ("but very expensive") food helps win fans for Tom
Etridge's "stylish" new bar-cum-restaurant, near Fulham
Broadway; service can be "lousy", though, and "it's outrageous
that they don't take cash!" / www.thefarmfulham.co.uk; 10.30 pm.

**Fat Boy's** £26 ❸❸❸
33 Haven Grn, W5   8998 5868   1–2A
431-433 Richmond Rd, TW1   8892 7657   1–4A
68 High St, TW8   8569 8481   1–3A
10a-10b Edensor Rd, W4   8994 8089   10–1A
"Always good and reliable" food underpins the appeal of these,
"cheap and cheerful" west London Thais (which, by day, operate
as greasy spoons); in Chiswick, you can BYO. / 11 pm;
no smoking area.

**Faulkner's E8** £26 ❷❷④
424-426 Kingsland Rd   7254 6152   1–1D
"Pure chippie heaven, worth driving out of your way for" –
this "jovial" institution ("long a feature of Dalston Market",
and recently refitted) serves "excellent fish", "big bags of chips",
and "mushy peas like they used to make 'em". / 10 pm; no smoking
area; need 8+ to book.

**Feng Sushi** £26 ❸❸④

26 Elizabeth St, SW1  7730 0033  2–4A
218 Fulham Rd, SW10  7795 1900  5–3B
101 Notting Hill Gate, W11  7727 1123  6–2B
21 Kensington Church St, W8  7937 7927  5–1A
13 Stoney St, SE1  7407 8744  9–4C

"Reliable" sushi and "some very good Bento box deals" win this "no-gimmicks" Japanese group a small fan club; the seating is a bit "cramped" and "uncomfortable", but you can always take away. / www.fengsushi.co.uk; 11 pm, Sun-Wed 10 pm, SE1 Thu-Sat 10.30 pm; SW1 & SE1 closed Sun; no smoking, SE1 smoking throughout; SW1 need 5+ to book.

**The Fentiman Arms SW8** £30 ❸❸❷

64 Fentiman Rd  7793 9796  10–1D

An unassuming Kennington boozer, which offers "simple but well-cooked meals"; it has a "fantastic beer garden".
/ www.geronimo-inns.co.uk; 9.45 pm; no Amex; no smoking area; need 8+ to book.

**Ferrari's SW17** £28 ④❸④

225 Balham High Rd  8682 3553  10–2C

"Nothing special, nothing bad" – this large, Balham/Tooting fringe Italian is a "friendly" venture, consistently praised as "a good option in an area bereft of decent places".
/ www.ferrarisrestaurants.co.uk; 11 pm; no smoking area.

**Ffiona's W8** £38 ❸❶❶

51 Kensington Church St  7937 4152  5–1A

"Ffiona is the key" to this "warm and cosy" Kensington bistro, whose "retro", "comfort food" adds to the impression of a "dinner party" ("just with someone else doing all the work").
/ www.ffionas.com; 11 pm; D only, closed Mon.

**Fifteen N1** £74 ⑤⑤⑤

15 Westland Pl  0871 330 1515  9–1C

"Great school food campaign, shame about the restaurant" – however "worthy" its founder's aims, many reporters can't help seeing Jamie Oliver's Hoxton two-year-old as a "monument to mediocrity", and even some who find it "good overall" (or are "huge Jamie fans") say it's "galling to pay so much for something so ordinary"; (n.b. the ground-floor trattoria is a cheaper option).
/ www.fifteenrestaurant.com; 9.30 pm; closed Sun D; no smoking; booking: max 6; set weekday L £38 (FP).

**The Fifth Floor Harvey Nichols SW1** £54 ④④⑤

Knightsbridge  7235 5250  5–1D

They're still tinkering with the lay-out, but Harvey Nics would needs a total rethink to rescue its "overpriced" top-floor dining room, where the "cold" décor is supposedly relieved by walls which change colour now and again – "well, at least it distracts you from what you're eating". / www.harveynichols.com; 11 pm; closed Sun D.

### The Fifth Floor (Café)
### Harvey Nichols SW1                    £40          ⑤⑤④
Knightsbridge   7823 1839   5–1D
"Appalling" food and "sloppy" service now seem endemic in the
"bright" and "busy" café of Harvey Nic's top floor food halls –
"only go if you need a coffee or are about to faint with hunger".
/ www.harveynichols.com; 10.30 pm, Sun 5 pm; closed Sun D; no smoking
area; no booking at L; set D £25 (FP).

### Fig N1                                £35          ④❸❸
169 Hemingford Rd   7609 3009   8–3D
This tiny and "cosy" Islington yearling has had a very mixed
reception – some find it "perfect" for an "inventive" bite, but to
doubters it's just "hyped and disappointing". / www.figrestaurant.co.uk;
10 pm; D only, closed Mon & Sun; no smoking.

### La Figa E14                          £33          ❸❷❸
45 Narrow St   7790 0077   11–1B
A Wapping sibling to Docklands' Il Bordello, similarly tipped for its
"top pizza" and other hearty Italian dishes; relatively speaking,
however, it attracts very little commentary from reporters. / 11 pm;
no smoking area.

### Fina Estampa SE1                     £35          ④❸④
150 Tooley St   7403 1342   9–4D
"Interesting food in an odd location" – that's the deal at this
"quaint" operation, near Tower Bridge, which offers
"fundamentally stodgy" Peruvian dishes, "done as well as perhaps
they can be". / www.finaestampa.co.uk; 10.30 pm; closed Sat L & Sun.

### La Finca SE11                        £25          ④④❷
185 Kennington Ln   7735 1061   10–1D
This long-in-the-tooth Kennington tapas bar (the Islington branch
is no more) is a "fun" and "busy" hang-out in a still under-served
area. / www.thefinca.co.uk; 11.30 pm; no Amex; no smoking area.

### Fine Burger Company                  £22          ❸❸④
50 James St, W1   7224 1890   3–1A  **NEW**
256 Muswell Hill Broadway, N10   8815 9292   8–1C
330 Upper St, N1   7226 0837   8–3D  **NEW**
37 Bedford Hill, SW12   8772 0266   10–2C
With its "posh" burgers, and "imaginative" toppings, this growing,
"upmarket fast food" chain gets a general thumbs-up from
reporters. / www.homebar.co.uk/fbc; 11 pm; no smoking.

### Fino W1                              £42          ❷❷❸
33 Charlotte St   7813 8010   2–1C
"Tapas taken to a new, more exciting level" – plus "superlative"
wines and "superb" service – have won fame for this Fitzrovia
basement yearling (which is done out "in defiantly non-Spanish
style"); even some fans, though, note that "prices seem stuck
on the 'up' escalator". / www.finorestaurant.com; 10.30 pm; closed Sun;
booking: max 12.

**Fiore SW1** NEW £45 ④❷④

33 St James's St  7930 7100  3–4C

*This St James's Italian newcomer (on the former Pétrus site, a sibling to nearby Al Duca) wins praise as a useful business rendezvous, thanks to its spacious layout and "enthusiastic" service; our visit – like that of some reporters – showed promise, but overall feedback is very mixed. / www.fiore-restaurant.co.uk; 10.30 pm; closed Sun L; smoking discouraged.*

**Fire & Stone WC2** NEW £27 ④❷❸

31-32 Maiden Ln  0845 330 0139  4–3D

*It was very early days when we visited this impressively airy and stylish new Covent Garden pizza place in June 2005 – to our mind, they need to shift the food up a notch to make it a truly useful destination. / Rated on Editors' visit; www.fireandstone.com.*

**The Fire Stables SW19** £38 ④④❷

27-29 Church Rd  8946 3197  10–2B

*A "vibrant" – and, on occasions, "horribly busy" – gastropub that's been quite a Wimbledon hit of recent years; the food, however, is "a bit nondescript". / www.thefirestables.co.uk; 10.30 pm; no Amex; no smoking area; booking: max 8, Sat & Sun.*

**FireHouse SW7** £46 ❸❷❸

3 Cromwell Rd  7584 7258  5–2C

*For a swanky joint in the heart of South Kensington, this club dining room (open to all at dinner) elicits surprisingly little feedback – such as there is though, says "staff can't do enough for you", and that the food can be "fantastic". / www.firehousesw7.com; 10 pm; D only, closed Mon & Sun.*

**Firezza SW11** NEW £23 ❶❷④

40 Lavender Hill  7223 5535  10–1C

*"Surpassing all expectations of how a pizza should look and taste", this "unbeatable" new south London mini-chain is off to a cracking start; primarily the branches are take-out, but there are a few (mainly alfresco) tables at the outlet listed. / 11.15 pm.*

**First Edition E14** £40 ④④④

25 Cabot Sq, Canary Wharf  7513 0300  11–1C

*It's "OK for a quick business lunch", but we can't help wishing that this Canary Wharf bar/restaurant – one of the few non-chain outfits in the locality – was something more; booths are available for greater privacy. / 11 pm; closed Sat & Sun.*

**First Floor W11** £39 ❸❸❶

186 Portobello Rd  7243 0072  6–1A

*An "elegant" dining room above a "buzzing" bar, in "the heart of Portobello Market" – it doesn't seem to have much of a following nowadays, but its fan club insists that its cooking is "consistently good". / www.firstfloorportobello.co.uk; 10.30 pm; closed Mon & Sun D; no Amex.*

### Fish Club SW11 `NEW` £30 ❷❷④

189 St John's Hill   7978 7115   10–2C

"Fresh fish served simply, cooked skillfully, and priced right" has made a local hit of this Battersea newcomer – a "very modern take" on the classic chippie formula. / www.thefishclub.com; 10 pm, Sun 9 pm; closed Mon; no Amex; no smoking.

### Fish Hoek W4 £43 ❶❷④

6-8 Elliott Rd   8742 0766   7–2A

"An amazing array of fish" – available in half or full portions, and cooked "to perfection" – makes this "friendly" Chiswick South African one of London's most "innovative" places for seafood; no one really cares that it's "cramped" and "noisy". / www.fishhoek.co.uk; 10 pm; closed Mon (except Aug-Dec); no Amex; no smoking area; set weekday L £19 (FP).

### Fish in a Tie SW11 £20 ❸❷❷

105 Falcon Rd   7924 1913   10–1C

"A triumph in cheap and cheerful eating", this "local jewel" – "on the wrong side of the tracks", near Clapham Junction – is "always packed to the rafters"; service is notably "friendly", but the key attraction is food for which "you could pay double elsewhere". / 11.45 pm; no Amex; no smoking area.

### Fish Shop EC1 £40 ❷❸④

360-362 St John's St   7837 1199   8–3D

"Very good fish" is helping this "bright" Islington outfit – with the air of an "upmarket chippie" – to make more waves; even fans, however, can find prices "a bit on the greedy side". / www.thefishshop.net; 10.30 pm; closed Mon & Sun D; no smoking area.

### fish! SE1 £39 ❸❸④

Cathedral St   7407 3803   9–4C

"Very fresh and simply-cooked" fish dishes are – after a failed expansion plan – "re-establishing" this "noisy", greenhouse-like place; it's at its best on Saturdays, when "the Borough Market surroundings add to the experience". / www.fishdiner.co.uk; 10.30 pm; no smoking area.

### Fishmarket
### Great Eastern Hotel EC2 £51 ④④⑤

40 Liverpool St   7618 7200   9–2D

Totally "soulless" it may be – and arguably "overpriced", too – but Conran's busy fish café by Liverpool Street station won more praise this year for its sometimes "interesting" dishes. / www.great-eastern-hotel.co.uk; 10.30 pm; closed Sat & Sun; booking: max 7 at L.

### Fishworks £43 ❷❸④

89 Marylebone High St, W1   7935 9796   2–1A
6 Turnham Green Ter, W4   8994 0086   7–2A
134 Upper St, N1   awaiting tel   8–3D   `NEW`

"Extremely fresh fish" – served "plainly and simply" – is proving a winning formula for these Chiswick and Marylebone restaurants-cum-fishmongers (part of a growing national chain); the thoroughly-restaurant prices, though, "are at odds with the café-style surroundings". / www.fishworks.co.uk; 10.30 pm; W4 closed Sun & Mon; W1 closed Mon; no smoking.

**5 Cavendish Square W1**  £53  ④❸❸
5 Cavendish Sq  7079 5000  3–1C
*A thirtysomething crowd finds it "fun" to visit the "grand" first-floor dining room of this "glamorous" – in a Versace sort of way – townhouse, just north of Oxford Street; the food, certainly in comparison, can seem "poor". / www.no5ltd.com; 11 pm; closed Sat L & Sun D; no booking, Fri & Sat.*

**Five Hot Chillies HA0**  £23  ❶❷❷
875 Harrow Rd  8908 5900  1–1A
*"Explosive flavours, bargain prices and total authenticity" win unanimous raves for this "packed" BYO cantina, in Sudbury – "as good as Indian food gets anywhere in the world!"*

**Flâneur EC1**  £44  ❷❸❷
41 Farringdon Rd  7404 4422  9–1A
*An "unusual situation" (within a "beautiful" food hall) contributes to the appeal of this Farringdon 'one-off' – be it for a "tasty" brunch, for "superb" cakes, or for a "very good" light lunch. / www.flaneur.com; 10 pm; closed Sun D; no smoking.*

**Florians N8**  £33  ④❸❸
4 Topsfield Pde  8348 8348  1–1C
*Quite a "stylish" Crouch End "perennial", whose "noisy" bar area is a particular local favourite; Italian fare that's "brilliant" for some reporters strikes others as "run-of-the-mill". / www.floriansrestaurant.co.uk; 11 pm; no Amex; no smoking.*

**Floridita W1**  £52  ⑤⑤❸
100 Wardour St  7314 4000  3–2D
*Ay, caramba! "Conran goes Cuban", at this Soho basement (which is, in fact, a joint venture with an outfit from Havana); if you go "for the live music and the rum", you can have a "great" (if "too loud") time, but the basic package – "forgettable" food and service "with attitude" – is eerily reminiscent of the Conran group's predecessor on this site, Mezzo (RIP). / www.floriditalondon.com; 2 am; D only, closed Sun.*

**Foliage**
**Mandarin Oriental SW1**  £67  ❷❶❷
66 Knightsbridge  7201 3723  5–1D
*"Complex dishes, with brilliant clarity of flavour" (from chef Chris Staines) have helped push this "extremely professional" Knightsbridge dining room to new heights this year; some reporters still discern a "lack of ambience", though – get a table with a "lovely park view" if you can. / www.mandarinoriental.com; 10.30 pm; booking: max 6; set always available £39 (FP).*

**La Fontana SW1**  £39  ❸❷❸
101 Pimlico Rd  7730 6630  5–2D
*"Unbeatable pasta with truffles (in season)" is what this Pimlico '60s-survivor still does best; those in search of a trattoria which is "not noisy" are unlikely to do better elsewhere. / 11 pm.*

### Food for Thought WC2　　　　£16　　❷④④
31 Neal St　7836 0239　4–2C
*"Queues are long and seating limited", at this "too cramped"
basement; "it's always worth it", though, for the "light" and
"nutritious" veggie fare that offers "the best value in Covent
Garden".* / 8.15 pm; closed Sun D; no credit cards; no smoking; no booking.

### The Food Room SW8　　　　£35　　❸❷④
123 Queenstown Rd　7622 0555　10–1C
*"Fine contemporary cooking" in "pleasant and uncluttered
surroundings" has helped win quite a following for this Battersea
yearling; its predecessor, the Stepping Stone (RIP), was a hard act
to follow, however, and – perhaps unfairly – it can seem an "also-
ran" in comparison.* / www.thefoodroom.com; 10.30 pm, Sat & Sun 11 pm;
closed Mon, Tue L, Sat L & Sun; no Amex; no smoking area.

### Food@TheMuse W11　[NEW]　　　£35
269 Portobello Rd　7792 1111　6–1A
*A chef with an impressive CV cooks at this new 'world cuisine'
restaurant-cum-gallery, in Notting Hill, which opened shortly
before this guide went to press; we sadly didn't manage to fit in a
visit, but newspaper reviews have been favourable.*
/ www.themuseat269.com; 11 pm; closed Mon L & Sun D; no smoking.

### Footstool SW1　　　　£32　　⑤⑤❸
St John's, Smith Sq　7222 2779　2–4C
*The food at this "canteen" in a Westminster crypt is "limited",
"predictable" and "expensive for what you get" – it's only really
recommendable around attendance at a concert in the hall
above.* / www.sjss.org.uk; L only, closed Sat & Sun; no smoking area.

### Formosa Dining Room
### The Prince Alfred W9　　　£37　　❸❸❷
5a Formosa St　7286 3287　6–1C
*The modern, white-walled dining annex of an "impressive"
Victorian boozer in Maida Vale; its "straightforward" cooking
is "of a high standard", if arguably "a bit pricey".* / 10.45 pm;
no Amex; no smoking.

### (The Fountain)
### Fortnum & Mason W1　　　£38　　④❸❸
181 Piccadilly　7734 8040　3–3D
*"Terrific breakfasts" and "great high teas" are highlights of the
"English nursery food" at this "comforting" bastion of old
St James's; "you expect the place to be stuck in a time warp,
and you're glad it is" – better visit now, before the major
redevelopment begins!* / www.fortnumandmason.co.uk; 7.45 pm; closed
Sun; no smoking area; no booking at L.

### 43 South Molton W1　[NEW]　　£39　　❸❸④
43 South Molton St　7647 4343　3–2B
*This odd new bistro, near Oxford Street, is curiously decked out
with old tins and so on; although our food was pretty good,
we couldn't help thinking that this place has its heart in the
adjoining club and bar facilities, rather than the eating.*
/ www.43southmolton.com; Rated on Editors' inspection; 10 pm.

**Four Regions** £34 ❸❸④
County Hall, Westminster Br Rd, SE1  7928 0988  2–3D
102-104 Kew Rd, TW9  8940 9044  1–4A
The "cavernous" County Hall branch of this Chinese duo
is mainly of interest because of its proximity to the Eye;
its Richmond-fringe forebear, though, is highly acclaimed locally
as the best oriental in the area. / www.fourregions.co.uk; 11.30 pm.

**The Four Seasons W2** £23 ❶⑤⑤
84 Queensway  7229 4320  6–1C
"The best crispy duck in the world" is served at this "hectic"
Bayswater Chinese (and the "pork dishes are also very good");
"dragon-like service keeps things moving at a fair whack".
/ 11.15 pm.

**1492 SW6** £35 ❸④❸
404 North End Rd  7381 3810  5–4A
"A really interesting Latin American menu" adds interest to this
"buzzing" and quite "funky" Fulham two-year-old; its dishes,
however, can seem "over-ambitious". / www.1492restaurant.com;
10.30 pm, Fri & Sat 11 pm; closed weekday L; no smoking area.

**The Fox EC2** £32 ❷④❷
28 Paul St  7729 5708  9–1C
Michael Belben's unmodified boozer "just outside the City limits"
makes an "atmospheric" and "romantic" destination in which
to enjoy this Eagle-founder's "original" cuisine; "the hit-and-miss
service is all part of the charm, I suppose". / 10 pm; closed
Sat & Sun; no Amex.

**Fox & Anchor EC1** £28 ❸❸❸
115 Charterhouse St  7253 5075  9–1B
The "classic, early-morning full fry-ups", at this "legendary"
Smithfield Market boozer, are "for the brave of heart" –
"make sure you get a pint to wash down all the grease". / closed
Sat & Sun.

**The Fox & Hounds SW11** £29 ❷❷❷
66 Latchmere Rd  7924 5483  10–1C
This "fantastic" Battersea gastropub is acclaimed for its
"delicious", largely Mediterranean cuisine, and its "good selection
of wines by the glass". / 10.30 pm; no Amex.

**The Fox Reformed N16** £30 ④❸❷
176 Stoke Newington Church St  7254 5975  1–1C
This "friendly" old Stokie institution is undoubtedly "a great wine
bar (especially for backgammon enthusiasts)"; its "comfort" food,
though, is "nothing to write home about". / www.fox-reformed.co.uk;
10.30 pm; closed weekday L; no smoking area.

**Foxtrot Oscar SW3** £35 ⑤④⑤
79 Royal Hospital Rd  7352 7179  5–3D
This "cliquey" Chelsea "bastion" still wins praise from the faithful
for its "great Bloody Marys" and its menu of "burgers and '70s
faves"; it's "not what it was", though, and the uninitiated
condemn a "drab" place, where the food is just "rubbish".
/ 11 pm.

### Frankie's SW3 `NEW` £42 ④④❸
3 Yeomans Row  7590 9999  5–2C
*Fans hail MPW and Franco Dettori's new Knightsbridge basement*
*(on the site of Chezmax, RIP) as a "fun" and "glamorous"*
*destination; prices are high, though, especially given the "slow"*
*service and "very ordinary" cuisine; (a Chiswick sibling is to open*
*in autumn 2005 in the location that was once Pug, RIP). / 11 pm;*
*set weekday L £27 (FP).*

### Franklins SE22 £40 ❷❷❷
157 Lordship Ln  8299 9598  1–4D
*"The best for miles around" – this "fantastic local eatery" wins*
*a hymn of praise from East Dulwich folk for its "simple" but*
*"delicious" fare, "great" service and "relaxed" atmosphere.*
*/ www.franklinsrestaurant.com; 10.30 pm; set weekday L £22 (FP).*

### Frantoio SW10 £37 ❸❷❷
397 King's Rd  7352 4146  5–3B
*Emerging (after a slow start) as a "great neighbourhood*
*restaurant", this "very friendly", "buzzy" and "good-value"*
*World's Ender offers an experience akin to "teleporting to Italy".*
*/ 11.30 pm; no smoking area.*

### Fratelli la Bufala NW3 `NEW` £27 ❶❷❸
45a South End Rd  7435 7814  8–2A
*This "splendid" new south Hampstead Italian occupies the*
*former site of Cucina (RIP); "fantastic" pizzas are complemented*
*by "excellent buffalo meat and cheese", and served in a setting*
*that's "warm", "welcoming" and "very lively".*
*/ www.fratellilabufala.com; 11 pm; no smoking area.*

### Frederick's N1 £47 ❸❸❷
106 Camden Pas  7359 2888  8–3D
*With its "beautiful high-ceilinged conservatory", this grand but*
*"friendly" Islington "favourite" has long been "a lovely place for*
*special occasions" (in "an area still surprisingly short of high-*
*quality options"). / www.fredericks.co.uk; 11.30 pm; closed Sun; no Amex;*
*no smoking area; set weekday L & pre-theatre £26 (FP).*

### The Freemasons SW18 £32 ❸❷❷
2 Wandsworth Common Northside  7326 8580  10–2C
*"Superbly presented" and "flavoursome" dishes are already*
*beginning to make quite a name for this "casual" and*
*"comfortable" new Wandsworth gastropub. / 10 pm; no smoking.*

### Freemasons Arms NW3 `NEW` £32 ④④❸
32 Downshire Hill  7433 6811  8–2A
*"The biggest beer garden in the neighbourhood" is among the*
*attractions of this "good new gastropub"; the dreaded*
*'Hampstead effect' is never far away, though – the food*
*is "dependable" going-on "dull". / www.freemasonsarms.co.uk;*
*10.45 pm; no smoking.*

### French House W1 £45 ❸④❷
49 Dean St  7437 2477  4–3A
*"There's something special" (and "intimate") about this "poky"*
*but "atmospheric" room, above a famous Soho pub; the food*
*may "play safe" but it's "consistently good" (unlike the sometimes*
*"unenthusiastic" service). / 11 pm; closed Sun D; booking: max 8.*

### Fresco W2 £18 ❷❷④
25 Westbourne Grove   7221 2355   6–1C
*"Delicious juices squeezed before your very eyes"* (and other *"freshly-prepared"* snacks) win rave reviews for this small Lebanese café, *"tucked-away"* in Bayswater – *"the queues outside speak for themselves"*. / 11 pm; no smoking area.

### Friends SW10 £36 ④④④
6 Hollywood Rd   7376 3890   5–3B
A younger crowd tips this cramped Chelsea Italian for *"great pizza for not much money"*; all-in-all, though, feedback is pretty *middle-of-the-road*. / 11.30 pm; closed weekday L, Sat D & Sun D; no Amex.

### Frocks E9 £37 ④④❸
95 Lauriston Rd   8986 3161   1–2D
Since it changed hands last year, this *"lovely"* and *"cosy"* Victoria Park bistro has seemed increasingly *"overpriced"*; for weekend brunch or romance, though, it still has its fans. / 11 pm; closed Mon, Tue L & Wed L.

### La Fromagerie Café W1 £29 ❶❷❷
2-4 Moxon St   7935 0341   3–1A
*"You're lucky if you can get a seat at the single trestle table"*, at this *"divine"* Marylebone cheese shop/food emporium, which offers *"gorgeous"* soups and salads, as well as dairy products; there's an *"interesting wine list"*, too. / www.lafromageriecafe.co.uk; 6.30 pm; L only; no smoking; no booking.

### The Frontline Club W2 £39 ④❷❸
13 Norfolk Pl   7479 8960   6–1D
Named after the war reporters' club with which it is associated, this *"bustling"* yearling near St Mary's has been a *"stylish"* addition to *"a dodgy part of Paddington"*; the *"evocative photographs"* on the walls, however, seem to be generating more interest than the *"pricey"* food. / www.frontlinerestaurant.com; 10.30 pm; closed Sat L & Sun; no smoking area.

### Fryer's Delight WC1 £9 ❸④⑤
19 Theobald's Rd   7405 4114   2–1D
*"No nonsense, no fuss"* – just a *"basic"*, *"cramped"* chippie, where the number of cabbies often to be found eating attests to a reputation as *"one of the best"*. / 10 pm; closed Sun; no credit cards; no booking.

### Fujiyama SW9 £19 ❷④❸
7 Vining St   7737 2369   10–2D
For a *"quick"* meal that's *"delicious, healthy, and filling"*, this *"good-value"* Brixton noodle bar incites nothing but praise; it now serves *"great sushi"* too. / www.newfujiyama.com; 12.45 am, Sat & Sun midnight; no Amex; no smoking area.

### Fung Shing WC2 £35 ❷❸⑤
15 Lisle St   7437 1539   4–3A
This *"ordinary"*-looking Chinatown fixture is sometimes tipped as *"London's best Chinese"* (in particular for its *"excellent seafood"*); ratings have see-sawed in recent years, though, and a number of *"ordinary"* meals were again noted this year. / 11.15 pm.

### Furnace N1 £30 ❸④❸

1 Rufus St 7613 0598 9–1D

*"Very good pizzas"* (plus a *"nice selection of starters"*) help make this *"buzzing"* spot a notably *"reliable"* destination, *"in the heart of Hoxton"*. / www.furnace.co.uk; 11 pm; closed Sat L & Sun; no Amex; no smoking area.

### Fuzzy's Grub £9 ❷❷❸

6 Crown Pas, SW1 7925 2791 3–4D
10 Well Ct, EC4 7236 8400 9–2B
62 Fleet St, EC4 7583 6060 9–2A

*"The best roast meat sandwiches in the world"* (*"with crackling even better than mum's!"*) and *"charming"* service make it well worth truffling out these *"brilliant"* British cafés. / www.fuzzysgrub.com; EC4 3 pm, SW1 4 pm; closed Sat & Sun; no credit cards; EC4 no smoking.

### Gabrielles W1 £46 ❸④❸

14 Heddon St 7494 2234 3–2C

Handily located just off Regent Street, this Provençal corner spot has an agreeable – if rather provincial – ambience, with nice outside tables for sunny days. / www.gabrielles.com; 10.30 pm; closed Sun; set weekday L & pre-theatre £27 (FP).

### Gaby's WC2 £25 ④④④

30 Charing Cross Rd 7836 4233 4–3B

*"Great falafels"*, and *"massive salt beef sandwiches"* are the trusty staples at this *"simple, cramped and canteen-like"* Covent Garden veteran (which is *"ideal for a pre-theatre bite"*). / www.gabys.net; 11.30 pm; no credit cards; no smoking area.

### La Galette W1 £28 ❸④④

56 Paddington St 7935 1554 2–1A

For a *"cheap and cheerful"* meal, the *"fabulous"* crêpes and *"jolly good"* cider at this smart Marylebone café make a *"welcome and tasty change"*. / www.lagalette.com; 10.45 pm; no smoking; need 6+ to book.

### Galicia W10 £27 ❷❸❷

323 Portobello Rd 8969 3539 6–1A

*"Plenty of Spaniards"* add authenticity to this no-nonsense North Kensington veteran, where the tapas are *"good-quality, and good-value, too"*. / 11.30 pm; closed Mon.

### Gallipoli £21 ❸❸❸

102 Upper St, N1 7359 0630 8–3D
107 Upper St, N1 7226 5333 8–3D
120 Upper St, N1 7359 1578 8–3D

*"For a fun night out at low prices"*, these trio of neighbouring *"warm"*, and *"boisterous"* Turkish bistros are an Islington *"mainstay"*; constantly *"oversubscribed"*, though, they risk becoming *"slapdash"*. / www.gallipolicafes.com; 11 pm, Fri & Sat midnight; 107 Upper St closed Mon.

**Galvin W1** NEW £38
66 Baker St 7486 3176 2–1A
*The Galvin brothers have quit big jobs at the Wolseley and
L'Escargot to set up this new (late-2005) 'bistro de luxe' on the
large former Marylebone site of Anda (RIP) – this should be one
to watch! (Price given is our guesstimate.)*

**Garbo's W1** £36 ④❸⑤
42 Crawford St 7262 6582 2–1A
*The "remarkable-value" smorgasbord is the star turn at this
"homely" Scandinavian veteran in Marylebone; other fare –
though mostly fine – can disappoint. / 10.45 pm; closed Sat L & Sun D;
no Maestro; set weekday L £23 (FP).*

**The Garden Café NW1** NEW £29 ❸②②
Inner Circle, Regent's Pk 7935 5729 8–4B
*With its beautiful location and large garden, this attractive
(if rather '70s) park café has long cried out for investment;
it finally got it this year, with the introduction of a simple menu
that's both well-realised and good value; summer sees a regular
programme of lunchtime jazz. / www.thegardencafe.co.uk; 9 pm;
no Amex; no smoking.*

**Garlic & Shots W1** £29 ④④④
14 Frith St 7734 9505 4–2A
*"Especially tasty, if you like garlic", or "the worst meal I have ever
eaten in London" – this Soho Goth "dive" (where absolutely
everything comes spiked with the pungent root) is a love-it-or-
hate-it affair. / www.garlicandshots.com; 11.15 pm, Thu-Sat 12.15 am;
D only; no Amex; no booking.*

**Garrison SE1** £35 ❷④❷
99-101 Bermondsey St 7089 9355 9–4D
*"A great buzz" and "simple" and "wholesome" cooking help win
local rave reviews for this dolled-up boozer, near Bermondsey
Antiques Market; it gets "crowded", though, and service can
be "haphazard". / 10 pm; no smoking in bar.*

**Gastro SW4** £37 ④⑤❸
67 Venn St 7627 0222 10–2D
*A "very Gallic", "shabby-chic" bistro, in "the heart of Clapham";
it didn't used to matter that it was "too cramped, too noisy and
too uncomfortable", but as service gets ever more "slapstick",
it's becoming ever more apparent that the food's "not up to the
price". / midnight; no credit cards; no smoking.*

**The Gate W6** £32 ❶②②
51 Queen Caroline St 8748 6932 7–2C
*"Almost enough to make you a veggie" – the "colourful" and
"enticing" creations at this "un-preachy" Hammersmith fixture
(in a converted church hall) make it "the best vegetarian
in town"; "lovely courtyard in summer". / www.thegate.tv; 10.45 pm;
closed Sat L & Sun.*

## Gaucho £32 ❷④④

Chelsea Farmers' Mkt, Sydney St, SW3   7376 8514   5–3C
30 Old Brompton Rd, SW7   7584 8999   5–2B

"The finest steaks this side of Buenos Aires" win rave reviews for
these basic bistros; the "rustic" Chelsea Farmers' Market branch
– with its outside tables – is "the original and still the best"
(and gets "packed for late weekend lunches"). / www.elgaucho.co.uk;
SW3 6.30 pm, SW7 11.30 pm; SW3 L only, SW7 D only; SW3 no credit
cards; SW3 no booking in summer, SW7 no bookings before 7 pm.

## Gaucho Grill £45 ❸④④

19 Swallow St, W1   7734 4040   3–3D
125 Chancery Ln, WC2   7242 7727   2–1D
89 Sloane Ave, SW3   7584 9901   5–2C
64 Heath St, NW3   7431 8222   8–1A
29 Westferry Circus, E14   7987 9494   11–1B
1 Bell Inn Yd, EC3   7626 5180   9–2C

"Absolutely fantastic" steaks win many plaudits for this would-be
"trendy" (and sometimes "loud") Argentinian chain, which is most
popular for business; otherwise, reports are mixed.
/ www.gauchosgrill.com; 11 pm; EC3 & WC2 closed Sat & Sun.

## LE GAVROCHE W1 £118 ❷❶❷

43 Upper Brook St   7408 0881   3–2A

"Exemplary" service (under Silvano Giraldin) and a wine list
of "biblical" proportions help set the scene at this "old-fashioned"
Mayfair basement (which is London's oldest temple of Gallic
gastronomy); prices are "dizzying", but Michel Roux Jr's "classic"
cuisine almost invariably "delivers the goods".
/ www.le-gavroche.co.uk; 10.45 pm; closed Sat L & Sun; jacket required;
smoking in bar only; set weekday L £50 (FP).

## Gay Hussar W1 £39 ④❷❶

2 Greek St   7437 0973   4–2A

"Even if it's only 70% authentic Hungarian", this "ancient" Soho
bastion – famed for its "Old Labour" associations – is still
treasured by some reporters for its "friendly and old-fashioned"
atmosphere and its "wholesome" fodder. / 10.45 pm; closed Sun.

## Geale's W8 £28 ④④⑤

2 Farmer St   7727 7528   6–2B

Since the Geale family sold out a few years ago, ratings at this
"stalwart" chippie, near Notting Hill Gate, have see-sawed;
fans find its fish 'n' chips "peerless" – others that the place
is "well past its peak". / www.geales.co.uk; 11 pm; closed Sun L;
no smoking area.

## Geeta NW6 £16 ❷❶⑤

57-59 Willesden Ln   7624 1713   1–1B

"Grim"-looking Kilburn veteran, long known for its "dependably
excellent" south Indian food, super-"friendly" service and
"impressive value-for-money"; the occasional report this year,
though, was a fraction less rapturous than usual. / 10.30 pm, Fri &
Sat 11.30 pm; no Amex.

### George & Vulture EC3     £38    ⑤④❷
3 Castle Ct   7626 9710   9–3C
It you're looking for the "heavy and uninspiring" English cooking
of legend, you won't find better than this "historic" City back-alley
chophouse. / L only, closed Sat & Sun.

### Getti     £39    ⑤④⑤
16-17 Jermyn St, SW1   7734 7334   3–3D
42 Marylebone High St, W1   7486 3753   2–1A
A glitzy West End Italian chain which inspires few reports...
perhaps because detractors find it "duller than dull". / 11 pm;
no smoking area.

### Ghillies     £40    ❸④❸
271 New King's Rd, SW6   7371 0434   10–1B
94 Point Pleasant, SW18   8871 9267   10–2B
"Eating on the deck by the Thames is fantastic", say fans of the
Wandsworth branch of this mini-chain; both here and in Fulham,
"simple and honest" fish is served in a "friendly", if not hyper-
efficient, manner. / 10 pm.

### Giardinetto W1  NEW    £52
39-40 Albemarle St   7493 7091   3–3C
Maurizio Vilona's "very good" Italian food – in "authentic
'slow cooking' style" – was never going to shine in the "tatty"
Fitzrovia basement he formerly occupied; let's hope for the best
in these smart new Mayfair premises, which aspire to be
everything the old ones were not. / www.giardinetto.co.uk; 11 pm; closed
Sat L; no smoking area.

### Gili Gulu WC2     £24    ④⑤④
50-52 Monmouth St   7379 6888   4–2B
"Bargain prices" help justify the continued existence of this
"cheap conveyor-belt sushi" outfit, near Covent Garden; there are,
however, "better options nearby". / 11 pm; no Amex; no smoking;
no booking.

### Ginger W2     £32    ❸❸④
115 Westbourne Grove   7908 1990   6–1B
"Nice curry, but no longer as cheap and special as it was" –
a neat summary of sentiment on this rather bleakly-decorated
Bayswater Bangladeshi. / www.gingerrestaurant.co.uk; 10.30 pm, Fri & Sat
11.30 pm; closed weekday L; no smoking area.

### Giraffe     £29    ④❷❸
6-8 Blandford St, W1   7935 2333   2–1A
270 Chiswick High Rd, W4   8995 2100   7–2A
7 Kensington High St, W8   7938 1221   5–1A
29-31 Essex Rd, N1   7359 5999   8–3D
46 Rosslyn Hill, NW3   7435 0343   8–2A
Royal Festival Hall, Riverside, SE1   7928 2004   2–3D  NEW
27 Battersea Rise, SW11   7223 0933   10–2C
"A fine variety" of "scrumptious" breakfast items make these
"colourful" diners a great brunch choice (even if they do get
"knee-deep in kids"); the 'proper' menu is "unexciting", though,
and "expensive for what it is". / www.giraffe.net; 11 pm; no smoking;
no booking at weekends.

### Glaisters SW10 £34 ④❸❷

4 Hollywood Rd 7352 0352 5–3B
*The cooking lacks interest, but fans find this long-established Chelsea brasserie a "relaxing and reliable" destination, and it has a "charming" garden room at the rear.* / www.glaisters.co.uk; 11 pm; no smoking area; set pre-theatre £22 (FP), set weekday L £22 (FP).

### Glas SE1 NEW £39 ❸❷④

3 Park St 7357 6060 9–4C
*"Unusual ingredients, such as reindeer" and "a lot of excellent Swedish herring" feature on the menu of this "slightly out-of-the-ordinary" Borough newcomer, where dishes come in "small but elaborate portions"; the setting is pretty, but cramped and cacophonous.* / www.glasrestaurant.com; 10 pm; closed Mon & Sun; no smoking.

### The Glasshouse TW9 £47 ❶❷❸

14 Station Pde 8940 6777 1–3A
*"Well worth the trek to Kew", this "light and airy" neighbourhood fixture – sibling to the legendary Chez Bruce – maintains all-round "admirable" standards, not least of "immaculate" cuisine and "knowledgeable" service.* / www.glasshouserestaurant.co.uk; 10.30 pm; no smoking; set weekday L £31 (FP).

### Globe Restaurant NW3 £40 ④❷④

100 Avenue Rd 7722 7200 8–2A
*"The Thursday drag cabaret is a must-see!", say fans of this Swiss Cottage spot, where "cheery" service offsets the rather "cold" décor; (it's also "very convenient for the Hampstead Theatre").* / www.globerestaurant.co.uk; 11 pm; closed Sat L & Sun D; no Amex; no smoking in restaurant.

### Golden Dragon W1 £23 ❸④⑤

28-29 Gerrard St 7734 2763 4–3A
*For a "great fast and cheap" meal, try the "huge" variety of lunchtime dim sum at this Chinatown fixture; other dishes are relatively "ordinary".* / 11.30 pm.

### Golden Hind W1 £16 ❷❷④

73 Marylebone Ln 7486 3644 2–1A
*"Just eat, don't worry about the cafeteria-style ambience" – this "age-old, BYO chippie" in Marylebone, serves "superb fish 'n' chips" (with "all the trimmings"), and it's "much better than the nearby Seashell".* / 10 pm; closed Sat L & Sun; no smoking area.

### Gonbei WC1 £26 ❷④④

151 King's Cross Rd 7278 0619 8–3D
*"Tucked-away" in the "very uninspiring area" near King's Cross, this small and very "authentic" Japanese "amazes" its fans with "sushi the way it should be made".* / 11 pm; D only, closed Sun; no Amex.

### Good Earth £38 ❶❷④

233 Brompton Rd, SW3 7584 3658 5–2C
143-145 The Broadway, NW7 8959 7011 1–1B
*"Keeping up their standards", these "smart" veterans offer a "fail-safe" formula of "wonderful" Chinese food at "fair" prices.* / 10.45 pm.

### Gopal's of Soho W1 £27 ❷④④

12 Bateman St 7434 1621 4–2A
*"Great" curry encourages fans to overlook the "tacky" décor and "sloppy" service at this Soho veteran. / 11.15 pm; closed Sun.*

### GORDON RAMSAY SW3 £91 ❶❶❷

68-69 Royal Hospital Rd 7352 4441 5–3D
*Head chef Mark Askew's "peerless" cuisine and maître d' Jean-Claude's "seamless" service combine to make Gordon Ramsay's Chelsea flagship once again London's undoubted number one dining room; if there is a quibble, it's that – for some tastes – the cooking is just too "clean and classic". / www.gordonramsay.com; 11 pm; closed Sat & Sun; jacket required; no smoking; booking: max 8; set weekday L £58 (FP).*

### GORDON RAMSAY AT CLARIDGE'S
### CLARIDGE'S HOTEL W1 £83 ❸❷❸

55 Brook St 7499 0099 3–2B
*This "luxurious" Art Deco dining room may have Gordon Ramsay's name over the door, but it's "not a patch on the Chelsea flagship" (and not much cheaper, either);
Mark Sargeant's cuisine can certainly scale "sublime" peaks, but too many reports of "pretty ordinary" meals undercut the rating overall. / www.gordonramsay.com; 11 pm; jacket required; no smoking; booking: max 8; set weekday L £50 (FP).*

### Gordon's Wine Bar WC2 £22 ⑤❸❶

47 Villiers St 7930 1408 4–4D
*"Full of nooks and dark crannies", this "amazing" candlelit cellar – London's oldest wine bar, near Embankment – is always "busy"; "forget the food" (cheese, pies, salads…), say diehard supporter – "go for the vino". / www.gordonswinebar.com; 11 pm; no Amex; no booking.*

### Goring Hotel SW1 £59 ❸❶❷

15 Beeston Pl 7396 9000 2–4B
*Being "a trifle staid" is "part of the appeal" of this "splendid" family-owned hotel, near Victoria, where "good, rather traditional food" is served by staff versed in "traditional courtesies"; let's hope their mid-2005 revamp doesn't wreck it!
/ www.goringhotel.co.uk; 10 pm; closed Sat L; no smoking area; booking: max 12; set Sun L £41 (FP).*

### Gourmet Burger Kitchen £20 ❷④④

49 Fulham Broadway, SW6 7381 4242 5–4A
50 Westbourne Grove, W2 7243 4344 6–1B
131 Chiswick High Rd, W4 8995 4548 7–2A
200 Haverstock Hill, NW3 7443 5335 8–2A **NEW**
331 West End Ln, NW6 7794 5455 1–1B
44 Northcote Rd, SW11 7228 3309 10–2C
333 Putney Bridge Rd, SW15 8789 1199 10–2B
*This "relentlessly busy" chain – the survey's most often mentioned – does "exactly what it says on the tin", offering "the best burgers on the planet", in "monster" portions, and with "every topping imaginable"; "great shakes", too ("if you still have room"). / www.gbkinfo.co.uk; 11 pm; no Amex; no smoking; no booking.*

### Gourmet Pizza Company £28 ❸④④

7-9 Swallow St, W1   7734 5182   3–3D
Gabriels Wharf, 56 Upper Ground, SE1   7928 3188   9–3A
18 Mackenzie Walk, E14   7345 9192   11–1C
"Odd-ball toppings make all the difference" to this "good-value"
pizza chain (which is, in fact, owned by PizzaExpress); the SE1
branch is notable for its "great views", across the river to St
Paul's. / www.gourmetpizzacompany.co.uk; 11.30 pm; no smoking area;
W1, need 8+ to book.

### Gow's EC2 £48 ④❸④

81-82 Old Broad St   7920 9645   9–2C
Plus ça change..., at this "old-fashioned" – yet recently refurbed
– City parlour; to fans, it's a "decent" fish place "attuned to the
needs of business" – to critics, it's "overrated" and "average".
/ www.ballsbrothers.co.uk; 9.30 pm; closed Sat & Sun; no smoking area;
booking: max 10.

### Goya £32 ④❷④

2 Ecclestone Pl, SW1   7730 4299   2–4B
34 Lupus St, SW1   7976 5309   2–4C
No longer under common ownership, these two tapas bars
(by Victoria Coach Station and in south Pimlico) are still both
useful stand-bys without much local competition; they are
otherwise pretty "ordinary". / 11.30 pm; no smoking area, Eccleston Pl.

### The Grapes E14 £39 ❸❸❶

76 Narrow St   7987 4396   11–1B
"It's a challenge to get a table", at this "cracking" old pub
in Docklands, whose "brilliant" seafood and "top fish 'n chips"
continue to please (nearly) all reporters; it has "amazing views
over the Thames", too. / 9.15 pm; closed Sun D; no smoking; set Sun L
£22 (FP).

### Gravy W4 £37 ❸④❸

142 Chiswick High Rd   8994 6816   7–2B
Notably "improved" this year, this attractive-looking Chiswick
bistro was consistently praised as a "good-value" destination.
/ www.gravyrestaurant.co.uk; 10.45 pm.

### Graze W9 NEW £40

215 Sutherland Ave   7266 3131   8–4A
Shortly before this guide went to press, Soren Jessen (of One
Lombard Street fame) conceded that the tapas formula offered
at this uncompromising Maida Vale newcomer (formerly Otto,
RIP) had been misconceived; look out for a relaunch with a more
conventional menu in late-2005. / www.graze.co.uk; 10.30 pm.

### Great Eastern Dining Room EC2 £34 ❷❷❷

54 Gt Eastern St   7613 4545   9–1D
Quite a veteran, by Shoreditch standards, Will Ricker's "friendly"
local linchpin offers "cheaper Nobu-ish fare" that's often "just as
good"; what really distinguishes it, though, is its "great buzz".
/ www.greateasterndining.co.uk; 10.45 pm; closed Sat L & Sun.

### Great Nepalese NW1 £23 ❷❷⑤
48 Eversholt St 7388 6737 8–3C
"A gem, by Euston station" – this "really friendly" fixture has
dished up "interesting" Nepalese specials (plus more standard
subcontinental fare) for over 20 years. / www.great-nepalese.co.uk;
11.30 pm; no smoking area.

### The Green NW2 £31 ❸❸❸
110 Walm Ln 8452 0171 1–1A
A "relaxed" and "pleasant" Willesden Green gastropub,
consistently hailed by reporters for its "good food" and
"agreeable service". / www.thegreen-nw2.co.uk; 10.30 pm; no Amex.

### The Green EC1 NEW £33 ❸❸❸
29 Clerkenwell Grn 7490 8010 9–1A
This "characterful" Clerkenwell corner site (once home to Novelli
in the City, RIP) has been retro-furbed into something akin to an
upmarket '80s wine bar (smoke and all); at lunchtime, it serves
a comforting menu to a business crowd – at night, it becomes
a tapas bar. / 11 pm, Thu-Sat midnight.

### The Green Olive W9 £41 ❸❸❸
5 Warwick Pl 7289 2469 8–4A
A "friendly" new team "seems to have bucked up standards"
at this "pleasant" Italian, near Little Venice – the cooking has
been notably more "interesting" of late. / 11 pm; no smoking area.

### Green's SW1 £55 ❸❷❷
36 Duke St 7930 4566 3–3D
The "clubby" ambience "lends gravitas" to a meal at this
"comfortable" St James's fixture, where "good, plain dishes"
(with much seafood) are served up by "friendly" staff.
/ www.greens.org.uk; 11 pm; closed Sun, May-Sep.

### The Greenhouse W1 £84 ❸❸❸
27a Hays Mews 7499 3331 3–3B
Last year, Marlon Abela set out to turn this Mayfair mews
"old favourite" into "a serious temple of gastronomy"; with its
"intricate" cuisine and "overwhelming" wine list, he's succeeded,
in a way, but the 'feel' is now "very corporate", and prices can
seem "off the scale". / www.greenhouserestaurant.co.uk; 11 pm; closed
Sat L & Sun; booking: max 4; set weekday L £53 (FP).

### Greenwich Park NEW
### Bar & Grill SE10 £39 ⑤❸④
King William Wk 8858 2437 1–3D
Right by the park entrance, this former corner boozer has
recently been revamped – without any wit or sensitivity – by the
local dining scene's Mr Big; the fat-filled daytime menu
we sampled on our July 2005 visit was frankly vile. / Rated
on Editors' visit; www.thegreenwichpark.com.

### Greig's W1 £54 ④④④
26 Bruton Pl 7629 5613 3–2B
"Top steaks and grills" are hailed by fans of this Mayfair mews
rival to the nearby Guinea Grill; critics, though, say "nothing
is good enough to make you want to go back". / www.greigs.com;
11 pm; no smoking area; set weekday L £23 (FP).

**Grenadier SW1** £37 ④④❷

18 Wilton Row 7235 3074 5–1D

This "super-secret" Belgravia tavern – which looks like it's straight out of a storybook – is in fact in all the tourist guides; "the food isn't that different from that in any pub, and a tad overpriced for what you get". / www.thespiritgroup.co.uk; 9 pm; no smoking; set Sun L £18 (FP).

**The Greyhound SW11** NEW £39 ❷❷❸

136 Battersea High St 7978 7021 10–1C

"A phenomenally good wine list" (actually there are two!) has helped win instant popularity for this "keen" Battersea newcomer – a restaurant "posing as a gastropub", serving some "really good" food; a fair number of reporters, however, rail at the "toppish" prices. / www.thegreyhoundatbattersea.co.uk; 9.30 pm; closed Mon & Sun D; no smoking in dining room; booking: max 6; set weekday L £25 (FP).

**The Greyhound NW10** £33 ④④④

64-66 Chamberlayne Rd 8969 8080 1–2B

Some reporters still vaunt this Queens Park yearling as a "good local gastropub"; one or two recent visits, though, have been plain "disappointing". / 10.30 pm, Sun 7 pm; closed Mon L; no smoking area.

**Grocer on Warwick Café W1** NEW £32 ❸❷❸

21 Warwick St 7437 7776 3–2D

This "rather different" Soho deli/diner (on the site of Sugar Club, RIP) serves "mix 'n' match" Pacific Rim dishes which generally "hit the spot"; "the individual items seemed expensive, but the overall bill wasn't too bad". / www.thegroceron.com; 11 pm; closed Sun L; no smoking.

**The Grove W6** £35 ④❸❸

83 Hammersmith Grove 8748 2966 7–1C

A "buzzy", mainly organic Hammersmith gastropub, with nice outside tables; it still mostly wins praise for a "good variety of well-executed dishes", but "the bill can mount", and some reporters feel it needs to "go back to basics". / www.groverestaurant.co.uk; 11 pm; no Amex; no smoking area.

**Grumbles SW1** £31 ④④❸

35 Churton St 7834 0149 2–4B

This '60s-veteran bistro in Pimlico continues to take reporters one of two ways – they either feel it's "nostalgic", "cosy" and "good-value", or "boring", "tired" and "dated". / www.grumblesrestaurant.co.uk; 11 pm; no Amex.

**The Guinea W1** £52 ❷❸❸

30 Bruton Pl 7499 1210 3–3B

"Some of the best steak you'll find", "world-renowned" steak 'n' kidney pies and "a good range of clarets" – that's the "no-frills" formula which sustains the popularity of this "dated" dining room (attached to an "olde-worlde" Mayfair pub). / www.theguinea.co.uk; 11 pm; closed Sat L & Sun; booking: max 8.

### The Gun E14 NEW £44 ❷❸❷
27 Coldharbour Ln 7515 5222 11–1C
*"A cracking addition to Dockland's dining"*, this *"brilliant nautical gastropub"* – with a *"nice"* waterside location, opposite the Dome – has certainly *"hit the ground running"*; it combines *"a proper pub feel on one side"* (the view side) with *"crisp white tablecloths"* on the other. / www.thegundocklands.com; 10.30 pm.

### Gung-Ho NW6 £30 ❷❷❷
328-332 West End Ln 7794 1444 1–1B
*"Consistently good"* cooking helps make this West Hampstead Chinese a *"popular local favourite"*; it's usually *"packed to the gills"*. / 11.30 pm; no Amex.

### The Gunmakers EC1 £31 ❸④❸
13 Eyre Street Hill 7278 1022 9–1A
*"Cosy little boozer"*, tucked away in Farringdon, serving *"good honest pub grub"*, albeit from a fairly *"limited"* menu. / www.thegunmakers.co.uk; 10 pm; closed Sat & Sun; no booking Fri D.

### Ha! Ha! £33 ④④④
43-51 Gt Titchfield St, W1 7580 7252 2–1B
6 Villiers St, WC2 7930 1263 4–4D
390 Muswell Hill Broadway, N10 8444 4722 8–1C
*"For a quick stop"*, some reporters would tip these busy wine bars; they can get *"darn noisy"*, though, and the food they offer is *"standard"*. / www.hahaonline.co.uk; 10 pm; W1 closed Sat & Sun; no smoking area.

### Haandi SW3 £34 ❷❸④
136 Brompton Rd 7823 7373 5–1C
This *"unexpected"* – and still too little-known – Knightsbridge basement offers some *"stunning"* Indian dishes (and in *"copious"* quantities, too). / www.haandi-restaurants.com; 11 pm, Fri & Sat 11.30 pm; no smoking area.

### Haché NW1 NEW £20 ❸❸④
24 Inverness St 7485 9100 8–3B
*"Burgers of all sorts, well crafted, and served with decent chips"* have made quite a name for this *"modestly priced"* Camden Town newcomer. / www.hacheburgers.com; 10.30 pm; no smoking.

### Hadley House E11 NEW £39 ❸❸④
27 Wanstead High St 8989 8855 1–1D
The menu *"may be a bit over-long"*, but *"good food in East London"* is not that easy to come by, making this small and *"bare"* Wanstead fixture well worth knowing about. / 10 pm; no Amex.

### HAKKASAN W1 £75 ❸④❷
8 Hanway Pl 7927 7000 4–1A
*"Hip, happening and simply great"* – this *"clubby"* basement, tucked away off Tottenham Court Road, serves some of *"the best Chinese food in London"* (including *"stunning"* dim sum), and has become the second most talked-about place in town; the service, though, can be *"appalling"*, and prices increasingly seem *"way too high"*. / midnight, Mon & Sun 11 pm; set weekday L £53 (FP).

### Halepi £33 ❸❷④
18 Leinster Ter, W2   7262 1070   6–2C
48-50 Belsize Ln, NW3   7431 5855   8–2A
*An odd couple of Greek restaurants – one old and kitsch
(Bayswater), the other "cold and clinical" (Belsize Park);
both serve hearty, "old-fashioned" fodder that fans say
is "the best". / NW3 11 pm, W2 11.45 pm; NW3 closed Mon L;
NW3 no smoking area.*

### Hamburger Union £21 ❸❸④
22-25 Dean St, W1   7437 6004   4–2A
4-6 Garrick St, WC2   7379 0412   4–3C
*A sort of "posh McDonalds" – these purveyors of "organic"
burgers and "huge" chips are widely hailed as "great additions
to the West End". / www.hamburgerunion.com; 10.30 pm; no Amex;
no smoking; no booking.*

### Hammersmith Café W6 £15 ❸❸⑤
1a Studland St   8748 2839   7–2B
*Near the cinema, a greasy spoon which also serves "great-value"
Thai "home-cooking". / 10.30 pm; closed Sun L; no credit cards.*

### Hampton's Restaurant KT8 £39 ④❷❸
Hampton Court Rd   8979 4740   1–4A
*A characterful location (overlooking the Thames, near the gate
to Hampton Court) is the highlight at this attractive dining room,
where accommodating staff offer a decent-enough menu.
/ www.hamptons-restaurant.com; 9.30 pm, Fri & Sat 10pm; closed
Sat L & Sun D; no smoking.*

### Harbour City W1 £25 ❸❷❸
46 Gerrard St   7439 7859   4–3B
*A Chinatown canteen where the "absolutely fresh" and
"very reasonably-priced" dim sum "continues to be a delight";
in other respects it's unremarkable. / 11.30 pm.*

### Hard Rock Café W1 £32 ④❸❷
150 Old Park Ln   7629 0382   3–4B
*"If you can cope with the noise", many reporters still claim you
get "the best burgers in town" at this famous old Piccadilly rocker;
it was sometimes "disappointing" this year, though.
/ www.hardrock.com; 1 am; no smoking; no booking.*

### Hardy's W1 £42 ❸❷❸
53 Dorset St   7935 5929   2–1A
*"Old-fashioned but much appreciated", this Marylebone wine bar
offers some "solid" British fare, and "a good long wine list" to go
with it. / 10.30 pm; closed Sat L & Sun; no Amex; no smoking area.*

### Hare & Tortoise £21 ❷❸④
15-17 Brunswick Sq, WC1   7278 4945   2–1D
373 Kensington High St, W14   7603 8887   7–1D   **NEW**
38 Haven Grn, W5   8610 7066   1–2A
296-298 Up' Rich'nd Rd, SW15   8394 7666   10–2B
*"Hearty noodles", "elegant sushi" and other "satisfying" dishes
from a "wide pan-Asian menu" make it well worth trying out this
"cheap, cheery and quick" chain. / 10.30 pm; no Amex; WC1 & W14
no smoking, SW15 & W5 no smoking areas.*

### Harlem £35 ④⑤④

78 Westbourne Grove, W2   7985 0900   6–1B
467 Brixton Rd, SW9   7326 4455   10–1D
The breakfasts, burgers and so on are good enough – "when they finally arrive" – at this would-be "hip" American mini-chain.
/ www.harlemsoulfood.com; 2 am, Sun midnight.

### Harry Morgan's NW8 £20 ❷❸❸

31 St John's Wood High St   7580 4849   8–3A
"Salt beef sandwiches to die for" and "chicken soup as good as mother makes" help ensure that this age-old kosher deli in St John's Wood is "always busy". / www.harryms.co.uk; 10 pm.

### Harry Ramsden's
### Regent Palace Hotel W1 £24 ④④⑤

Sherwood St   7287 3148   3–3D
"Northerners everywhere should rejoice", say fans of this offshoot of the famous chippie chain, near Piccadilly Circus; its ratings are undercut, though, by those who dismiss it as "vile and formulaic".
/ www.harryramsdens.co.uk; 11 pm; no smoking area.

### The Hartley SE1 £32 ❸④❷

64 Tower Bridge Rd   7394 7023   1–3C
This "buzzy" Bermondsey gastropub (a mile or so south of Tower Bridge) has been "a wonderful addition to the area"; it serves a "short" menu that "hits the right balance between gastro and pub". / www.thehartley.com; 10 pm; closed Sun D; no smoking area.

### Harwood Arms SW6 £30 ❸❸❷

29 Walham Grove   7386 1847   5–3A
"Steer clear when Chelsea's playing at home", but otherwise this chilled pub in a quiet Fulham backstreet is a "great local", not least "for Sunday lunch". / 11 pm.

### The Havelock Tavern W14 £31 ❶⑤❷

57 Masbro Rd   7603 5374   7–1C
Olympia's "fantastic local secret" is well and truly out nowadays, and – thanks to its "gutsy" and "excellent-value" cooking – this "super-gastropub" is always "chaotically busy"; none of this, however, excuses the "graceless" service.
/ www.thehavelocktavern.co.uk; 10 pm; no credit cards; no booking.

### The Haven N20 £32 ❸❸❷

1363 High Rd   8445 7419   1–1B
For its many fans, this "lovely" Whetstone restaurant lives up to its name, offering "everything you might expect to find in the West End"; the food is "not inspirational", but it is "consistently good", and "getting a table can be difficult". / www.haven-bistro.co.uk; 11 pm; no smoking.

### Haz E1 £29 ❷❷❸

9 Cutler St   7929 7923   9–2D
"A stone's throw from Liverpool Street", this "energetic" ("noisy") modern Turkish restaurant offers a winning package of "fresh, simple and tasty" food, "super" service and a "light" and "airy" setting; the set meals offer especially "good value".
/ www.hazrestaurant.com; 11.30 pm.

### Hazuki WC2 £29 ❸❷❸
43 Chandos Pl 7240 2530 4–4C
A "sweet little Japanese", handily located near Charing Cross;
it's a "very friendly" place, offering "reasonably-priced" grub.
/ www.sushihazuki.co.uk; 10.30 pm; closed Sun L.

### Henry J Beans SW3 £27 ④④❷
195-197 King's Rd 7352 9255 5–3C
For a burger, ribs ("in huge portions") or brunch, this formulaic
old-timer has its place; its secret trump card though, is its vast
garden, in the heart of Chelsea. / www.henryjbeans.com; 10.30 pm;
no booking.

### The Highgate NW5 £32 ④④④
79 Highgate Rd 7485 8442 8–2B
A "busy" Kentish Town gastropub, with "lots of potential";
but while some reporters say it offers "an all-round good
experience", others think that "something's missing". / 9.30 pm;
no smoking area.

### The Hill NW3 £33 ④④❷
94 Haverstock Hill 7267 0033 8–2B
Decoration using "Grandma's tables and chairs" creates
a "trendy" vibe at this boozer, north of Chalk Farm; otherwise,
it can seem to offer "mediocre everything" – perhaps the new
chef will perk things up? / www.geronimo-inns.co.uk; 10.30 pm; no Amex.

### Hole in the Wall W4 NEW £34 ❸❸❷
12 Sutton Lane North 8742 7185 7–2A
"One of the better pub gardens in west London" is the star
feature at this newly-converted Chiswick gastropub, which offers
a "simple" menu of hearty dishes. / 10 pm; no smoking area.

### Homage NEW
### Waldorf Hilton WC2 £49 ❸❸④
22 Aldwych 7759 4080 2–2D
Even Roy Ackerman's well-publicised conversion of this potentially-
elegant Covent Garden ballroom has piqued hardly any interest
amongst reporters – though its "classic" Gallic dishes are done
to a good standard, a return visit found it largely deserted.
/ www.homagerestaurant.co.uk; 11 pm; closed Sat L & Sun L; no smoking area;
booking: max 6; set weekday L & pre-theatre £31 (FP).

### Home EC2 £38 ❸❷❷
100-106 Leonard St 7684 8618 9–1D
"One of the 'original' Shoreditch venues", this "hip" but "friendly"
basement bar and ground-floor restaurant wins unanimous praise
for its "buzzing" ambience and "very good" food; "I've known
it since it was a quarter of the size, and it's still consistent".
/ www.homebar.co.uk; 10.30 pm; closed Sat L & Sun.

### Hope & Sir Loin EC1 £35 ❸④⑤
94 Cowcross St 7253 8525 9–1A
"A great breakfast" – but "only if you like a lot of meat" – is the
stand-out attraction at this "poorly-decorated" Smithfield pub;
thanks to the local licensing laws, you can wash it down with
a pint, or a bottle of bubbly. / breakfast & L only, closed Sat & Sun.

### Hot Stuff SW8 £14 ❷❷❸
19 Wilcox Rd 7720 1480 10–1D
"Awesome Indian and West African food... and so cheap!" –
this "cramped" BYO destination looks "like a greasy spoon",
but doesn't cook like one; "you have to book". / www.eathotstuff.com;
9.45 pm; closed Sun.

### The House N1 £43 ❸❸❸
63-69 Canonbury Rd 7704 7410 8–2D
"Traditional French provincial food" and "knowledgeable" service
help make this "popular" (and "noisy") Islington two-year old
"more than a gastropub"; it is getting "a bit pricey", though.
/ www.inthehouse.biz; 10.30 pm; closed Mon L; no Amex; no smoking area;
set weekday L £30 (FP).

### Hoxton Apprentice N1 £33 ④❸❷
16 Hoxton Sq 7739 6022 9–1D
"A great community project", this "interesting" "training
restaurant" – overseen by catering supremo Prue Leith –
has been "well done" (and has a lovely terrace, on Hoxton
Square); arguably the food "lacks sparkle", but it's usually "well-
cooked and well-presented". / www.hoxtonapprentice.com; 11 pm; closed
Mon; no Amex.

### Hoxton Square Bar & Kitchen N1 £31 ④④❸
2-4 Hoxton Sq 7613 0709 9–1D
This concrete-chic Hoxton linchpin is best-known as a bar,
with some fantastically-located alfresco tables; it also does
tolerable, simple food, served charmingly, but sometimes very
slowly. / www.barworks.com; 10 pm; no smoking area.

### Hudson's SW15 £32 ④❷❸
113 Lower Richmond Rd 8785 4522 10–1A
Locals may decry "the conversion of the terrace into a new
room", but the ratings for this "reasonable all-rounder" –
a Putney linchpin – have strengthened in recent times;
its breakfasts are of particular renown. / 10.30 pm.

### Hunan SW1 £39 ❶❶④
51 Pimlico Rd 7730 5712 5–2D
"Let Mr Peng order for you", when you visit this "bustling" Pimlico
spot, where almost all reporters are "bowled over" by the "varied,
very fresh, and original" cooking – for some, "the best Chinese
food in London". / 11 pm; closed Sun; no smoking area.

### Huong-Viet
### An Viet House N1 £23 ❶④❸
12-14 Englefield Rd 7249 0877 1–1C
"Incredibly tasty" Vietnamese cooking makes this "cheap" and
"chaotic" Dalston community centre "canteen" extremely
popular, and service sometimes "suffers" accordingly; licensed,
but you can BYO. / 11 pm; closed Sun; no Amex.

**Hush W1** £54 ④❸❷

8 Lancashire Ct 7659 1500 3–2B

A "secluded" cobbled courtyard location, just off Bond Street,
sets the tone at this "stylish" Mayfair hang-out; the food has
"improved, after a lull", but can still seem "unnecessarily pricey"
– the "buzzy" bar remains a safer bet. / www.hush.co.uk; 11 pm;
closed Sun; booking: max 12; set pre-theatre £35 (FP).

**I Thai**
**The Hempel W2** £65

31-35 Craven Hill Gdns 7298 9001 6–2C

New owners of this Bayswater hotel look set to relaunch this Zen-
minimalist dining room – apparently with the same name,
but possibly with a revised formula – in late-2005; hence this
'holding' entry. / www.the-hempel.co.uk; 10.30 pm; closed Sun D.

**The Ifield SW10** £33 ❸❷❷

59 Ifield Rd 7351 4900 5–3B

A "buzzy" and charmingly louche Chelsea-fringe gastropub;
it's yet to win back the following it once enjoyed, but "good grub"
and "relaxed charm" still attract keen local support (even if it can
be "too smoky"). / 11 pm; Mon-Thu D only; no smoking in dining room.

**Ikeda W1** £65 ❸❸④

30 Brook St 7629 2730 3–2B

You get some of the "best sushi in town" – but, boy, is it "pricey"
– at Mrs Ikeda's low-key Mayfair fixture, of a quarter of a
century's standing. / 10.30 pm; closed Sat L & Sun; set weekday L
£30 (FP).

**Ikkyu W1** £28 ❸❸❸

67a Tottenham Court Rd 7636 9280 2–1C

"No-frills, 'proper' Japanese food" helps maintain the consistent
popularity of this basement veteran, near Goodge Street tube –
"language difficulties with the staff only add to the authenticity".
/ 10 pm; closed Sat & Sun L; no Maestro; no smoking area.

**Imperial China WC2** £36 ❷❷❷

25a Lisle St 7734 3388 4–3B

This "tucked-away" Chinatown venture is a "pleasant" place that
"doesn't feel like all the others" thereabouts; it's "reliable" all-
round, but the "fantastic dim sum" has a particular following.
/ www.imperial-china.co.uk; 11.15 pm.

**Imperial City EC3** £39 ❷❷❷

Royal Exchange, Cornhill 7626 3437 9–2C

"Well-executed and presented" Chinese dishes have made these
"tightly-packed" cellars (under the Royal Exchange) a "long-
running favourite for business dining".
/ www.orientalrestaurantgroup.co.uk; 10.30 pm; closed Sat & Sun; smoking
in bar only.

**Inaho W2** £29 ❶⑤⑤

4 Hereford Rd 7221 8495 6–1B

"There's only one waiter" ("who vanishes all the time") at this
"teeny-tiny" and "very cramped" Bayswater Japanese;
the dazzling food, however – "melt-in-your-mouth" sushi and
other "luscious tidbits" – more than "makes up for it". / 11 pm;
closed Sat L & Sun; no Amex or Maestro; no smoking; set weekday L £17 (FP).

### Inc Bar & Restaurant SE10 £37 ④❷❷
7 College Approach   8858 6721   1–3D
*Though the food plays second fiddle to the designer (Laurence Llewelyn-Bowen) at this Greenwich bar/restaurant, most reports are of a "good" overall experience; it's best avoided at weekends, though, when it's "heaving". / www.incbar.com; 10 pm; D only; no Amex.*

### Incognico WC2 £45
117 Shaftesbury Ave   7836 8866   4–2B
*Due for a relaunch in late-2005, this Theatreland site — no longer associated with the Ladenis family — is apparently aiming to put a more Italianate spin on what was traditionally a pretty French formula. / www.incognico.com; 11.30 pm; closed Sun L.*

### L'Incontro SW1 £55 ❸❸④
87 Pimlico Rd   7730 6327   5–2D
*Last year, sentiment on this "very pricey" Pimlico spot seemed to be heading in precisely the right direction — this year's reports, however, are a tussle between those who proclaim it a "top Italian", and those who just find it "bland".
/ www.lincontro-restaurant.com; 11.30 pm; closed Sun L; set weekday L £34 (FP).*

### India Club
### Stand Continental Hotel WC2 £18 ④④⑤
143 Strand   7836 0650   2–2D
*"Unchanged since a visit in the '70s" — this "shambolic", Formica-chic BYO canteen is cherished by its fans as a "weird time warp from the last days of the Raj"; even if the food is "as cheap as chips", though, some reporters feel an "overhaul" can't be put off much longer. / 10.45 pm; no credit cards; booking: max 6.*

### Indian Ocean SW17 £22 ❷❷❸
216 Trinity Rd   8672 7740   10–2C
*"Every year we try loads of curry houses, but this is still one of the best" — for "solid" subcontinental fare, this Wandsworth veteran is hard to beat. / 11.15 pm; no smoking area.*

### Indigo
### One Aldwych WC2 £51 ❸❷❸
1 Aldwych   7300 0400   2–2D
*"Tables overlooking the bar are best", at this "light and airy" mezzanine dining room, whose "consistent" cooking and "comfortable" setting make it a "classy" venue for business (and also pre-theatre, or for brunch). / www.onealdwych.com; 11.15 pm; no smoking at breakfast.*

### Iniga SW3 NEW £45 ④④❸
2a Pond Pl   7589 6589   5–2C
*We've lost track of the number of restaurants we've visited in this 'difficult' Chelsea basement; mixed early reports on this latest Italian incumbent support the view that it "will go the way of all the others" — a shame, as our visit was rather good!
/ www.iniga.com; 11.30 pm; D only.*

### Inn the Park SW1 £41 ④⑤❸

St James's Pk 7451 9999 2–3C

*Why on earth did the Royal Parks give this "superbly-located" St James's Park one-year-old to Oliver Peyton to manage? – his 'form' suggested that it would end up a "horribly missed opportunity", and many reporters do indeed find it "incredibly badly-run", and dismiss its "expensive" British cooking as notably "average". / 8.30 pm; no smoking.*

### Inshoku SE1 £23 ❸❸❸

23-24 Lower Marsh 7928 2311 9–4A

*"Unfailingly good for a quick bite" – this "Japanese caff", near Waterloo, does a wide range of noodle, sushi and other dishes at "budget" prices. / 10.15 pm; closed Sat L & Sun; no smoking area.*

### Inside SE10 £36 ❷❸④

19 Greenwich South St 8265 5060 1–3D

*Serving "the best food in Greenwich by miles", "this fabulous local" is going from strength to strength; at peak times it can get "very buzzy", but the ambience can suffer when it's quiet. / www.insiderestaurant.co.uk; 11 pm; closed Mon, Tue L & Sun D; no smoking area.*

### Isarn N1 NEW £34 ❸❸④

119 Upper St 7424 5153 8–3D

*Perhaps our expectations of this new Islington Thai, run by the sister of 'Mr Hakkasan' (Alan Yau), were too high, but it struck us as a pretty middle-of-the-road all-rounder (though an early reporter proclaimed the food "more inspiring than average"). / Rated on Editors' visit; 11.30 pm; no smoking.*

### Ishbilia SW1 £38 ❷❷④

9 William St 7235 7788 5–1D

*"Very fresh" and "subtle" dishes make this "friendly" Knightsbridge café a "top Lebanese" for the few reporters who comment on it. / www.ishbilia.com; 11.30 pm.*

### Ishtar W1 NEW £27 ❸❸④

10-12 Crawford St 7224 2446 2–1A

*This "good-value", if slightly "variable", Turkish newcomer is "a welcome addition to Marylebone", which – say fans – deserves more of a following. / www.ishtarrestaurant.com; midnight; no smoking.*

### Island
### Royal Lancaster Hotel W2 £42 ❸❸❸

Lancaster Ter 7551 6070 6–2D

*Sceptics say "it won't be changing our opinions on hotel dining", but this strikingly-designed modern newcomer – semi-detached from the Royal Lancaster – wins more bouquets than brickbats for its moderately "creative" cooking; some tables have good Hyde Park views, too. / www.islandrestaurant.co.uk; 11 pm; no smoking area; booking: max 10.*

**Istanbul Iskembecisi N16**  £23  ❸④④

9 Stoke Newington Rd  7254 7291  1–1C

*This long-established Turkish restaurant in Dalston
is "not outstanding, but good"; it's "quite upmarket" by local
standards, too. / www.londraturk.com; 5 am; no Amex.*


**Italian Kitchen WC1**  £36  ❸❸❸

43 New Oxford St  7836 1011  2–1C

*After a number of disappointing years, this "kitsch" Bloomsbury
Italian is finally getting back on track, and is now generally
praised for its "interesting dishes at reasonable prices".
/ www.italiankitchen.uk.com; 10.45 pm.*


**Itsu**  £26  ❸❸④

1 Hanover Sq, W1  7491 9799  3–2C  **NEW**
103 Wardour St, W1  7479 4790  3–2D
118 Draycott Ave, SW3  7590 2400  5–2C
Level 2, Cabot Place East, E14  7512 5790  11–1C

*"A top take on the sushi belt" – these "slick" conveyor-joints
serve a mix of traditional and "new wave" dishes; falling ratings,
however, increasingly support those who find them "overrated".
/ www.itsu.co.uk; 11 pm, W1 Fri & Sat midnight, SW3 10 pm; E14 closed
Sat & Sun; no smoking; no booking.*


**THE IVY WC2**  £57  ❸❷❶

1 West St  7836 4751  4–3B

*This legendary Theatreland haunt may not – for the first time
in a decade – be voted reporters' No 1 favourite, but its
"magical" charm, egalitarian staff, and reliable "comfort" food
still make "hard to beat"; (the new owner, rag trade millionaire
Richard Caring, seems to plan no sweeping changes).
/ www.the-ivy.co.uk; midnight; booking: max 6; set weekday L £41 (FP).*


**Iznik N5**  £24  ④❸❷

19 Highbury Park  7354 5697  8–2D

*"Beautiful decoration" – Ali Baba-style – maintains the special
appeal of this Turkish restaurant in Highbury; those who
remember its glory days, however, may feel that it's
"gone downhill". / 11 pm; no Amex.*


**Jaan**
**The Howard WC2**  £57  ❸❷④

12 Temple Pl  7300 1700  2–2D

*Paul Peters's "inventive and well-executed" fusion fare –
plus "efficient" service and a secret "sun-trap" terrace –
win plaudits for this dining room near Temple tube; some find
it "overpriced", though, and the interior can seem "uninspiring".
/ 10.30 pm; closed Sat L & Sun L.*


**Jade Garden W1**  £26  ❸④④

15 Wardour St  7437 5065  4–3A

*"Reliable" Chinatown fixture that's "good for (somewhat limited)
dim sum"; Sunday lunchtimes are "busy" and "stressed".
/ www.londonjadegarden.co.uk; 11.30 pm.*


**for updates visit www.hardens.com**

## Jashan £21 ❷❶④

1-2 Coronet Pde, Ealing Rd, HA0   8340 9880   1–1A
19 Turnpike Ln, N8   8340 9880   1–1C
*"They look like bog-standard curry houses, but they aren't" –
these suburban Indian restaurants provide "really friendly" service
and "varied and deeply tasty" south Indian cuisine.*
/ www.jashanrestaurants.co.uk; 10.30 pm; N8 D only, closed Mon; no Amex;
HA0 no smoking.

## Jenny Lo's Tea House SW1 £23 ❷❷④

14 Eccleston St   7259 0399   2–4B
*For a "delicious" bowl of rice or noodles that's "so fresh and
cheap", Jenny Lo's "efficient" Belgravia venture "always hits the
spot"; "fluorescent lighting, stark walls and communal tables",
however, is a combination that "doesn't make you linger".* / 10 pm;
closed Sat L & Sun; no credit cards; no booking.

## Jim Thompson's £31 ④④❷

617 King's Rd, SW6   7731 0999   5–4A
889 Green Lanes, N21   8360 0005   1–1C
*"Amazing displays" of Thai "knick-knacks" add to the "cosy"
ambience of these "buzzy" hang-outs, where "reasonable" food
comes at "reasonable prices".* / www.jimthompsons.com; 11 pm;
no smoking area.

## Jin Kichi NW3 £33 ❶❷④

73 Heath St   7794 6158   8–1A
*"Always packed, for a reason", this "cramped" but "great-value"
Hampstead Japanese is again applauded by reporters for its
"very authentic, fresh and tasty" fare – this includes "the best
yakitori", as well as "outstanding sushi".* / www.jinkichi.com; 11 pm;
closed Mon & weekday L.

## Joe Allen WC2 £40 ④④❷

13 Exeter St   7836 0651   4–3D
*As a spot "to chill after the theatre" – with "star spotting" thrown
in – this underground Covent Garden "institution" can still make
a "fun" destination; service is "hit-and-miss", though, and even
some fans say the American food "can be pretty bad" – opt for
the famous off-menu burger.* / www.joeallen.co.uk; 12.45 am; no smoking
area; set pre-theatre & brunch £22 (FP).

## Joe's Brasserie SW6 £28 ④❸❸

130 Wandsworth Bridge Rd   7731 7835   10–1B
*"You don't go for the cuisine", but for John Brinkley's "interesting"
and "ridiculously cheap" wine, to this "always-buzzing" hang-out,
in deepest Fulham.* / www.brinkleys.com; 11 pm.

## Joe's Café SW3 £37 ❸④❷

126 Draycott Ave   7225 2217   5–2C
*"Perfect for watching ladies-who-lunch not eating" –
this Brompton Cross shopaholics' refuge does "delicious
brunches" and "the best salads".* / 11 pm; breakfast & L only;
no booking at weekends.

### Joy King Lau WC2 £23 ❷④④
3 Leicester St 7437 1132 4–3A
*"The place looks typical"*, but the food at this *"popular and bustling"* Chinese, off Leicester Square, is *"better than most"*.
/ 11.30 pm.

### Julie's W11 £46 ⑤④❶
135 Portland Rd 7229 8331 6–2A
This *"fabulous"* Holland Park Gothic labyrinth is *"still magic, after all these years"*, especially for those of a romantic disposition (or for a party); the food, though, is *"dire"*. / www.juliesrestaurant.com; 11.30 pm.

### Julie's Wine Bar W11 £46 ④❸❶
135 Portland Rd 7727 7985 6–2A
As at the neighbouring restaurant, *"wonderful Gothic décor"* (*"with private nooks and crannies"*) is the strength of this *"timeless"* Holland Park hang-out; also similarly, the food is *"never amazing"*. / www.juliesrestaurant.com; 11.30 pm.

### The Junction Tavern NW5 £31 ❸❷❷
101 Fortess Rd 7485 9400 8–2B
After a bit of a roller coaster performance, this *"pleasant"* Kentish Town gastroboozer seem to be settling down – the menu is *"attractive"*, and the results can be *"very good"*. / 10.30 pm; no Amex; booking: max 12.

### Just Gladwins EC3 £50 ❸④④
Minster Ct, 1 Mark Ln 7444 0004 9–3D
Service can be *"amateur"*, but fans say the *"reliable"* cooking at this City basement (whose ratings rose this year) makes it *"ideal for an upmarket business lunch"*. / www.justgladwins.com; L only, closed Sat & Sun; no smoking area.

### Just India SW15 £32 ④❷④
193 Lower Richmond Rd 8785 6004 10–1A
This modern Putney Indian has won a name locally for its *"surprising"* and *"well-presented"* cuisine; under its new owners, though, it's taking increasing flak for *"bland"* and *"uninspiring"* cooking. / www.justindia.org; 11 pm; no Amex; no smoking area.

### Just Oriental SW1 £34 ❸❷❷
19 King St 7976 2222 3–4D
The basement of Just St James offers a *"reliable"* oriental snack menu that's relatively *"inexpensive"* by the standards of the area. / www.juststjames.com; 11 pm; closed Sat L & Sun; set weekday L £21 (FP).

### Just St James SW1 £47 ④④④
12 St James's St 7976 2222 3–4D
*"A perfect layout for business"* makes this *"well-spaced"* and *"serene"* – but also slightly *"strange"* and *"cavernous"* – former banking hall a handy St James's rendezvous; prices can seem *"optimistic"*, though, given the *"so-so"* food and *"average"* service. / www.juststjames.com; 11 pm; closed Sat L & Sun; set pre-theatre £29 (FP).

### Just The Bridge EC4 £37 ④④❸
1 Paul's Walk 7236 0000 9–3B
*It has "great" views – of Tate Modern and the 'wobbly' bridge – but this hard-edged City brasserie can seem "quiet"; it's not helped by cooking that's a mite "dull". / www.justthebridge.com; 9.45 pm; closed Sun D; booking: max 11.*

### K10 EC2 £27 ❶❸❸
20 Copthall Ave 7562 8510 9–2C
*"A well-stocked conveyor-belt brings an interesting array of dishes" ("not just traditional sushi"), at this "excellent" City basement – it gets "very busy", so "arrive early". / www.k10.net; L only, closed Sat & Sun; no smoking; no booking.*

### Kai Mayfair W1 £50 ❷⓿❷
65 South Audley St 7493 8988 3–3A
*A zillion spiritual miles from Chinatown, this "comfortable" and "quiet" Mayfair oriental offers "impeccable" service and a wine list strong in first-growth clarets; the food is "imaginative" and "interesting", too... but "be prepared for a huge bill". / www.kaimayfair.com; 10.45 pm.*

### Kaifeng NW4 £45 ❷❷❸
51 Church Rd 8203 7888 1–1B
*"The best Kosher Chinese food in town" wins uniform praise for this Harrow stalwart; that said, even if it's a style of cooking that rarely comes cheap, it can seem "unnecessarily expensive" here. / 10.30 pm; closed Fri; no smoking.*

### Kandoo W2 £24 ❸❷④
458 Edgware Rd 7724 2428 8–4A
*"Good Persian cooking" makes it worth knowing about this BYO spot, at the top end of the Edgware Road. / 11.30 pm; no Amex.*

### kare kare SW5 £33 ❷❷❸
152 Old Brompton Rd 7373 0024 5–2B
*"Fresh and light" cuisine and "exceptional" service are generating a devoted local following for this "innovative" Earl's Court Indian. / www.karekare.co.uk; 11.30 pm; no smoking area; set weekday L £19 (FP).*

### Kastoori SW17 £21 ❶❶④
188 Upper Tooting Rd 8767 7027 10–2C
*"Outstanding" Gujarati/East African veggie "delicacies" make it "worth the trek" to this family-run Tooting spot, where "lovely" service enlivens the rather "drab" environment. / 10.30 pm; closed Mon L & Tue L; no Amex or Maestro; booking: max 12.*

### Kasturi EC3 £29 ❸❸❸
57 Aldgate High St 7480 7402 9–2D
*"Good food" – "even if it ends up costing a bit more than you expected" – makes this pleasant City subcontinental a handy stand-by, near Aldgate. / www.kasturi-restaurant.co.uk; 11 pm, Sat 9.30 pm; closed Sun L; no smoking area.*

**sign up for the survey at www.hardens.com**

## Katana
### The International WC2     £35     ❸❸④
116 St Martin's Ln   7655 9810   4–4B
*"Handily-located near the Coliseum", this "reasonably-priced" pan-Asian bar/restaurant is most worth knowing about for its "pre- and post- theatre deals".* / www.theinternational.uk.com; 11.30 pm, Sun 9.30 pm.

## Kazan SW1     £31     ❸❷❸
93-94 Wilton Rd   7233 7100   2–4B
*With its "nice Turkish food" and "good atmosphere", this (much smarter) spin-off from the Sofra group is emerging as one of Pimlico's few "good evening-out" destinations.* / www.kazan-restaurant.co.uk; 10.45 pm; no Amex; no smoking area.

## Ken Lo's Memories SW1     £46     ❷❷❸
67-69 Ebury St   7730 7734   2–4B
*"Amazing consistency over the years" makes this "pricey" Belgravia veteran "London's top Chinese" for many reporters; after a "modern" facelift, the room feels "bright" and "livelier", too.* / 11.15 pm; closed Sun L.

## Ken Lo's Memories of China W8     £47     ❷❷❸
353 Kensington High St   7603 6951   7–1D
*"It feels like a neighbourhood Chinese", but fans go wild about the "excellent-quality" cooking at this low-key oriental, near Olympia; it doesn't wow everyone, though (and some find prices "extortionate").* / 11 pm; set weekday L & set D £24 (FP).

## Kensington Place W8     £48     ❸❸④
201-209 Kensington Church St   7727 3184   6–2B
*It was a seminal modern British restaurant in the '90s, but this "noisy" landmark, just off Notting Hill Gate, is more a favoured "canteen" for well-heeled locals nowadays; generally the cooking seems to be "resting on its laurels", but "delicious, seasonal fish" is a highlight.* / www.egami.co.uk; 11 pm; set weekday L £32 (FP).

## Kettners W1     £33     ④❸❶
29 Romilly St   7734 6112   4–2A
*"Charmingly faded" but "amazing", this historic Soho landmark comes complete with a champagne bar (and "pianists everywhere"); its performance has been very iffy in recent years, but, of late, its "posh" PizzaExpress (plus burgers) formula has seemed more of a "solid bet".* / www.kettners.com; midnight; no smoking area; need 7+ to book.

## Kew Grill TW9     £43     ❸❸④
10b Kew Grn   8948 4433   1–3A
*"Excellent" steaks figure in many reports on AWT's year-old venture, near Kew Green; "it's a shame he didn't buy a bigger place, though" – it's "too small" and "too crowded" – and, given the prices, some reporters find the experience "easily forgotten".* / www.awtonline.co.uk; 10.30 pm; closed Mon L; no smoking.

**Khan's W2**                                    £15      ❷④④

13-15 Westbourne Grove   7727 5420   6–1C
"Honest", "value-for-money" Indian scoff maintains the
"consistent" appeal of this vast Bayswater landmark; on the
downside, service can be "slow", and alcohol is a no-no.
/ www.khansrestaurant.com; 11.45 pm; no smoking area.


**Khan's of Kensington SW7**          £28      ❸❷④

3 Harrington Rd   7581 2900   5–2B
There are no culinary fireworks at this "accommodating" Indian –
just "well-cooked" and "tasty" dishes, at prices which are
"reasonable", for South Kensington. / 11 pm, Fri & Sat midnight;
no smoking area.


**Khyber Pass SW7**                       £25      ❸❷④

21 Bute St   7589 7311   5–2B
Reporters seem to "rather miss the old flock wallpaper" at this
once-grungy Kensington old-timer (which was refitted a couple
of years ago), known for its "good-value" cooking. / 11.15 pm;
no smoking area; need 4+ to book.


**Kisso SW5** NEW                          £35      ❸❷❸

251 Old Brompton Rd   7584 9920   5–3A
"A welcome addition to Earl's Court", this "fusion-type" Japanese
(replacing Bar Japan, RIP) offers "carefully prepared" and
"reasonably-priced" dishes in a modern setting.


**Koba W1** NEW                            £38      ❷❶❸

11 Rathbone St   7580 8825   2–1C
A new Fitzrovia Korean with a stylish "modern" look; we very
much agree with the early reporter who thought the food –
cooked at your table – "lovely", and the service "charming".
/ Rated on Editors' visit; 11 pm; closed Sun L.


**Konditor & Cook**                       £16      ❶❸④

Curzon Soho, Shaftesbury Av, W1   7292 1684   4–3A  NEW
46 Gray's Inn Rd, WC1   7404 6300   9–1A
10 Stoney St, SE1   7407 5100   9–4C
22 Cornwall Rd, SE1   7261 0456   9–4A
"Amazing cakes", "irresistible savouries", and "coffee to die for"
make for "long queues" at these small café/take-aways; a new
sit-down branch in Soho's Curzon Cinema opened in July 2005,
and is already busy. / www.konditorandcook.com; 11 pm; no smoking;
no booking.


**Kovalam NW6**                           £23      ❷❷⑤

12 Willesden Ln   7625 4761   1–2B
"Excellent food for the price" and "amazingly friendly" service
help make this "naff"-looking subcontinental (with a south Indian
bias) a top Kilburn-fringe destination. / www.kovalamrestaurant.co.uk;
11 pm, Fri & Sat midnight; no smoking area.


**sign up for the survey at www.hardens.com**

**Kulu Kulu**  £21  ❷④④

76 Brewer St, W1   7734 7316   3–2D
51-53 Shelton St, WC2   7240 5687   4–2C
39 Thurloe Pl, SW7   7589 2225   5–2C
"Very tasty and amazingly cheap sushi" wins acclaim for this duo
of 'kaiten' (conveyor-belt-style) Japanese cafés; the Regent Street
site is a bit of "a dive", though (and "don't expect to linger").
/ 10 pm; SW7 10.30 pm; closed Sun; no Amex; no smoking area,
WC2 no smoking; no booking.

**Kurumaya EC4** NEW  £28  ④④⑤

76-77 Watling St   7236 0236   9–2B
This Japanese newcomer – with ground floor conveyor-sushi,
and downstairs restaurant – is, say supporters, "a useful,
if modest, addition to the City"; sceptics don't disagree, and feel
"they're lucky there's so little competition" in the area.
/ www.kurumaya.co.uk; 9.30 pm; closed Sat & Sun; no Amex; no smoking.

**Kwan Thai SE1**  £37  ❷❷❸

Unit 1, Hay's Galleria   7403 7373   9–4D
It's testament to the 'plain vanilla' charms of this attractive Thai
(with river views towards the City), that although it's voted
a 'top oriental' by some reporters, no one actually wastes any
words on it! / www.kwanthairestaurant.co.uk; 10 pm; closed Sat L & Sun;
no smoking area; set weekday L £24 (FP).

**The Ladbroke Arms W11**  £37  ❷❸❷

54 Ladbroke Rd   7727 6648   6–2B
With its "delicious, imaginative and fairly-priced cooking",
this ever-popular Notting Hill gastroboozer offers standards
"well above its peers"; get there early, especially if you want
a table on the "lovely" terrace. / www.capitalpubcompany.co.uk;
9.45 pm; no booking after 7.30 pm.

**Lahore Kebab House E1**  £19  ❷⑤⑤

2-4 Umberston St   7488 2551   11–1A
"Some of the finest food in town for under £20" (not just
"the best kebabs", but "fabulous" curries and BBQ chops) has
long made it worth braving the "awful", bare Formica décor
at this legendary East End Pakistani canteen; as this guide goes
to press, it is more than doubling the size – fingers crossed they
don't bite off more than they can chew. / 11.30 pm; no Amex;
need 12+ to book.

**Lamberts SW12**  £38  ❶❶❷

2 Station Pde   8675 2233   10–2C
"Book early", if you want a table at this "outstanding local",
behind Balham station, which a number of locals note "is only
beaten around here by Chez Bruce!" / www.lambertsrestaurant.com;
10.30 pm; closed Mon, Tue-Fri D only, Sat & Sun open L & D; no Amex;
no smoking area.

**(Winter Garden)**
**The Landmark NW1**                £69        ④❸❷

222 Marylebone Rd   7631 8000   8–4A

*"The beautiful atrium" ("complete with palm trees") of this
luxurious Marylebone hotel provides a "fantastic" setting for
a "brilliant afternoon tea" or a "great Sunday brunch";
the adjoining dining room proper (to which the formula price
shown relates) is of little interest.* / www.landmarklondon.co.uk;
10.45 pm; no smoking area; booking: max 12.

**Lanes**
**East India House E1**             £44       ❸❷❸

109-117 Middlesex St   7247 5050   9–2D

*"Well-executed" food, "accommodating" service and an air
of "easy sophistication" have come together to make this City-
fringe yearling "a good safe choice, particularly for a business
lunch".* / www.lanesrestaurant.co.uk; 10 pm; closed Sat L & Sun.

**The Lanesborough SW1**            £93        ④❸❷

Hyde Park Corner   7259 5599   5–1D

*"You can't beat the setting" – a "delightful and airy"
conservatory – in the dining room of this "splendid" hotel;
"breakfasts and afternoon teas are its forte", though – "lunch
and dinner are less impressive" (and arguably "way overpriced").*
/ www.lanesborough.com; 11.30 pm; set weekday L £37 (FP), brunch £57
(FP), set D £62 (FP).

**Langan's Coq d'Or SW5**           £35       ❸❸❸

254-260 Old Brompton Rd   7259 2599   5–3A

*This "informal" but "professional" Earl's Court stand-by serves
"good-quality, old-fashioned French food at decent prices"
(and also does a "very good Sunday brunch"); its following among
reporters, however, remains surprisingly small.*
/ www.langansrestaurants.co.uk; 11 pm.

**Langan's Bistro W1**              £34        ④❷❷

26 Devonshire St   7935 4531   2–1A

*This "cramped", but "cosy" and "civilised" veteran Marylebone
bistro can sometimes deliver "good", "un-mucked-about-with"
food, but it is "rather inconsistent".* / www.langansrestaurants.co.uk;
11 pm; closed Sat L & Sun.

**Langan's Brasserie W1**           £48        ④❸❷

Stratton St   7491 8822   3–3C

*"There's still a great buzz, and the food is good enough",
according to the extensive and devoted fan club of this once-great
Mayfair brasserie; others – mystified by its ongoing popularity –
think it needs a "total revamp".* / www.langansrestaurants.co.uk;
11.45 pm; closed Sat L & Sun.

**Lansdowne NW1**                   £39       ❷❸❷

90 Gloucester Ave   7483 0409   8–3B

*Despite having The Engineer down the road, this "laid-back"
gastropub is, for many reporters, "first choice in Primrose Hill";
"cramped" and "always busy", it serves "fresh" and "interesting"
dishes to a "lively meedja crowd".* / 10 pm; closed Mon L; no Amex
or Maestro.

### La Lanterna SE1      £32    ❸❷❸
6-8 Mill St    7252 2420    11–2A
*"The smell of garlic hits you as you go in" to this "lively" Italian joint, near Butlers Wharf; it serves "simple" and "dependable" grub, with pizza a highlight. / www.millstreetcafe.co.uk; 11 pm; closed Sat L; no smoking area.*

### Latium W1      £40    ❷❷❸
21 Berners St    7323 9123    2–1C
*"The best value in the West End?" – perhaps not quite, but "consistently interesting" and "accomplished" Italian cooking is putting this "reliable" yearling, north of Oxford Street, firmly on the map; it's equally good for "a corporate lunch or a relaxed dinner with friends". / www.latiumrestaurant.com; 10.30 pm; closed Sat L & Sun.*

### Latymers W6      £22    ❷❸⑤
157 Hammersmith Rd    8741 2507    7–2C
*"Very plain and very basic" it may be, but the dining area at the back of this Hammersmith gin palace houses "one of the best value-for-money, authentic Thais in town". / 10 pm; closed Sun D; no Amex; no smoking; no booking at L.*

### Laughing Gravy SE1      £39    ❸❸❷
154 Blackfriars Rd    7721 7055    9–4A
*"Eclectic" décor and "lovely" service help create a "cosy" ambience at this family-run Southwark outfit, where the cooking is somewhere between "inexpert" and "distinctive". / 10 pm; closed Sat L & Sun; no Amex.*

### Launceston Place W8      £49    ④❸❷
1a Launceston Pl    7937 6912    5–1B
*"Tucked-away in a beautiful backstreet", this Kensington townhouse still exudes a romantic allure (of a fairly "grown-up" sort); sadly, though, the cooking "has slipped" of late, being judged "barely adequate" in some cases. / www.egami.co.uk; 11 pm; closed Sat L & Sun D; set always available £33 (FP).*

### Laureate W1   **NEW**      £27    ❸❷❸
64 Shaftesbury Ave    7437 5088    4–3A
*On the fringe of Chinatown, this pleasant new corner Chinese is already gathering something of a following, not least for its "quality dim sum". / 11.15 pm.*

### Lavender      £27    ④❸❷
112 Vauxhall Walk, SE11    7735 4440    2–4D
171 Lavender Hill, SW11    7978 5242    10–2C
24 Clapham Rd, SW9    7793 0770    10–1D
*"A permanent buzz from local twenty- and thirtysomethings" creates a "great ambience" at these "chilled" south London eateries, which serve "reliable" bistro fodder at "fair" prices. / 11 pm; SW9 closed Mon L, SE11 closed Sat L & Sun.*

### Leadenhall Tapas Bar EC3      £26    ④④④
27 Leadenhall Mkt    7623 1818    9–2D
*Characterfully-housed in the eaves of the City's Leadenhall Market, this "cheap and cheerful" spot makes a handy rendezvous. / 10 pm; closed Sat & Sun.*

**The Ledbury W11** NEW  £58  ❷❶❷
127 Ledbury Rd   7792 9090   6–1B
*"Finally, a proper grown-up restaurant in Notting Hill";
this "calmly-decorated" newcomer (sibling to The Square,
Chez Bruce, etc) — where "knowledgeable" staff serve up Brett
Graham's "original" (if rather ornate) cuisine — has emerged
as the 'high-end' opening of the year.* / www.theledbury.com; 11 pm;
no smoking.

**Lemonia NW1**  £27  ④❶❶
89 Regent's Park Rd   7586 7454   8–3B
*This "large", "loud" and "lively" Primrose Hill taverna has long
been a north London institution — its Greek fare may be "nothing
special", but the atmosphere is "unbeatable".* / 11.30 pm; closed
Sat L & Sun D; no Amex.

**Leon W1** NEW  £18  ❷❷❸
35-36 Gt Marlborough St   7437 5280   3–2C
*"Wholesome" victuals — salads, wraps, grills, juices —
with "vibrant" tastes have made this "superior organic take-away-
with-tables", by Liberty's, a great hit with most reporters;
"why hasn't it been done before?"* / www.leonrestaurants.co.uk; 10 pm;
no smoking.

**Levant W1**  £40  ④④❶
Jason Court, 76 Wigmore St   7224 1111   3–1A
*As a "loud" and "exotic" West End party destination (complete
with belly-dancing), this basement Lebanese, near the Wigmore
Hall, has a strong following; the food is only "averagely good",
though, and some reporters find the prices "exorbitant".*
/ www.levant.co.uk; 11.30 pm.

**Levantine W2**  £35  ④④❸
26 London St   7262 1111   6–1D
*This initially promising souk-style yearling, near Paddington
station, has induced very mixed reviews; some reporters did hail
its "wonderful" food and "fun" style, but there were also
a number of "major let-downs".* / www.levant.co.uk; 11.30 pm.

**The Light E1**  £37  ④④④
233 Shoreditch High St   7247 8989   9–1D
*A "light", "spacious" and "no-frills" bar/restaurant north
of Liverpool Street; it's mainly a drinking destination, nowadays,
but the food is OK (and "there's always a cheap menu on offer").*
/ www.thelightE1.com; 11 pm; closed Sat L & Sun D.

**The Light House SW19**  £43  ❸❷④
75-77 Ridgway   8944 6338   10–2B
*"Interesting" fusion dishes and "very personal" service make this
modern five-year-old one of Wimbledon's better eateries;
some reporters find it "overpriced", though, and the setting —
while "light and airy" — can seem "lifeless".* / 10.30 pm; closed Sun D;
no smoking area; set weekday L £28 (FP).

## Lightship E1  £43  ④④❶
5a Katharine's Way, St Kath's Dock   7481 3123   9–3D
*Is this "quirky" former lightship, near Tower Bridge, just a "smelly old boat"?; it depends on your point of view – romantics proclaim it "a winner every time", but foodies may find the Scandinavian cuisine "mediocre". / www.lightshipx.com; 10 pm; closed Mon L, Sat L & Sun; set weekday L £28 (FP).*

## Lilly's E1  NEW  £33  ❷❷❷
75 Wapping High St   7702 2040   11–1A
*"Much more sophisticated than it needs to be", this "relaxing" all-day brasserie (with boothed seating) has been a "top-class" addition to the "Wapping scene". / www.lillysrestaurant.co.uk; 11 pm; smoking in bar only; set weekday L £18 (FP).*

## Lindsay House W1  £74  ❸❸❷
21 Romilly St   7439 0450   4–3A
*On most accounts, Richard Corrigan's "gorgeous" Soho townhouse offers "sublime" and "faultless" meals; support is still undercut, however, by the minority of reporters which complains of "astronomical" bills for cooking that's "good, but not outstanding". / www.lindsayhouse.co.uk; 11 pm; closed Sat L & Sun; no smoking area; set weekday L & pre-theatre £48 (FP).*

## Lisboa Patisserie W10  £5  ❸④④
57 Golborne Rd   8968 5242   6–1A
*You get "the best custard tarts in London", at this famous Portuguese café in North Kensington (where pasteis da nata are the house speciality); it gets "too busy", though, and service can be "very slow". / 8 pm; L & early evening only; no Amex; no booking.*

## Little Bay  £24  ❸❷❷
140 Wandsworth Br Rd, SW6   7751 3133   10–1B  NEW
228 Belsize Rd, NW6   7372 4699   1–2B
228 York Rd, SW11   7223 4080   10–2B
171 Farringdon Rd, EC1   7278 1234   9–1A
*"For the prices", the food is "little short of astonishing" at this "funky" small bistro chain; "why can't others do it?" / www.little-bay.co.uk; 11.30 pm; NW6 no credit cards.*

## Little Earth Cafe  NEW
## Triyoga NW3  £15  ❷❸④
6 Erskine Rd   7449 0700   8–3B
*London's first raw-food café occupies a few tables in the lobby of a my-body-is-a-temple Primrose Hill yoga centre; its simple, vibrant, veggie dishes are excellent... if you like that sort of thing. / 8 pm, Sat 6 pm; closed Sun D; no smoking.*

## Little Italy W1  £55  ④④④
21 Frith St   7734 4737   4–2A
*"They practically dance on the tables", at this late-night Soho Italian, which fans find "positively adorable"; less starry-eyed reporters, however, just dismiss it as "hugely expensive" for what it is. / 4 am, Sun 11.30 pm.*

**The Little Square W1**   £38   ④❸❸

3 Shepherd Mkt   7355 2101   3–4B

*A "bijou" Mayfair bistro, "in the romantic setting of Shepherd Market"; it's a "patchy" performer, though, and can "fail to live up to its undoubted promise". / 11 pm; set weekday L £22 (FP).*

**Livebait**   £40   ④④④

21 Wellington St, WC2   7836 7161   4–3D
43 The Cut, SE1   7928 7211   9–4A

*"Good-quality fish at sensible prices" still wins quite a following for this white-tiled ("lavatorial") chain; ebbing ratings, however, reflect the number of reporters who find the formula "faded" and too "pricey". / www.santeonline.co.uk; WC2 11.30 pm, SE1 11 pm, Sun 9 pm; WC2 closed Sun; no smoking area.*

**LMNT E8**   £25   ❸❸❶

316 Queensbridge Rd   7249 6727   1–2D

*"Amazing", "totally mad" décor ("like an Egyptian boudoir") has won fame for this "quirky" Hackney venture; the food is surprisingly "innovative", too, and it comes at "great-value" prices. / www.lmnt.co.uk; 10 pm; no Amex.*

**Lobster Pot SE11**   £41   ❶❷❸

3 Kennington Ln   7582 5556   1–3C

*"The sound of seagulls and fog-horns" transports you from an ugly Kennington junction to the "weird and wonderful world" of this "bizarre" Breton venture; "ten minutes in, you forget the absurdity", allowing you to focus on the "superb" Gallic fish cooking. / www.lobsterpotrestaurant.co.uk; 11 pm; closed Mon & Sun; no smoking area; booking: max 8; set weekday L £24 (FP).*

**LOCANDA LOCATELLI
CHURCHILL INTERCONT'L W1**   £56   ❷❷❷

8 Seymour St   7935 9088   2–2A

*Giorgio Locatelli's "swish" modern Italian on Portman Square delivers "straightforward cooking of the highest calibre"; it is, for many reporters, simply London's top Italian. / www.locandalocatelli.com; 11 pm, Fri & Sat 11.30 pm; closed Sun; booking: max 8.*

**Locanda Ottoemezzo W8**   £58   ❸❷❷

2-4 Thackeray St   7937 2200   5–1B

*The "rustic" cooking is "very good" and staff "will do anything to help" at this "down-to-earth" Kensington Italian; some reporters still feel it's "ludicrously overpriced", though. / 10.45 pm; closed Sat L & Sun; set weekday L £34 (FP).*

**Loch Fyne**   £34   ④④④

2-4 Catherine St, WC2   7240 4999   2–2D
676 Fulham Rd, SW6   7610 8020   10–1B
175 Hampton Rd, TW2   8255 6222   1–4A

*"Could do better!" – even some reporters who say this national seafood chain makes a "pleasant" stand-by concede that it's an "uninspired" choice. / www.lochfyne.com; 10 pm-11 pm; no smoking area.*

**Loco** £36 ④④❸
Locale) 222 Munster Rd, SW6   7381 6137   10–1B   NEW
Mensa) 3b Belvedere Rd, SE1   7401 6734   2–3D
Locale) 1 Lawn Terrace, SE3   8852 0700   1–4D
*"Generally good, but misfires not unknown" – a fair summary
of the performance of this small Italian chain; the airy Blackheath
original is the best-known branch, but the "buzzy" 'Mensa' outlet
by County Hall and the "cheerful" new other 'Locale' in Fulham
also rate a mention.* / www.locorestaurants.com; 10.30 pm; SE3 closed
Mon, Tue-Fri L & Sun D; no smoking area.

**Lola's N1** £46 ❸❸❸
359 Upper St   7359 1932   8–3D
*Given the comings-and-goings of numerous chefs over the years,
reporters' loyalty to this "calm" and "classy" Islington venture –
above the Antiques Market – is impressive ; perhaps the (post-
survey) return of a Juliet Peston protégée to the stove will herald
an era of greater stability.* / 11 pm; closed Sun D; booking: max 14.

**Lomo SW10** £28 ④④❸
222-224 Fulham Rd   7349 8848   5–3B
*A "former-favourite" Chelsea tapas bar, now drifting; some
"disappointing" dishes have been reported of late.* / www.lomo.co.uk;
midnight; D only.

**Lonsdale W11** £39 ⑤⑤④
48 Lonsdale Rd   7727 4080   6–1B
*"Nothing can prepare you for the size of the portions" – "tiny" –
at this "pretentious" Notting Hill bar, which once had quite
a 'name' for its cooking.* / www.thelonsdale.co.uk; 11.30 pm; book only
at D.

**The Lord Palmerston NW5** £29 ❷④❷
33 Dartmouth Park Hill   7485 1578   8–1B
*It's "nothing fancy", but – thanks to the range of "gorgeous"
dishes prepared with "a light touch" – this "way above-average"
Dartmouth Park gastropub "can get as crowded as hell".*
/ 10 pm; no Amex; no booking.

**Lots Road SW10** £35 ❸❸❸
114 Lots Rd   7352 6645   5–4B
*"Tucked-away", by the entrance to Chelsea Harbour, this popular
gastropub exudes a "friendly" hustle and bustle, especially
at weekends; "great burgers" are a highlight.* / 10 pm; no Amex;
no smoking area.

**Lou Pescadou SW5** £38 ❸❷④
241 Old Brompton Rd   7370 1057   5–3A
*"Very fresh seafood" and "a witty maître d'" help ensure that this
"old-fashioned" Gallic fish restaurant, in Earl's Court, "never fails
to impress" its loyal following.* / midnight.

**Louvaine SW11** NEW £31 ④❷❸
110 St John's Hill   7223 8708   10–2C
*This rather romantic-looking new Gallic bistro looks set to gather
a reasonable Wandsworth following – early reports are mainly
favourable, if a bit up-and-down.* / www.louvaine.co.uk; 10.30 pm; closed
Mon, weekday L & Sat L; no Amex; no smoking area.

#### Love India SW3 NEW £30
153 Fulham Rd   7589 7749   5–2C
*We always thought that the subterranean Tandoori of Chelsea
(RIP) was an overlooked period gem; it took on this new,
more modern format shortly before this guide went to press –
the old chef remains, but prices are now significantly lower.*

#### Lowiczanka
#### Polish Social & Cultural Assoc'n W6 £27   ❸❷❸
238-246 King St   8741 3225   7–2B
*This "unusual and pleasing" small café, attached to a
Hammersmith cultural centre, serves simple Polish grub
at "cheap" prices, to a crowd of locals and émigrés. / 10 pm, Fri &
Sat 11 pm; no smoking area.*

#### Luc's Brasserie EC3 £39   ④④④
17-22 Leadenhall Mkt   7621 0666   9–2D
*"Squashed-in" over Leadenhall Market, this Gallic brasserie
seems to be rather losing its way under new ownership;
n.b. owing to a dispute with the Corporation of London, it was
closed as this guide went to press. / L only, closed Sat & Sun.*

#### Lucio SW3 £46   ❷❶❷
257 Fulham Rd   7823 3007   5–3B
*"Suddenly very fashionable" – this Chelsea yearling is a "happy"
sort of place, where "really tasty" Italian dishes are served
by "very sweet" staff. / 10.45 pm; no smoking area.*

#### Lucky Seven W2 £31   ❸④❷
127 Westbourne Park Rd   7727 6771   6–1B
*Tom Conran's "fun", "faux-American" diner, in Bayswater, serves
"burgers straight off the set of 'Grease'" (and milkshakes "which
make your straw stand to attention"). / 11 pm; closed Mon L; no credit
cards; no booking.*

#### Luigi's WC2 £47   ⑤④④
15 Tavistock St   7240 1795   4–3D
*"Old-fashioned" Covent Garden Italian that's still hailed as a
"pleasant" destination by its diehard older fan club; some younger
bloods rail at "indifferent" food and "inflated" prices.
/ www.luigisofcoventgarden.com; 11.30 pm; closed Sun; set pre-theatre
£26 (FP).*

#### Luna Rossa W11 NEW £39   ④⑤④
192 Kensington Park Rd   7229 0482   6–1A
*"Bring back 192!" – this successor to that famous Notting Hill
restaurant wins some praise for its pizza and pasta dishes, but its
air of "semi-organised chaos" leaves many reporters cold.
/ 11.30 pm; no Amex; no smoking area.*

#### Lundum's SW7 £45   ❷❶❶
119 Old Brompton Rd   7373 7774   5–2B
*"Beautiful and romantic" décor and "attentive" staff win the
highest praise for the Lundum Family's "elegant" but "homely"
South Kensington restaurant, where a "classic" menu comes with
a "Scandinavian twist" – highlights include seafood and the
Sunday buffet brunch. / www.lundums.com; 11 pm; closed Sun D;
set weekday L £29 (FP).*

**sign up for the survey at www.hardens.com**

### Ma Cuisine £30 ❸❸❸

6 Whitton Rd, TW1   8607 9849   1–4A
9 Station Approach, TW9   8332 1923   1–3A

"Straightforward" Gallic "comfort food" at "jolly good" prices
makes John McClement's "cramped", "old -school" bistros very
popular with most reporters; the new sibling to the Twickenham
original is "a huge asset to Kew Village". / TW1 10.30 pm,
TW9 11 pm; no Amex; no smoking.

### Ma Goa SW15 £31 ❷❷❸

244 Upper Richmond Rd   8780 1767   10–2B

"Sumptuous" and "genuine" Goan cuisine is served by "lovely
people", at this "cosy", if "slightly poky", Putney "gem".
/ www.ma-goa.com; 11 pm; D only, ex Sun open L & D; no smoking.

### Made in China SW10 £35 ❷❷④

351 Fulham Rd   7351 2939   5–3B

"Freshly-prepared" food at "reasonable prices" is making this
Chelsea two-year-old a bit of a "local favourite"; it's "a bit
canteen-like", though – "they need to turn the lights down
or something". / 11.30 pm.

### Made in Italy SW3 £34 ❷⑤❸

249 King's Rd   7352 1880   5–3C

"It's a bit of a squeeze", but "great fun", at this "loud" Chelsea
fixture, which is known for its "fabulous" and "very authentic"
pizza; service, though, is "useless". / 11.30 pm; closed weekday L;
no Amex.

### Madhu's UB1 £29 ❶❷❸

39 South Rd   8574 1897   1–3A

With its "great smells, textures and ingredients" the food "takes
some beating for authenticity", at this pleasant Southall Indian –
the best all-rounder in this curry-dominated suburb.
/ www.madhusonline.com; 11.30 pm; closed Tue, Sat L & Sun L.

### Maggie Jones's W8 £43 ❸❸❶

6 Old Court Pl   7937 6462   5–1A

"Like the '90s never happened" (or the '80s, for that matter),
this "cheesy" rustic Kensington veteran can still make a "lovely"
destination for those with romance in mind; it offers "simple"
going-on "basic" English fare. / 11 pm; set Sun L £28 (FP).

### Maggiore's WC2 £49 ❷❷❶

33 King St   7379 9696   4–3C

"In the midst of Covent Garden's tourist hell", this "wonderfully
romantic" venture (complete with "magical" inside courtyard)
comes as a "very nice surprise"; but that's not all – the food
is "very competent", and the "massive" wine list is "simply
stunning". / www.maggiores.uk.com; 10.45 pm; no smoking; set weekday L
£30 (FP), set pre-theatre £22 (FP), set Sun L £20 (FP).

### Maison Bertaux W1 £9 ❷❸❸

28 Greek St   7437 6007   4–2A

It may be "cramped and too expensive", but reporters
"feel good" at this "ungentrified" bastion of old Soho (est. 1871);
the coffee is notoriously "indifferent", but it's the "top-class
pâtisserie that matters". / 9 pm; no credit cards; no smoking area;
no booking.

### Malabar W8 £30 ❷❷❸
27 Uxbridge St 7727 8800 6–2B
*"Standards never slip"*, at this *"old-favourite"* curry house, off Notting Hill Gate; it has a big fan club, thanks to its *"sophisticated"* and *"slightly different"* curries, which offer *"great value"*. / www.malabar-restaurant.co.uk; 11.15 pm.

### Malabar Junction WC1 £30 ❸❷❸
107 Gt Russell St 7580 5230 2–1C
A very *"civilised"* and *"spacious"* – if slightly *"characterless"* – Bloomsbury venture, where *"courteous"* staff dish up some notably *"delicate"* south Indian dishes (including a *"wide veggie selection"*). / 11.30 pm; no smoking area.

### The Mall Tavern W8 £36 ❸❸❸
71-73 Palace Gardens Ter 7727 3805 6–2B
This *"busy"* gastropub, just off Notting Hill Gate, serves an *"interesting and constantly-changing menu"* (even if it *"doesn't always come off"*); it has a *"fantastic"* courtyard. / 10.45 pm; set pre-theatre £22 (FP).

### Malmaison EC1 £41 ❸❸❷
18-21 Charterhouse St 7012 3700 9–1B
*"Elegant"* décor and a slightly *"secluded"* feel make this Clerkenwell design-hotel dining room a surprise *'hit'* on the ambience front; the food – though a less reliable attraction – is generally *"good value"*. / www.malmaison.com; 10.30 pm; no smoking area; set weekday L £27 (FP).

### Mamounia W1 NEW £50 ❸④❸
37a Curzon St 7629 2211 3–4B
This Mayfair newcomer (on the former site of the Curzon, RIP) has no relation to the famous Marrakech hotel, and the menu – unlike the decorative style – only 'nods' to Morocco; it's quite a handy spot, though, comfortably furnished and offering straightforward cooking. / Rated on Editors' visit; www.mamouniarestaurant.co.uk; 11 pm.

### La Mancha SW15 £33 ❸❷❷
32 Putney High St 8780 1022 10–2B
*"Good tapas and paella"* contribute to the *"all-round"* appeal of this large and *"lively"* Putney hang-out. / www.lamancha.co.uk; 10 pm; need 6+ to book.

### Mandalay W2 £18 ❶❶④
444 Edgware Rd 7258 3696 8–4A
*"The friendliest restaurant in London"* may be this *"drab"* shop-conversion, near Edgware Road tube, where *"truly enthusiastic"* proprietors serve up *"delicious"* Burmese dishes (*"a cross between Indian and Chinese"*) at *"very reasonable prices"*; book ahead. / 10.30 pm; closed Sun; no smoking.

### Mandarin Kitchen W2 £27 ❶④④
14-16 Queensway 7727 9012 6–2C
It's *"a complete zoo"* – and *"booking doesn't seem to make any difference"* – but this *"scruffy"* Queensway oriental remains a *"brilliant"* choice for seafood; *"you mustn't miss the lobster"* (of which they claim to serve more than anywhere else in the UK!). / 11.15 pm.

### Mangal E8    £15    **❶❷❸**

10 Arcola St    7275 8981    1–1C
*"A lesson in how to do simple things well"* – this *"fantastic-value"*
Turkish caff, in Dalston, offers *"wonderful"* kebabs and
*"good mezze"*; *"try to spend over 20 quid, without having to be
wheeled home"*. / midnight; no credit cards.

### Mango Room NW1    £33    **❷**④**❷**

10 Kentish Town Rd    7482 5065    8–3B
*"The plantain is pure perfection"*, and *"you feel like you were
somewhere cooler than Camden Town"*, when you visit this
*"cosy"*, *"laid-back"* Caribbean – *"a really top place for a fun
evening"*. / www.mangoroom.co.uk; 11 pm; no Amex; no smoking area.

### Mango Tree SW1    £45    **❷❸**④

46 Grosvenor Pl    7823 1888    2–4B
A popular Belgravia-fringe destination, where the *"delicious and
beautifully presented"* Thai fare is *"expensive, but worth it"*;
its office-block setting, however, is *"bland"* and *"barn-like"*.
/ www.mangotree.org.uk; 11 pm.

### Manicomio SW3    £43    **❸❸❸**

85 Duke of York Sq    7730 3366    5–2D
*"Great for a weekend lunch"*, this Italian two-year-old –
*"conveniently-located"* near Sloane Square – benefits from
*"a perfect traffic-free terrace"*; its *"deli-style"* cuisine strikes some
reporters as *"sophisticated"*, but others as *"nothing special"*.
/ www.manicomio.co.uk; 10.30 pm; no smoking area.

### Manna NW3    £34    ④**❸❸**

4 Erskine Rd    7722 8028    8–3B
Primrose Hill's veggie veteran of nearly four decades' standing has
been *"too variable"* in recent times – it can be *"first-rate"*, but it
can also be *"really disappointing"*. / www.manna-veg.com; 10.45 pm;
closed weekday L; no Amex; no smoking.

### Manzi's WC2    £45    **❸**④④

1 Leicester St    7734 0224    4–3A
*"Never a poor meal in 40 years"* – reporters who *"like Manzi's
just how it is"* are unstinting in their praise for this *"old-
fashioned"* Theatreland fish veteran; doubters, however, dismiss
it as *"venerable, but with nothing else to commend it"*.
/ www.manzis.co.uk; 11.15 pm; closed Sun L.

### Mao Tai    £38    **❷❸❸**

96 Draycott Ave, SW3    7225 2500    5–2C
58 New King's Rd, SW6    7731 2520    10–1B
With their *"classic"* Chinese cuisine, these *"consistent"* orientals
– in Parson's Green and at Brompton Cross – continue to please;
they're *"certainly not cheap"*, though, and some reporters feel
that they *"need to re-invent themselves"*. / www.maotai.co.uk;
11.30 pm; no smoking area.

### Marechiaro SW3    £34    **❸**⑤④

257 Kings Rd    7351 2417    5–3C
Made in Italy's offshoot, a few yards further down the King's
Road, is a chip off the old block – the pasta (in particular)
is *"good"*, but the service can be *"useless"*. / 11.30 pm; closed
weekday L; no Amex.

### Marine Ices NW3     £26    ❸❷❷

8 Haverstock Hill   7482 9003   8–2B

*Seventy-five this year, the Mansi family's "really atmospheric" Belsize Park veteran remains every north London child's dream, thanks to "Britain's best ice cream"; "the mains are worth a look, too", in particular the "reliable" pizza.* / www.marineices.co.uk; 11 pm; no Amex; no smoking.

### Maroush     £40    ❷④④

I) 21 Edgware Rd, W2   7723 0773   6–1D
II) 38 Beauchamp Pl, SW3   7581 5434   5–1C
III) 62 Seymour St, W1   7724 5024   2–2A
IV) 68 Edgware Rd, W2   7724 9339   6–1D
V) 3-4 Vere St, W1   7493 3030   3–1B
"Garden") 1 Connaught St, W2   7262 0222   6–1D

*"Consistent, high-quality Lebanese food" has long made this upmarket Middle Eastern group a London benchmark; branches vary in style and appeal, but most are open till late – the (cheaper) café sections of I, II and V offer good-value early-hours re-fuelling.* / www.maroush.com; 11.30 pm-3.30 am.

### Masala Zone     £23    ❸❸❸

9 Marshall St, W1   7287 9966   3–2D
147 Earl's Court Rd, SW5   7373 0220   5–2A   **NEW**
80 Upper St, N1   7359 3399   8–3D

*A "snazzy"-looking Indian chain, which serves "spicy" street-food at "affordable" prices; it's a good formula for a meal that's "fast and convenient" as well as "interesting and satisfying".* / www.realindianfood.com; 11 pm; no Amex; no smoking; no booking.

### Mash W1     £40    ⑤⑤④

19-21 Gt Portland St   7637 5555   3–1C

*With its "totally unmemorable" food and "poor" service, Oliver Peyton's once-trendy joint, north of Oxford Street, "just doesn't cut it as a restaurant" any more; something of a revamp was completed as this guide went to press, but we can't honestly say we're holding our breath for news of major improvement.* / www.mashbarandrestaurant.co.uk; 10.30 pm; closed Sun.

### The Mason's Arms SW8     £32    ❸④❸

169 Battersea Park Rd   7622 2007   10–1C

*Despite its uncompromisingly "urban" location, by Battersea Park BR, this long-established gastroboozer remains an ever-popular – and sometimes "too busy" – destination; the food is a touch variable, but can be "very good".* / 10 pm.

### Matilda's SW11   **NEW**     £34    ④⑤❸

74-76 Battersea Bridge Rd   7228 6482   5–4C

*Though "much touted" in the media, this "airy" Battersea gastropub has had a mixed and muted reception from reporters; service can be "clueless", and the Italian menu often "promises more than it delivers" – "excellent meat and cheeseboards" are the safest bet.* / www.matilda.tv; midnight; no Amex.

**Matriciano SW6** NEW                    £36            ④④④
108-110 New King's Rd   7731 2142   10–1B
*Initial reports on this relaunched Parson's Green Italian (formerly
of Brompton Cross) are very up-and-down; supporters insist it's
"trying hard" and "getting busier". / 11.30 pm; closed Mon L & Tue L;
no smoking area.*

**Matsuri**                              £60            ❷❷④
15 Bury St, SW1   7839 1101   3–3D
Mid City Place, 71 High Holborn, WC1   7430 1970   2–1D
*"Particularly great sushi" is a mainstay of the often-"stunning"
cuisine of these "bland"-looking St James's and Holborn
Japaneses; service comes "with a smile", and , in SW1, you also
get "lots of whirling knives" at the "fabulous" teppan-yaki.
/ www.matsuri-restaurant.com; 10 pm; WC1 closed Sun; set D £35 (FP).*

**Mawar W2**                             £23            ❸④⑤
175a Edgware Rd   7262 1663   6–1D
*A tacky cellar, near Edgware Road tube, where you get "good"
Malaysian dishes at low, low prices. / 10.30 pm; no smoking area.*

**Maxwell's**                            £31            ④❸❸
8-9 James St, WC2   7836 0303   4–2D
76 Heath St, NW3   7794 5450   8–1A
*"I don't go often, but when I do it still seems good" – these
predictable but "still entertaining" Hampstead and Covent
Garden burger-veterans continue to do an OK job.
/ www.maxwells.co.uk; midnight; NW3 closed weekday L;
WC2 no smoking area.*

**maze W1** NEW                          £50            ④④④
10-13 Grosvenor Sq   7107 0000   3–2A
*The press has, for the most part, raved, but we just can't see the
point of Gordon Ramsay's Mayfair newcomer – leaving aside the
hit-and-miss quality of the 'grazing' dishes on our July 2005 visit,
the service we had was too slow to make the place 'handy',
and too laboured to make it 'fun'. / Rated on Editors' visit; 11 pm;
smoking in bar only.*

**McClements TW1**                       £67            ❸④⑤
2 Whitton Rd   8744 9610   1–4A
*Is Michelin's approval (ever to be feared) giving John McC's
"cramped" Twickenham veteran ideas "above its station"? –
the food is often "first-rate", but many reporters now find this
a "looking-down-your-nose" sort of place, charging "grasping"
prices. / www.mcclementsrestaurant.com; 10.30 pm; closed Mon & Sun;
no smoking; set weekday L £41 (FP).*

**Medcalf EC1**                          £32            ❷❸❷
40 Exmouth Mkt   7833 3533   9–1A
*The "deliberately basic" look and "very British" menu go down
well with a "hip" clientèle at this "bustling", "café-style"
Clerkenwell yearling; by night, it's much more of a bar.
/ www.medcalfbar.co.uk; 10 pm; closed Fri D & Sun D; no Amex.*

**for updates visit www.hardens.com**                  130

**Mediterranean Kitchen** £31 ⑤④④
50-51 St Martin's Ln, WC2   7836 8289   4–4C
25-35 Gloucester Rd, SW7   7589 1383   5–2B   NEW
127 Kensington Church St, W8   7727 8142   6–2B   NEW
3-5 Campden Hill Rd, W8   7938 1830   5–1A
334 Upper St, N1   7226 7916   8–3D
*For snacks or pre-theatre (on St Martin's Lane), this "friendly",*
*"no-frills" chain has its fans; reports are still patchy, though,*
*and the food can be "very disappointing" on occasions. / 11 pm;*
*no smoking area.*

**Mediterraneo W11** £38 ❸❸❸
37 Kensington Park Rd   7792 3131   6–1A
*This "cramped" trattoria remains a popular Notting Hill*
*destination, thanks to its "fun" ambience and "sensibly-priced"*
*food; the feeling that it's "not what it used to be", though,*
*runs through a number of reports. / 11.30 pm; no smoking area;*
*booking: max 10.*

**Mehek EC2** £30 ❷❷❸
45 London Wall   7588 5043   9–2C
*Notably consistent standards make this smart Indian, near the*
*Barbican, a handy City stand-by. / www.mehek.co.uk; 11 pm; closed*
*Sat & Sun; no smoking area.*

**Mekong SW1** £22 ❸❷④
46 Churton St   7630 9568   2–4B
*A "popular" Pimlico Vietnamese/Thai, with a name locally for*
*"dependable" and "reasonably-priced" food; "for better*
*atmosphere, sit upstairs if you can". / 11.15 pm; no Amex.*

**Mela WC2** £33 ❸❸❸
152-156 Shaftesbury Ave   7836 8635   4–2B
*"Different" and "tasty" dishes at "good-value prices for the West*
*End" have made quite a name for this "reliable" Indian,*
*by Cambridge Circus; over the years, though, its standards have*
*drifted noticeably. / www.melarestaurant.co.uk; 11.30 pm; no smoking area.*

**Melati W1** £28 ④❸④
21 Gt Windmill St   7437 2745   3–2D
*"Reasonably-priced Malaysian food" maintains the appeal of this*
*slightly "seedy"-looking Soho veteran, especially as a pre-theatre*
*destination; (n.b. it's under different ownership from Melati*
*on nearby Peter Street, which is also quite good). / 11.30 pm, Fri &*
*Sat midnight; no smoking area.*

**Memories of India SW7** £27 ❸❷④
18 Gloucester Rd   7581 3734   5–1B
*This "unassuming", "moderately-priced" Indian of "above-*
*average" standards is worth knowing about in South Kensington.*
*/ 11.15 pm.*

**Menier Chocolate Factory SE1** NEW £33 ④❷❷
51-53 Southwark St   7378 1712   9–4B
*An intriguing new South Bank theatre-cum-dining venue; the food*
*may be "essentially average", but a "combined theatre/dining*
*package" offers the prospect of a "fun" and "cheap" evening.*
*/ www.menierchocolatefactory.com; 11 pm; closed Mon D, Sat L & Sun L.*

**Le Mercury N1**  £24  ④❷❶
140a Upper St  7354 4088  8–2D
*"So cosy and candlelit", this "old-style", "romantic" budget bistro
in Islington has many fans; the food's no better than "not bad",
but it's so "incredibly cheap" that "you can't go wrong". / 1 am.*

**Mesclun N16**  £34  ④④④
24 Stoke Newington Church St  7249 5029  1–1C
*Small, once-culinarily-acclaimed café-style venture, which – for a
few fans – is "still one of Stoke Newington's gems"; too much
of the limited feedback it induces nowadays, however, says it's
"lost it". / www.mesclunrestaurant.co.uk; 10.30 pm; closed Mon,
Tue-Thu D only.*

**Meson don Felipe SE1**  £23  ④④❶
53 The Cut  7928 3237  9–4A
*"It feels like you're on holiday every time", at this "squashed",
"basic" and "incredibly noisy" tapas bar, near the Old Vic. / 11 pm;
closed Sun; no Amex; no booking after 8 pm.*

**Meson los Barilles E1**  £26  ❷❸④
8a Lamb Street  7375 3136  9–1D
*"Good and reliable" tapas and "simply-cooked fresh fish" are
among the culinary highlights at this "authentic" Spanish
bar/restaurant, in Spitalfields Market. / 11 pm; closed Sat & Sun D.*

**Messanges** NEW
**Cadogan Hotel SW1**  £45  ❸❷④
75 Sloane St  7235 7141  5–1D
*The launch of this modestly trendified Knightsbridge dining room
induced scant feedback; the little there was, praised its
"good match" of "old-world service" and "mouth-watering food"
– our visit was pleasant enough, but didn't dazzle.
/ www.cadogan.com; 10.30 pm.*

**Mestizo NW1** NEW  £27  ❷❷④
103 Hampstead Rd  7387 4064  8–4C
*"High-quality food at good prices" makes this new Mexican
restaurant – five minutes' walk north of Warren Street tube –
a "gem", according to one early reporter; we didn't find
it especially atmospheric, but it's certainly interesting.
/ www.mestizomx.com; midnight; no smoking area.*

**Le Metro**
**Capital Hotel SW3**  £32  ❸❸❸
28 Basil St  7591 1213  5–1D
*"Tucked away, by Harrods", this recently refurbished basement
brasserie is "a good stand-by", thanks not least to its "simple"
and "reasonably-priced" fare. / www.capitalgrp.co.uk; 9 pm; closed
Sun D; need 5+ to book.*

**Metro EC3** NEW
1 Seething Ln  7702 2020  9–3D
*If it lives up to its aspirations, this large new brasserie, pâtisserie
and bar – scheduled to open in late-2005 – should make a very
handy all-day City destination; it is designed so that, on fine-
weather days, the whole glass front of the establishment can
be removed.*

**Metrogusto N1**   £42   ❸❶❷

13 Theberton St   7226 9400   8–3D
*When it's on form – which has become much more the norm
again of late – this Islington side street spot can be a "terrific
local", offering "imaginative" cooking, "personable" service and
an "excellent" wine list.* / www.metrogusto.co.uk; 10.30 pm, Fri & Sat
11 pm; Mon-Thu D only; smoking in bar only; booking: max 8, Sat & Sun.

**Meza W1**   £30   ④❸❸

100 Wardour St   7314 4002   3–2D
*Conran's large new tapas bar, on the ground floor of the Soho site
that was Mezzo (RIP), has induced spectacularly little feedback
(and hardly any of that from London-based reporters) – perhaps
it's because, in our personal view, the place lacks anything
resembling a soul.* / 1.30 am; closed Sun L; smoking in bar only.

**Mezzanine**
**Royal National Theatre SE1**   £35   ⑤⑤⑤

South Bank   7452 3600   2–3D
*Even some reporters who find the RNT's in-house dining room
"a pleasant pre-show dinner venue" admit that "the cooking
is not what it was"; harsher critics boo it as "a total dud".*
/ www.nationaltheatre.org.uk; 11 pm; D only (open for L at matinée), closed
Sun; no smoking.

**Michael Moore W1**   £46   ❸❸④

19 Blandford St   7224 1898   2–1A
*Michael Moore's fans find him a "very charming and creative
chef", and sing the praises of his small and "friendly"
Marylebone dining room; à la carte, it can seem "rather
overpriced", though, and sceptics find their experience "a mixed
bag".* / www.michaelmoorerestaurant.com; 11.30 pm; closed Sun; no smoking.

**Michiaki W1**   NEW   £35   ❸④④

40-42 Baker St   7486 3898   2–1A
*Baker Street is an 'anonymous' thoroughfare, and that feeling has
rubbed off on this ambitious new minimalist Japanese (from the
Royal China people); it is hailed by some (but not all) early
reporters for its "terrific" food and "reasonable" prices.*
/ www.michiaki.co.uk; 11pm, Fri-Sun 11.30 pm; closed Sun; no smoking;
set weekday L £23 (FP).

**Mildred's W1**   £27   ❷④❸

45 Lexington St   7494 1634   3–2D
*"Proof that veggie food isn't all mung beans!" – this "cramped"
Soho stalwart generates "queues out the door", thanks to its
"diverse" and "really tasty" fare; the veggie-burger is especially
recommended.* / www.mildreds.co.uk; 11 pm; closed Sun; only Maestro;
no smoking area; no booking.

**Mimmo d'Ischia SW1**   £52   ④❸④

61 Elizabeth St   7730 5406   2–4A
*Mimmo's "personal" style helps create a "unique" experience for
fans of this Belgravia veteran Italian; even many reporters who
applaud its "high-quality" ("if not exciting") cooking, though,
find the bills "eye-watering".* / www.mimmodischia.co.uk; 11.30 pm;
closed Sun.

**Mint Leaf SW1**  £50  ❸❷❷
1 Suffolk Pl  7930 9020  2–2C
*"Not at all the triumph of style over substance you might expect"
– this "smooth" and "dimly-lit" basement, near Trafalgar Square,
offers "beautifully-presented" Indian dishes "of high quality";
there's a "good bar", too. / www.mintleafrestaurant.com; 11 pm; closed
Sat L & Sun.*

**Mirabelle W1**  £65  ❸❸❷
56 Curzon St  7499 4636  3–4B
*Fans still see MPW's "grand Art Deco dame" as a "great"
Mayfair "all-rounder", serving "classic Gallic cuisine"
(complemented by a "cellar to die for"); its ratings continue
to drift, though, with critics finding it "dated", "tired" and
"impersonal". / www.whitestarline.org.uk; 11.15 pm; set Sun L £40 (FP), set
weekday L £39 (FP).*

**Miraggio SW6**  £30  ❷❷❷
510 Fulham Rd  7384 9774  5–4A
*The Aiello family now run this modest-looking, Parson's Green
Italian, which is universally hailed for its "fantastic", "authentic"
cuisine at "very reasonable" prices. / 11 pm.*

**Mirch Masala**  £22  ❶④④
1416 London Rd, SW16  8679 1828  10–2C
213 Upper Tooting Rd, SW17  8672 7500  10–2D
171-173 The Broadway, UB1  8867 9222  1–3A
*"Unbelievable", "home-style" Indian cooking "at great prices"
puts branches of this "basic" south London chain among the
capital's top budget destinations. / midnight; no Amex;
SW17 no smoking, SW16 no smoking area.*

**Mirto SW6**  £35  ❸❶④
839 Fulham Rd  7736 3217  10–1B
*"A charming owner" helps compensate for the "lack of
atmosphere" at this 'difficult' Fulham site; most reporters say its
Sardinian cooking is "fabulous", but there was also the odd
"disappointment" this year. / 11 pm; closed Mon.*

**Missouri Grill EC3** 🆕  £40  ❷❶④
76 Aldgate High St  7481 4010  9–2D
*"Simple and satisfying" cooking – not especially American in style
– and exceptional service have helped make this bravely-sited
newcomer (opposite Aldgate tube) quite a "classy" City lunching
destination; it's not inexpensive, though, and the evenings can
be "dead". / www.missourigrill.com; 11 pm; closed Sat & Sun.*

**Mitsukoshi SW1**  £53  ❷❷⑤
Dorland Hs, 14-20 Lower Regent St  7930 0317  3–3D
*The "excellent" sushi is amongst the best in town at this West
End department store basement (even if it does badly "need a
make-over") – "sit at the counter, and let the chef sort out your
order". / www.mitsukoshi-restaurant.co.uk; 10 pm; no smoking area;
set weekday L £25 (FP).*

## Miyabi
### Great Eastern Hotel EC2 £37 ❷④⑤
Liverpool St 7618 7100 9–2D
*"Top-quality sushi"* and *"good basic Japanese cooking"* again win
praise for this small City café; its *"cramped"*, though, and – being
part of the Conran empire – *"a bit more expensive than its
competitors"*. / www.miyabi.co.uk; 10.30 pm; closed Sat L & Sun; booking:
max 6.

## Miyama W1 £55 ❷❷⑤
38 Clarges St 7499 2443 3–4B
*The sushi is "excellent"*, at this long-established Mayfair
*Japanese, but the "cold" décor perennially "needs a re-design".*
/ 10.30 pm; closed Sat L & Sun L.

## Mju
### Millennium Knightsbridge SW1 £70 ❷❷④
16-17 Sloane St 7201 6330 5–1D
*Despite Tom Thomson's "delicious", "experimental" fusion fare,
this Knightsbridge dining room has never gathered much of a
following among reporters – the airport-lounge style doesn't help.*
/ www.milleniumhotels.com; 10.30 pm; closed Sun; no smoking area;
set weekday L £41 (FP).

## Mohsen W14 £25 ❷❷④
152 Warwick Rd 7602 9888 7–1D
*"Brilliant fresh Persian dishes"* and *"an honest welcome"* help
ensure this *"modest"* BYO café, opposite Olympia's Homebase,
is usually *"filled with local Iranians"*. / 11.30 pm; no credit cards.

## Momo W1 £47 ④④❷
25 Heddon St 7434 4040 3–2C
*The "exuberant" and "exotic" ambience of Mourad Mazouz's
souk-style West End Moroccan makes it a natural place to party;
standards, however, have declined of late – its "expensive" dishes
can be "tasteless", and service is ever more "blasé".*
/ www.momoresto.com; 11.30 pm; closed Sun L.

## Mon Plaisir WC2 £40 ❸❸❷
19-21 Monmouth St 7836 7243 4–2B
*"Like stumbling into a bit of France"*, this *"romantic"* Covent
Garden *"stalwart"* of half a century's standing can still weave its
magic (not least for *"the best-value pre-theatre menu in town"*);
there's a slight feeling that the food *"is not as good as it used
to be"*, but, for most reporters, it's *"still worth a go"*.
/ www.monplaisir.co.uk; 11.15 pm; closed Sat L & Sun; set weekday L £24
(FP), set pre-theatre £22 (FP).

## Mona Lisa SW10 £20 ❸❶④
417 King's Rd 7376 5447 5–3B
*The "sheer variety of the clientèle"* – *"taxi drivers rub shoulders
with Chelsea matrons"* – makes for a *"warm and friendly
atmosphere"* at this crowded institution; by day a greasy spoon,
by night it knocks out Italian dishes at *"incredible-value"* prices.
/ 11 pm; closed Sun D; no Amex; no smoking area.

**Mongolian Barbecue**          £26     ⑤⑤⑤
12 Maiden Ln, WC2  7379 7722  4–3D
162 The Broadway, SW19  8545 0021  10–2B
*These DIY-wok joints "used to be fun"; they inspire little
commentary nowadays, mainly to the effect that they are
"boring", "badly-staffed" and "a waste of money". / 11 pm;
SW19 D only.*

**Monmouth Coffee Company**     £10     ❶❷❸
27 Monmouth St, WC2  7645 3560  4–2B
2 Park St, SE1  7645 3560  9–4C
*For "top-class caffeine kicks", this micro-chain – with its
"wonderful selection of coffees" – is London's "absolute best";
the Borough Market branch – with its larger range of "yummy
cakes, pastries and savouries" – has more of an 'on-trade' than
the smaller Covent Garden shop. / www.monmouthcoffee.co.uk; L &
afternoon tea only; closed Sun; no Amex; no smoking; no booking.*

**Montpeliano SW7**             £56     ④④④
13 Montpelier St  7589 0032  5–1C
*With its "excellent" Knightsbridge location, this "very '70s"
trattoria is hailed by diehard fans as "the perfect British Italian" –
as ever, though, doubters just find it a "temple to mediocrity".
/ 11.55 pm; set D £36 (FP), set weekday L £32 (FP).*

**Monza SW3**                   £41     ❸❷❸
6 Yeomans Row  7591 0210  5–2C
*This "intimate", lesser-known Italian, in a Knightsbridge
backstreet, is "not especially cheap, but is reliably good".
/ www.monza.co.uk; 11 pm; closed Mon L & Sun; set weekday L £25 (FP).*

**Morel SW4** NEW               £40     ❸④⑤
14 Clapham Park Rd  7627 2468  10–2D
*Prix-fixe Clapham newcomer, on the difficult site that was Thyme
(RIP); some of the cooking is "very fine" (but not all of it), and the
ambience can be "a let-down". / www.morelrestaurant.co.uk; 10.30 pm;
D only, ex Sun L only; no Amex; no smoking.*

**The Morgan Arms E3**          £40     ❷④❷
43 Morgan St  8980 6389  1–2B
*"Surprisingly good, for the area" – this "buzzy" Bow gastroboozer
offers an "imaginative" menu (plus "well-kept beers, and a wide
selection of wines"). / www.geronimo-inns.co.uk; 10 pm; closed Sun D.*

**Morgan M N7**                 £46     ❶❸④
489 Liverpool Rd  7609 3560  8–2D
*Many reporters leave "awe-struck" by the cuisine at Monsieur
Meunier's Islington/Holloway-fringe yearling; the ambience of his
pub-conversion is "chilly", though, and we can personally vouch
for the advice staff now give customers: "don't park in a side
street". / www.morganm.com; 10 pm; closed Mon, Tue L, Sat L & Sun D;
no Amex; no smoking; booking: max 6.*

**Moro EC1** £40 **❶❷❷**

34-36 Exmouth Mkt 7833 8336 9–1A
*Samantha and Samuel Clark's "innovative" and "delicious"
Spanish/North African cuisine makes a visit to this "buzzy"
Clerkenwell hotspot "a sublime gastronomic experience"; service
– after an 'iffy' patch – "has improved", too. / www.moro.co.uk;
10.30 pm; closed Sun; booking essential ex Sat L.*

**Moroccan Tagine W10** £19 **❸❸❸**

95 Golborne Rd 8968 8055 6–1A
*This "cheap and friendly" North African café in the heart
of North Kensington's flea market is a handy stand-by for "good"
and simple grub. / www.moroccantagine.com; 11 pm; no Amex;
no smoking area.*

**Mosaica
The Chocolate Factory N22** £37 **❶❷❷**

Unit C005, Clarendon Rd 8889 2400 1–1C
*A Wood Green wonder, where the food is "superb" and the
service "unsurpassed"; the fact this it has an "unsettling" location
(a converted factory, "in the middle of an industrial estate") only
boosts its appeal. / www.mosaicarestaurant.com; 9.30 pm; closed Mon,
Sat L & Sun D; no smoking area.*

**Mosaico W1** £48 **❸❷④**

13 Albemarle St 7409 1011 3–3C
*This "discreet" and "plush" – and rather boring – Mayfair
basement has something of a business following; the Italian food
is "refined", but "you pay through the nose for it".
/ www.mosaico-restaurant.co.uk; 10.45 pm; closed Sat L & Sun.*

**Moshi Moshi** £24 ④④④

Waitrose, Canada Pl, E14 7512 9201 11–1C
Unit 24, Liverpool St Station, EC2 7247 3227 9–2D
*The sushi is "not the best in town", but "impressive queues"
confirm the all-round usefulness of these "fun" and "dependable"
City conveyor-joints. / www.moshimoshi.co.uk; 9.30 pm; EC2 closed
Sat & Sun; no Amex; no smoking; E14 no booking.*

**Motcombs SW1** £46 ④**❷❸**

26 Motcomb St 7235 6382 5–1D
*A "louche" (and slightly mature) crowd continue to patronise this
"reliable" Belgravia veteran, which is perhaps seen to best
advantage at lunchtime. / www.motcombs.co.uk; 11 pm; closed Sun D.*

**Moti Mahal WC2** NEW £45 ④**❷❸**

45 Gt Queen St 7240 9329 4–2D
*The fact that a restaurant operator has four outlets in Delhi
doesn't necessarily kit it out to meet the needs of London's
diners-out – despite the smart contemporary décor, this pricey
new Covent Garden Indian struck us, on our July 2005 visit,
as just too 'traditional' for current tastes. / Rated on Editors' visit.*

**Mr Chow SW1** £63 ④④④

151 Knightsbridge 7589 7347 5–1D
*Once-glamorous '60s-throwback, known for its "Chinese food,
served Italian-style"; it "doesn't quite gel" these days, though,
not helped by its "real rip-off" prices. / www.mrchow.com; midnight.*

**Mr Jerk**  £18  ❶❸❸

189 Wardour St, W1   7287 2878   3–1D
19 Westbourne Grove, W2   7221 4678   6–1C
*"Food this good for this price is hard to find in central London" –
these "cramped", "friendly" Caribbean cafés (in Soho and
Bayswater) offer "huge" portions of "scrummy" curries, fried
plantains and BBQ dishes; "queue early". / www.mrjerk.co.uk; 10 pm,
Sun 8 pm.*

**Mr Kong WC2**  £22  ❷❸⑤

21 Lisle St   7437 7341   4–3A
*"Authentic" cooking ("go for the chef's specials") make this "un-
distinguished"-looking Chinese "the best in Chinatown", for some
reporters; "it can't be emphasised too much how important it is
to avoid the basement". / 2.45 am.*

**Mr Wing SW5**  £45  ❷❷❷

242-244 Old Brompton Rd   7370 4450   5–2A
*This pricey 'party-Chinese', in Earl's Court, has always had its
"peaks and troughs foodwise"; for most reporters, though,
it offers a "fabulous" experience, "time and time again".
/ www.mrwing.com; 11.30 pm.*

**Murano TW9**  £38  ④❸❸

110 Kew Rd   8948 8330   1–4A
*"Wholesome" cooking and "reasonable" prices win the support
of some (if not quite all) of the locals who comment on this
"pleasant" Italian, near Richmond Bridge.
/ www.muranorestaurant.co.uk; 11.15 pm; no smoking.*

**Mustards Brasserie EC1**  £34  ④❷❸

60 Long Ln   7796 4920   9–1B
*It may feel like "a brasserie in a Midlands market town",
but "better cooking" won somewhat more enthusiastic support
this year for this Smithfield stand-by. / www.mustards.co.uk; 10.30 pm;
closed Sat & Sun.*

**MVH SW13**  £46  ❷❸❷

5 White Hart Ln   8392 1111   10–1A
*Michael von Hruschka's "unusual" – and, for some, "over-
complicated" – cuisine is delivered "with panache" at this brave,
Barnes venture; the upstairs bar ('Hell') is "dark and sinful",
the ground-floor restaurant ('Heaven') is light and "serene".
/ 11 pm; Mon-Wed D only; no smoking area.*

**Nahm**
**Halkin Hotel SW1**  £70  ❸④④

5 Halkin St   7333 1234   2–3A
*"The best Thai food outside Thailand", or "nothing special"? –
there's little middle ground in views on David Thompson's
Belgravia dining room; most reports do agree, though, that it's
"very pricey", and has "no atmosphere". / www.nahm.como.bz;
11 pm; closed Sat L & Sun L; no smoking; booking: max 8; set weekday L
£44 (FP).*

### Naked Turtle SW14 £42 ④④④
505 Upper Richmond Rd   8878 1995   10–2A
*"Singing waitresses"* help make this Sheen wine bar a *"fun"* and
*"different"* destination in an area *"with few other options"*;
it doesn't attract nearly the number of rave reviews it once did,
though. / www.naked-turtle.com; 11 pm; D only, ex Sun open L & D;
no smoking area.

### Nam Long SW5 £34 ⑤⑤❸
159 Old Brompton Rd   7373 1926   5–2B
The *"brilliant see-and-be-seen bar"* has long been the main point
of this Earl's Court Vietnamese; the once-creditable food,
however, has become *"increasingly poor"* in recent years.
/ 11.30 pm; D only, closed Sun; no trainers.

### Nancy Lam's Enak Enak SW11 £39 ❸④④
56 Lavender Hill   7924 3148   10–1C
*"Nancy is larger than life"* (in person as well as on TV) and –
subject to her other commitments – cooks at this Battersea
dining room (which was *"recently extended and modernised"*);
fans say hers is the *"yummiest oriental home-cooking"*, but one
or two reporters feel it's *"not up to the prices"*. / www.nancylam.com;
10.30 pm; closed Tue–Sat L, Sun D & Mon.

### Nando's £21 ④④④
Branches throughout London
*"Functional"* chain, liked for its *"basic"* and *"honest"* fast-food
formula of *"fresh"* grilled chicken, Portuguese-style (*"you choose
the level of spices"*); outlets are generally *"child-friendly"*, but, by
night, can be *"too noisy and smoky"*. / www.nandos.co.uk; 11.30 pm;
no Amex; no smoking areas; no booking.

### Nanglo SW12 £23 ❷❷④
88 Balham High Rd   8673 4160   10–2C
A modern Nepalese on Balham's main drag; its curries are *"of a
very high standard"* and, for the staff, *"nothing is too much
trouble"*.

### Napulé SW6 £30 ❸⑤❸
585 Fulham Rd   7381 1122   5–4A
Service can be *"a let-down"* – *"like you've crashed the waiters'
private party"* – but this *"authentic"* Fulham Italian can still
be *"fun"*; *"very tasty"* pizzas are the menu highlight. / 11 pm;
closed weekday L; no Amex.

### Nathalie SW3 £45 ❸❶⑤
3 Milner St   7581 2848   5–2D
With its *"very decent modern French food"* and *"intimate"*
surroundings, this quietly-sited Chelsea yearling *"deserves to be
better known"* – as it is, a *"lack of buzz"* is the main problem.
/ www.nathalie-restaurant.co.uk; 10.30 pm; closed Sun.

### Nautilus NW6 £26 ❶❶④
27-29 Fortune Green Rd   7435 2532   1–1B
*"Still good, despite the change of management"* –
this *"traditional"*, kosher chippie in West Hampstead continues
to serve *"brilliant fish in matzo meal"*, with *"loads of chips"*.
/ 9.30 pm; closed Sun; no Amex; mainly non-smoking.

**Navarro's W1**  £25  ❸❷❷

67 Charlotte St   7637 7713   2–1C
*Central London's leading traditional tapas bar – a Fitzrovia
veteran, where "fresh and delicious" dishes are served in a
"very pretty" and "authentic" tiled setting. / www.navarro.co.uk;
10 pm; closed Sat L & Sun.*

**Neal Street WC2**  £56  ④④④

26 Neal St   7836 8368   4–2C
*"Despite your poor reviews, it's the best!", says one of the
(few) advocates of TV-chef Antonio Carluccio's Covent Garden
Italian; as ever, though, many reporters just dismiss the whole
experience as "so very ordinary, and so very expensive".
/ www.carluccios.com; 10.30 pm; closed Sun; no smoking area; set pre-theatre
£37 (FP).*

**New Culture Revolution**  £23  ❸❸④

75 Southampton Row, WC1   7436 9708   2–1D
305 King's Rd, SW3   7352 9281   5–3C
157-159 Notting Hill Gate, W11   7313 9688   6–2B
42 Duncan St, N1   7833 9083   8–3D
43 Parkway, NW1   7267 2700   8–3B
*"Reliably good, very cheap" Chinese noodles and dumplings in a
"completely no-frills" setting – that's the well-liked formula for this
small "Wagamama-esqe" chain. / 10.30 pm; no smoking area; need 4+
to book.*

**New Mayflower W1**  £26  ❷④④

68-70 Shaftesbury Ave   7734 9207   4–3A
*A "good" and "straightforward" Cantonese, on the edge
of Chinatown; it offers some of London's best food in the early
hours. / 3.45 am; D only.*

**New Tayyabs E1**  £16  ❶❸❸

83 Fieldgate St   7247 9543   9–2D
*"Insanely busy, but worth the wait"; "poshed-up" décor
(and more space) has done nothing to change the basic appeal
of this "astounding" Pakistani East End caff, which serves
"fabulous" grills, naans and dry curries at "rock bottom" prices;
BYO. / www.tayyabs.co.uk; 11.30 pm; no smoking area.*

**New World W1**  £32  ❸④④

1 Gerrard Pl   7734 0677   4–3A
*Lunchtime is "trolley heaven", at this "authentic" and "very busy"
Chinatown behemoth, which serves "brilliant dim sum"
at "tiny prices"; at other times, it is unremarkable. / 11.45 pm;
no smoking area; no booking, Sun L.*

**Newton's SW4**  £34  ④④❸

33 Abbeville Rd   8673 0977   10–2D
*"Reliable" cooking makes this well-established bistro
a "good local" for some Clapham reporters.
/ www.newtonsrestaurants.co.uk; 11 pm; no smoking area; set weekday L
£19 (FP).*

**Nicole's W1**  £53  ④❸④
158 New Bond St   7499 8408   3–3C
*During shopping excursions – and, more surprisingly, for a
"business lunch treat", too – this Mayfair fashion store basement
makes a pretty "reliable" rendezvous; "especially in the
evenings", though, "it can lack atmosphere".* / 10.45 pm; closed
Sat D & Sun; smoking in bar only.

**Nikita's SW10**  £40  ⑤❸❷
65 Ifield Rd   7352 6326   5–3A
*You "go for the vodka, not the food", to this subterranean Russian
stalwart, on the fringe of Chelsea, whose illicit booths offer
"London's most romantic dining possibilities".*
/ www.nikitasrestaurant.com; 11.30 pm; D only, closed Sun; no smoking area.

**Niksons SW11**  £39  ④④❸
172-174 Northcote Rd   7228 2285   10–2C
*The "lively" bar is the highlight at this popular Battersea local;
the pretty rear dining room offers "unimpressive" food at prices
which strike some reporters as excessive.* / www.niksons.co.uk; 10 pm;
Mon-Thu closed L; no smoking area.

**No 77 Wine Bar NW6**  £29  ④④❷
77 Mill Ln   7435 7787   1–1B
*A "warm" and "casual" West Hampstead stand-by, where
"burgers are still the top menu attraction".* / 11.30 pm, Mon & Tue
10.30 pm; no Amex.

**Noble Rot W1**  3-5 Mill St   7629 8877   3–2C
*As this guide was going to press, Soren 'One Lombard Street'
Jessen's "stylish" Mayfair venture announced a major change
of style; it's always seemed more successful as a club than as a
restaurant, and the aim seems to be to make it more that way
inclined.* / www.noblerot.com; 11 pm; closed Sat L & Sun; set weekday L
£37 (FP).

**NOBU
METROPOLITAN HOTEL W1**  £84  ❷④④
Old Park Ln   7447 4747   3–4A
*"Still amazing after all these years" – this "slick" ("Manhattan-
vibe") Mayfair star-magnet continues to maintain a towering
reputation for its "divine" Japanese-fusion cuisine; the bill is an
"arm and a leg job", though, and service can be "arrogant".*
/ www.noburestaurants.com; 10.15 pm, Fri & Sat 11 pm; no smoking area;
booking: max 12.

**Nobu Berkeley W1**  NEW  £84
15-16 Berkeley St   7290 9222   3–3C
*As this guide goes to press, the latest opening from Matsuhisa
Nobu's legendary international group is poised to launch
in extraordinarily swanky premises, near the Ritz; it looks likely
that this will be THE 'hot ticket' of late-2005.* / D only, closed Sun;
need 6+ to book.

**Noodle Noodle** £22 ❷❸④
18 Buckingham Palace Rd, SW1 7931 9911 2–4B
Vauxhall Bridge Rd, SW1 7828 8565 2–4B
*"There's not much else just by Victoria", so it's worth knowing*
*about these "quick" and "very well-priced" cafés, which serve*
*"huge bowls of noodles and veg". / www.noodle-noodle.co.uk; 10.45 pm;*
*no smoking.*

**Noor Jahan** £30 ❷❷④
2a Bina Gdns, SW5 7373 6522 5–2B
26 Sussex Pl, W2 7402 2332 6–1D
*"Superb" dishes – there's "never an off night" –*
*and "professional" (if sometimes "humourless") service have*
*made this South Kensington curry house a local "favourite" for*
*many years; its Bayswater spin-off is also "excellent", if rather*
*"dull". / 11.30 pm.*

**North Sea Fish WC1** £28 ❸❷⑤
7-8 Leigh St 7387 5892 8–4C
*"Proper fish 'n' chips" in "huge portions" are the deal at this this*
*"basic" and "old-fashioned" Bloomsbury caff.*
*/ www.northseafishrestaurant.co.uk; 10.30 pm; closed Sun; no smoking.*

**The Northgate N1** £33 ❷❷❷
113 Southgate Rd 7359 7392 1–1C
*"Food above gastropub expectations" – with dishes that are*
*"uniformly well thought-out and executed" – is winning much*
*local acclaim for this "tasteful" De Beauvoir boozer; service*
*is "very friendly", too. / 11 pm; closed weekday L; no Amex.*

**Nosh TW1** £34 ④❸④
139 St Margarets Rd 8891 4188 1–4A
*With its "friendly" service and "modestly-priced" (if "limited")*
*menu, this "high-ceilinged" St Margarets venture makes a useful*
*stand-by. / www.nosh-restaurant.co.uk; 10.15 pm; closed Sun.*

**Noto EC2** £29 ❸❸⑤
2-3 Bassishaw Highwalk 7256 9433 9–2B
*"Tokyo café meets the Square Mile", at this "no-frills" oriental,*
*near London Wall, which is "always crowded with Japanese*
*expats"; "lunch is set meals for City workers in a hurry –*
*at dinner, the pace slows and the menu lengthens".*
*/ www.noto.co.uk; 9.30 pm; closed Sat & Sun; no Amex.*

**Notting Grill W11** £48 ❸④❸
123a Clarendon Rd 7229 1500 6–2A
*"Properly aged and flavourful steaks" are the top draw to AWT's*
*"fun" pub-conversion, on the fringe of Holland Park; it's not*
*pushing back any frontiers, though, and some reporters leave*
*"rather unimpressed". / www.awtonline.co.uk; 10.30 pm, Fri & Sat*
*11.30 pm; closed weekday L; no smoking area.*

**Notting Hill Brasserie W11**  £46  ❷❶❶
92 Kensington Park Rd 7229 4481 6–2B
*This "secret" townhouse "gem" has "gone from strength
to strength" since its 2003 relaunch; it offers "perfect romantic
dining" (complete with "excellent but not intrusive live music"),
as well as Mark Jankel's "sophisticated" cuisine – "'brasserie'
doesn't really do it justice". / 11 pm; closed Sun D; no smoking area;
set weekday L £32 (FP).*

**Noura**  £39  ❸❷④
122 Jermyn St, SW1 7839 2020 3–3D NEW
16 Hobart Pl, SW1 7235 9444 2–4B
2 William St, SW1 7235 5900 5–1D NEW
16 Curzon St, W1 7495 1050 3–4B NEW
*This Paris-based Lebanese chain is ramping up its London
operations, with three new openings this year; the strain
is showing, though, with the increasingly "industrial" performance
of the once-"classy" Belgravia original, and the "pushy" service
at its second opening, in Jermyn Street (replacing Chinatamani,
RIP). / www.noura.co.uk; 12.30am, Thu-Sat 1am, William St midnight.*

**Novelli in the City**
**The Capital Club EC4**  £45  ④④④
15 Abchurch Ln 7717 0088 9–3C
*"Original" cuisine is still mentioned in most feedback on J-C
Novelli's year-old régime at this anodyne City basement; reports
were much more mixed this year, though, and included some real
disasters. / www.londoncapitalclub.com; 9 pm; closed Sat & Sun.*

**Nozomi SW3** NEW  £60
15 Beauchamp Pl 7838 1500 5–1C
*This smart new Japanese opened on the Knightsbridge site that
was Floriana (RIP) shortly before this guide went to press;
we didn't find time to visit, but early newspaper reviews have
tended to deride it as a Eurotrash haven, of limited culinary
merit. / www.nozomi.co.uk.*

**Numero Uno SW11**  £33  ❸❷❷
139 Northcote Rd 7978 5837 10–2C
*"Cheap, cheerful and atmospheric", this Battersea "local
favourite" is "invariably packed", thanks to its "good-value",
"solid" cooking and "friendly" service. / 11.30 pm; no Amex.*

**Nuovi Sapori SW6** NEW  £33  ❷❶❸
295 New King's Rd 7736 3363 10–1B
*A Fulham newcomer which hides a notably "friendly" heart
behind a rather unpromising façade; that's not the only surprise –
the reasonably-priced Italian cuisine is "great", too. / 11 pm;
closed Sun.*

**Nyonya W11**  £26  ❸❸④
2a Kensington Park Rd 7243 1800 6–2B
*"Tasty" and "reasonably-priced" Thai fare makes this "noisy",
"canteen-style" operation – just north of Notting Hill Gate –
a handy stand-by. / www.nyonya.co.uk; 10 pm; no smoking.*

**O'Conor Don W1** £34 ❷❷❷

88 Marylebone Ln 7935 9311 3–1A

*Back on form, this "special" Irish pub in Marylebone boasts
a "quiet" dining room serving hearty scoff, which is "perfect for
a bowsie sort of lunch"; ('bowsie', Irish English, adj: raffish,
drunken). / www.oconordon.com; 10 pm; closed Sat & Sun.*


**O'Zon TW1** £25 ❸❷❸

33-35 London Rd 8891 3611 1–4A

*"A great selection of Thai, Chinese and Malaysian dishes, all to
a good standard" is on offer at this "efficient" all-you-can-eat
Twickenham café. / www.ozon.co.uk; 10.30 pm, Fri & Sat 11.30 pm.*


**The Oak W2** £38 ❷❸❷

137 Westbourne Park Rd 7221 3355 6–1B

*"Thin, crisp and perfectly-formed" pizza and an "attractive and
buzzy" setting have helped make this former boozer "one of the
trendier Notting Hill hang-outs"; (the upstairs room is also now
open again – an early report says it's "effortlessly cool, with an
eclectic tapas-style menu"). / 10 pm; Mon-Thu closed L; no booking.*


**Occo W1** NEW £35 ❷④❸

58 Crawford St 7724 4991 2–1A

*"A nice twist on modern Moroccan food, at fair prices" has
helped get this new Marylebone pub-conversion (formerly the
Street, RIP) off to "a good start"; a regular tips the 'tapas'
in preference to the main menu. / 10 pm; no smoking area.*


**Odette's NW1** £50 ❸❸❶

130 Regent's Park Rd 7586 5486 8–3B

*"Mirrors all around" and "subtle" lighting create a "fantastic",
ultra-"romantic" atmosphere at this "posh" Primrose Hill
"favourite"; in the first full year of the new régime, however,
ratings for its "lovely" cuisine slipped rather, and there was the
occasional incident of "grumpy" service. / 10.30 pm; closed
Sat L & Sun D; no smoking; set weekday L & Sun L £34 (FP).*


**Odin's W1** £45 ❷❶❶

27 Devonshire St 7935 7296 2–1A

*This "tranquil" Marylebone "old faithful" – adorned with the late
Peter Langan's "gorgeous" art collection – offers a "classic",
"time-warped" experience; the reasonably-priced cooking
"doesn't bowl you over, but is much better than average and
always dependable". / www.langansrestaurants.co.uk; 11 pm; closed
Sat & Sun; no smoking area; booking: max 10.*


**Old Parr's Head W14** £19 ❸❷④

120 Blythe Rd 7371 4561 7–1C

*"Great" Thai food and "cheery" staff make it worth knowing
of this budget oriental – part of a traditional boozer, hidden-away
in Olympia. / www.theoldparrshead.com; 10 pm; no Amex; no smoking.*

### Ye Olde Cheshire Cheese EC4 £35 ④④❶

145 Fleet St 7353 6170 9–2A

"There's a real, ancient feel", at this famous (and touristy) City-fringe tavern that "dates back to Dickens" (and beyond); its traditional fare tends to be "pricey" and "average", but doesn't provoke any serious complaints. / www.yeoldecheshirecheese.com; 9.30 pm; closed Sun D; no smoking area; no booking, Sat & Sun.

### Oliveto SW1 £39 ❷❸④

49 Elizabeth St 7730 0074 2–4A

"Excellent pizzas" are the top tip at this "cheerful" (but "cramped" and "noisy") Sardinian – one of the few reasonably-priced places in Belgravia, it's "always busy". / 11 pm; booking: max 7 at D.

### Olivo SW1 £43 ❷❸④

21 Eccleston St 7730 2505 2–4B

An "original" menu of "delicious, simple dishes", and a "wonderful Sardinian wine list" draw some reporters back time and again to this "cramped" and "energetic" ("very noisy") Belgravia fixture. / 11 pm; closed Sat L & Sun L.

### Olley's SE24 £29 ❶❷④

67-69 Norwood Rd 8671 8259 10–2D

This "converted railway arch overlooking Brockwell Park" is an unlikely setting in which to enjoy "some of the very best fish and chips in the capital" – "worth the above-par prices". / www.olleys.info; 10.30 pm; closed Mon L.

### 115 at Hodgson's WC2 £38 ④④❷

115 Chancery Ln 7242 2836 2–2D

After a year under new management, these pretty and intriguing glazed-roofed premises, in the heart of 'Legal Land', are substantially the same as ever – "a good place for a business lunch"; the basic basement makes an informal local stand-by. / www.115.uk.com; 11 pm; closed Mon-Wed D, Sat & Sun; no smoking area.

### 1 Blossom Street E1 £44 ④④④

1 Blossom St 7247 6530 9–1D

"Exceptionally well-spaced tables" ("for the City") and a "sublime Italian wine list" are the two particular selling-points of this otherwise rather "dull" basement, north of Liverpool Street. / www.1blossomstreet.com; 9 pm; closed Sat & Sun.

### 1 Lombard Street EC3 £65 ❸❸❸

1 Lombard St 7929 6611 9–3C

"A perfect location for City lunches" – plus "reliable" standards overall – make for a "buzzy" atmosphere at this former banking hall, by Bank; it can seem a touch "overpriced", though, and "the brasserie is better value than the dining room". / www.1lombardstreet.com; 10 pm; closed Sat & Sun; no smoking in dining room.

**One-O-One**
**Sheraton Park Tower SW1**   £73   ❷❸⑤
101 Knightsbridge   7290 7101   5–1D
Pascal Proyart's "sublime" seafood is hailed by fans as "the best
in town" – "it doesn't even seem that expensive when it tastes
this good"; the "airport-lounge" décor of this Knightsbridge hotel
dining room, however, is "so bad it's funny".
/ www.oneoonerestaurant-luxurycollection.com; 10.15 pm; no smoking area;
set weekday L £47 (FP).

**Opium W1**   £49   ⑤⑤❸
1a Dean St   7287 9608   3–1D
"Good cocktails and a clubby vibe" are the reasons to visit this
Vietnamese basement on the fringe of Soho – no one really
mentions the food. / www.opium-bar-restaurant.com; 9.30 pm; D only,
closed Sun.

**OQO Bar N1**   NEW   £33   ❷❷❷
4-6 Islington Grn   7704 2332   8–3D
Incomparably better than your typical Islington bar/restaurant,
this stylish newcomer serves up top-quality, light oriental dishes
in a stylishly understated setting; good-looking cocktail list, too.
/ Rated on Editors' visit; www.oqobar.co.uk; 10.45 pm, Thu-Sat 11.45 pm.

**L'Oranger SW1**   £77   ❸❸❸
5 St James's St   7839 3774   3–4D
A "safe" St James's choice – this "expensive but impressive"
establishment offers an "enjoyable all-round" experience,
comprising "rich" modern French cuisine and "attentive" service,
in an "intimate" and "clubby" setting that can suit both business
and romance. / 10.45 pm; closed Sat L & Sun; no smoking area; booking:
max 8; set weekday L £52 (FP).

**The Oratory SW3**   £28   ④④❸
232 Brompton Rd   7584 3493   5–2C
"Excellent wines at reasonable prices" are helping to 'up' the
profile of John Brinkley's brasserie near the Brompton Oratory –
the grub's only "pretty average", but the atmosphere can
be "frenetic". / www.brinkleys.com; 11 pm; no smoking.

**Oriel SW1**   £34   ⑤⑤❸
50-51 Sloane Sq   7730 2804   5–2D
Given this Sloane Square brasserie's "drab" food and "churlish"
service, it's easy to conclude that it's "only its location" –
a prominent corner-site – which keeps it in business; breakfast
is "a weekend institution". / www.tragusholdings.com; 10.45 pm;
no smoking area; no booking.

**Oriental City Food Court NW9**   £21   ❸④⑤
399 Edgware Rd   8200 1188   1–1A
This "amazingly authentic"-feeling food court is part of a
disorientatingly oriental north London shopping mall, and offers
a bewildering choice of basic dishes – quite a culinary adventure
for the price of a tube ticket (to Colindale). / 8 pm; L & early evening
only; no Amex; no booking.

**Original Tajines W1**          £30          ❸❸❷
7a Dorset St   7935 1545   2–1A
A "tiny" and "unpretentious" North African bistro, off Baker
Street, with "good-natured" service and an "interesting" menu
of "authentic-tasting" Moroccan dishes. / www.originaltajines.com;
10.30 pm; closed Sat L; no Amex.

**Orrery W1**          £68          ❸❷❸
55 Marylebone High St   7616 8000   2–1A
Often hailed as "the best Conran", this "spacious" room,
overlooking a Marylebone churchyard, impresses many reporters
with its "knowledgeable" staff, "stylish" cuisine and "incredibly
diverse" wine list; prices are "sky high", though, and the setting
strikes some as "dull". / www.orrery.co.uk; 11 pm; no smoking area;
booking: max 12; set weekday L £40 (FP), set Sun L £46 (FP).

**Orso WC2**          £43          ④❸❸
27 Wellington St   7240 5269   4–3D
A "long-term favourite", this Covent Garden Italian dispenses
"solid, if unspectacular" fare in an ever-"buzzy" basement
setting; its standards currently seem to be on the 'up'.
/ www.orso.co.uk; midnight; no smoking area; set weekday L £24 (FP).

**Oscar**
**Charlotte Street Hotel W1**          £55          ⑤⑤④
15 Charlotte St   7806 2000   2–1C
This boldly-muralled design-hotel fixture, in Fitzrovia, is perhaps
best-liked for a "power breakfast"; it can be too "noisy" for
serious dining, though, especially as the "pretentious" food can
be rubbish. / www.firmdalehotels.com; 11 pm; closed Sun L; no smoking area.

**Oslo Court NW8**          £48          ❷①❸
Charlbert St, off Prince Albert Rd   7722 8795   8–3A
"It'll never win any style awards" – its "greying" clientèle would
be horrified if it did – but this "unfailing" St John's Wood
"time warp" almost invariably wows reporters with its "gigantic"
portions of "creamy" scoff ("leave room for the sweet trolley"),
and its "amazing", "old-fashioned" service. / 11 pm; closed Sun.

**Osteria Antica Bologna SW11**          £36          ④④④
23 Northcote Rd   7978 4771   10–2C
This "basic" but "cosy" Battersea Italian once had a strong foodie
following; it's "not what it was", though, and – while still
a "favourite" for some – can be "maddeningly inconsistent"
nowadays. / www.osteria.co.uk; 11 pm; set weekday L £23 (FP).

**Osteria Basilico W11**          £42          ❷❸❷
29 Kensington Park Rd   7727 9957   6–1A
"Great bustle" has helped make this "cramped" Italian – where
"humorous" staff deliver "solid" cooking (and "great pizza") –
a Notting Hill "institution"; "do all you can to avoid the
basement!" / www.basilico.co.uk; 11.30 pm; no booking, Sat L.

**Osteria dell'Arancio SW10**  £37  ❸❸❷

383 King's Rd   7349 8111   5–3B

"Decent and affordable" cooking (from a "limited" menu) and
a wine list "with many interesting finds" win support from most
reporters for this "creative" new Chelsea Italian; it's not for
everyone, though, and sceptics say "it'll have to work hard, in the
face of so much local competition". / www.osteriadellarancio.co.uk;
11.30 pm; closed weekday L; no smoking area; set weekday L £23 (FP).

**Ottolenghi**  £36  ❶❸❷

63 Ledbury Rd, W11   7727 1121   6–1B  **NEW**
287 Upper St, N1   7288 1454   8–2D  **NEW**

"Out-of-this-world" salads and cakes have made this "effortlessly
cool" deli-duo an instant smash-hit with Notting Hill and
(especially) Islington trendies; "they're up there as contenders for
best breakfast, too". / www.ottolenghi.co.uk; W11 8 pm, Sat 7 pm,
Sun 6 pm, N1 11 pm; W11 L only; N1 no Amex; no smoking;
W11 no booking, N1 booking for D only.

**(BRASSERIE)
OXO TOWER SE1**  £47  ⑤⑤❸

Barge House St   7803 3888   9–3A

"At least they can't screw up the view", from the eighth floor
of this South Bank landmark; just as well, as – with its "severely
overpriced" food and "amateur" service – it's now topped the
survey's 'most disappointing' nominations for five years in a row!
/ www.harveynichols.com; 11 pm; booking: max 8.

**(RESTAURANT)
OXO TOWER SE1**  £66  ⑤⑤❷

Barge House St   7803 3888   9–3A

Even fans of this South Bank landmark dining room – which
shares the "stunning" views of the adjoining brasserie – say its
prices are "outrageous"; outright critics find its standards just
"rubbish". / www.harveynichols.com; 11.30 pm; booking: max 14;
set weekday L £36 (FP).

**Ozer W1**  £29  ④❸❸

4-5 Langham Pl   7323 0505   3–1C

"Much cheaper and more basic than when it started", this once-
ambitious Turkish restaurant is now "basically a Sofra",
with sometimes "dull" cooking; still, it's a handy destination,
near Broadcasting House. / www.sofra.co.uk; midnight.

**Pacific Oriental EC2**  £48  ❸④⑤

1 Bishopsgate   7621 9988   9–2C

It's a bit "functional", but this large, two-level (grander upstairs)
oriental is generally hailed as "a reasonable City stand-by".
/ www.orientalrestaurantgroup.co.uk; 9 pm; closed Sat & Sun; no smoking area.

**Page in Pimlico SW1**  £29  ❸❸❸

11 Warwick Way   7834 3313   2–4B

Reports on the Thai cuisine at one of Pimlico's nicer boozers were
more upbeat this year; staff are "mainly Aussie, and 100%
smiley". / www.frontpagepubs.com; 10 pm; closed Sat L & Sun L; no smoking.

### Il Pagliaccio SW6 £28 ④❷❶
182-184 Wandsworth Bridge Rd   7371 5253   10–1B
*"Full almost every night", this "loud and bustling" "party"-Italian
in deepest Fulham offers pizza and other fare that's "not the
greatest, but competent and good-value". / www.paggs.co.uk; midnight.*

### Le Pain Quotidien W1 NEW £22 ❷④❷
72 Marylebone High St   7486 6154   2–1A
*"Excellent coffee and breads" are the star turns at this "fun" and
"buzzy" new Marylebone outpost of an international café/bakery
franchise; bearing in mind the "erratic" service, it's a better bet
for breakfast or coffee than for lunch. / 6.45 pm; L & afternoon tea
only; no smoking.*

### The Painted Heron £40 ❶❶❸
112 Cheyne Walk, SW10   7351 5232   5–3B
205-209 Kennington Ln, SE11   7793 8313   1–3C
*"Not your generic Indian" – thank to its "exquisite"
(and "very different") cuisine, and "first-class" service, this "posh"
Chelsea and Kennington mini-chain is at last making quite
a name for itself. / www.thepaintedheron.com; SE11 10.30 pm,
SW10 11 pm; SW10 closed Sat L; SE11 no smoking area.*

### Le Palais du Jardin WC2 £46 ❸④❸
136 Long Acre   7379 5353   4–3C
*"A great central location" and "dependable" food (including
"spectacular seafood platters") make this very large and
"bustling" Covent Garden brasserie a useful rendezvous;
sometimes, however, service "couldn't care less". / 11.30 pm.*

### The Palmerston SE22 £36 ❶❸❸
91 Lordship Ln   8693 1629   1–4D
*"Top-quality cooking" – from "an inventive menu which changes
regularly" – is creating a growing reputation for this East Dulwich
gastropub. / www.thepalmerston.co.uk; 10 pm; no Amex; no smoking area;
set weekday L £24 (FP).*

### Pampa £40 ❷④❸
4 Northcote Rd, SW11   7924 1167   10–2C
60 Battersea Rise, SW11   7924 4774   10–2C
*"Bring your ear plugs", if you visit these "cramped", "no-
nonsense" Argentinians; service is "indifferent", but they serve
"great steaks". / 11 pm, Fri & Sat 11.30 pm; D only.*

### Pan-Asian Canteen
### Paxton's Head SW1 £26 ❸❷❸
153 Knightsbridge   7589 6627   5–1D
*"Very tasty fare" ("even if the menu is a bit limited") makes
it worth seeking out this modernistic, communal-tables oriental
dining room, on the first floor of a palatial Knightsbridge pub.
/ www.thespiritgroup.com; 10.30 pm; no Amex; no smoking area.*

### Panzella SW11 £31 ❷❷❸
78 Northcote Rd   7350 2385   10–2C
*This "pleasant" Battersea corner trattoria attracts only modest
feedback from reporters; such as it is, however, tends to confirm
our view that this is a "fantastic local", with "very good pasta"
and charming service. / 11.30 pm; closed weekday L; no Amex;
no smoking area.*

### Papageno WC2 £36 ④❷❶
29-31 Wellington St   7836 4444   4–3D
*"Great decoration" and a "fun atmosphere" have made this new
Theatreland son-of-Sarastro a worthy chip off the old block;
the food ("fine") is actually something of an improvement!*
*/ www.papagenorestaurant.com; 11.45 pm.*

### The Papaya Tree W8 £30 ❸④⑤
209 Kensington High St   7937 2260   7–1D
*A handy Thai stand-by in a Kensington basement;
the "reasonably-priced set lunch" is a highlight. / 10.45 pm;
no smoking area.*

### Pappa Ciccia £26 ❷❷❸
105-107 Munster Rd, SW6   7384 1884   10–1B
41 Fulham High St, SW6   7736 0900   10–1B
90 Lower Richmond Rd, SW15   8789 9040   10–1A
*"Fresh and well-cooked" Italian dishes – with "massive pizzas"
a speciality – have made this "squashed" but "fun" chain a local
institution (aided, at SW6 branches, by the BYO policy).*
*/ www.pappaciccia.com; 11 pm; Fulham High St no smoking area.*

### Pappagallo W1 £45 ❸❷❸
54-55 Curzon St   7629 2742   3–4B
*"A real find for Mayfair" – this year-old relaunch of Ristorante
Italiano wins praise for its "upmarket" décor, "efficient" service
and "good prices"; it's still little-known, though, which can make
for a lack of atmosphere in the evenings. / 11 pm; closed
Sat L & Sun L.*

### Paradise by Way of
### Kensal Green W10 £34 ④④❷
19 Kilburn Ln   8969 0098   1–2B
*"A shabby-chic, arty-farty crowd, plus the odd celeb'" has long
been a defining feature of this "quirky" and "relaxed" pub-
conversion; its food "ranges from good to OK".*
*/ www.paradisebywayofkensalgreen.co.uk; 10.30 pm; no Amex.*

### Paradiso Olivelli £28 ④④④
3 Gt Titchfield St, W1   7436 0111   3–1C   **NEW**
9 St Christopher's Pl, W1   7486 3196   3–1A   **NEW**
35 Store St, WC1   7255 2554   2–1C
31 Catherine St, WC2   7836 3609   4–2D   **NEW**
W12 Centre, Shepherd's Bush Gn, W12   8222 6682   7–1C
61 The Cut, SE1   7261 1221   9–4A
*Low-key chain delivering "basic, but always reliable" Italian
dishes, not least "good pizza". / www.ristoranteparadiso.co.uk; midnight;
WC1 closed Sun.*

### The Parsee N19 £31 ❷❸⑤
34 Highgate Hill   7272 9091   8–1C
*"Wonderfully subtle cooking" – "a million miles from your typical
curry house" – win raves for Cyrus Todiwala's Highgate Indian;
even some ardent fans of the food "wouldn't go back", though –
the interior is just so "miserable". / www.theparsee.com; 10.45 pm;
D only, closed Sun; no smoking area.*

**Pasha SW7** £43 ④④❶
1 Gloucester Rd 7589 7969 5–1B
*"Ask for one of the hidden nooks", if you visit this "exotic" South Kensington Moroccan – the "romantic" décor is a much stronger attraction that the "OK" food and service.*
*/ www.pasha-restaurant.co.uk; 10.45 pm; closed Sun L; booking: max 10 at weekends; set weekday L £21 (FP).*

**Pasha N1** £34 ④❸❸
301 Upper St 7226 1454 8–3D
*A large but "cramped" Turkish restaurant in Islington, which continues to pack 'em in, even if the cooking is no more than "standard". / 11.30 pm, Fri & Sat midnight.*

**Passione W1** £55 ❷❸❸
10 Charlotte St 7636 2833 2–1C
*"The highest-quality ingredients prepared with love and care" still win raves for Gennaro Contaldo's "busy" and "noisy" Fitzrovian; this year's feedback was a bit up and-down though, with one or two reporters finding the place "overrated". / www.passione.co.uk; 10.15 pm; closed Sat L & Sun.*

**Pasta Brown** £33 ⑤④⑤
31-32 Bedford St, WC2 7836 7486 4–3C
35-36 Bow St, WC2 7379 5775 4–2D
*Despite the odd fan among reporters, these West End pasta joints are too often dismissed as "ambience-free", "tourist-trade" dives. / www.pastabrown.com; 11 pm, Sun 6 pm.*

**Patara** £46 ❶❷❸
15 Greek St, W1 7437 1071 4–2A **NEW**
3-7 Maddox St, W1 7499 6008 3–2C
181 Fulham Rd, SW3 7351 5692 5–2C
9 Beauchamp Pl, SW3 7581 8820 5–1C
*"The most delicious Thai food" – "perfumed to perfection" – underpins the high popularity of this small group; its "serene" charms are perhaps best appreciated at the spacious new Soho branch. / 10.30 pm; no smoking area; set weekday L £31 (FP).*

**Paternoster Chop House EC4** £50 ④④④
Warwick Ct, Paternoster Sq 7029 9400 9–2B
*By St Paul's, another new "bland" and "loud" dining room from the celebrated (why?) Conran 'design' studio; "it's OK but ridiculously overpriced – i.e. a classic City lunch venue".*
*/ www.conran.com; 10.30 pm; closed Sat & Sun D; smoking in bar only.*

**Patio W12** £25 ④❶❷
5 Goldhawk Rd 8743 5194 7–1C
*This "quirky", "cosy" and "personal" Polish restaurant, off Shepherd's Bush Green, is ideally suited to a party (or romance) on a budget; its cuisine is somewhere between "hearty" and "heavy". / 11 pm; closed Sat L; no smoking area.*

**Pâtisserie Valerie** £22 ❸④❸

17 Motcomb St, SW1   7245 6161   5–1D
Hans Cr, SW1   7590 0905   5–1D   NEW
105 Marylebone High St, W1   7935 6240   2–1A
162 Piccadilly, W1   7491 1717   3–3C   NEW
44 Old Compton St, W1   7437 3466   4–2A
215 Brompton Rd, SW3   7823 9971   5–1C
Duke of York Sq, SW3   7730 7094   5–2D   NEW
27 Kensington Church St, W8   7937 9574   5–1A   NEW
37 Brushfield St, E1   awaiting tel   9–2D   NEW
*"Yummy breakfast pastries" are still done very well by this
expanding café/pâtisserie chain which claims to have introduced
croissants to London in the '30s – go to the Soho original for
maximum authenticity; other light fare (availability varies from
branch to branch) is reliable, too.* / www.patisserie-valerie.co.uk;
6.30 pm; no booking.

**Patterson's W1** £51 ❷❷❸

4 Mill St   7499 1308   3–2C
*Raymond Patterson's "impressive" cooking, and service
"that genuinely cares" make this family-run Mayfair two-year-old
a "value-for-money" package of a type "rare in central London";
unsurprisingly, it's beginning to gather quite a following.*
/ www.pattersonsrestaurant.com; 11 pm; closed Sat L & Sun; no smoking area.

**Paul** £18 ❸⑤④

115 Marylebone High St, W1   7224 5615   2–1A
29-30 Bedford St, WC2   7836 3304   4–3C
*"Excellent coffee" and "delicious" pastries (from breakfast on)
compensate for sometimes "unbelievably slow" service at these
"Parisian-style" café/bakeries; it's a shame that, as the
UK operation grows (now including railway station take-aways),
standards generally are "slipping".* / 7.30 pm-8.30 pm; no Amex;
no smoking; no booking.

**Pearl**
**Marriot Hotel WC1** £64 ❸④④

252 High Holborn   7829 7000   2–1D
*Jan Tanaka's "unusual" cuisine can be "terrific", so it's a shame
that this "depressingly sterile" Holborn dining room – with its
"outrageous" prices and "slow and pompous" service – seems
tailor-made to take the edge off the experience.*
/ www.pearl-restaurant.com; 10 pm; closed Sun D; no smoking area;
set weekday L £43 (FP).

**The Peasant EC1** £38 ④④④

240 St John St   7336 7726   8–3D
*Fans say you get "quirky but tasty food" at this characterful
gastropub (with dining room above), north of Smithfield; service
can be "inattentive", though, and the cooking strikes some
reporters as "too complex" or "overpriced".* / www.thepeasant.co.uk;
11 pm; closed Sat L & Sun.

**Pellicano SW3** £44 ❸❷④

19-21 Elystan St   7589 3718   5–2C
*"Sometimes wonderful, sometimes OK" – this "friendly" Chelsea
backstreet Italian has its fans, but it never seems to have found
a consistent stride; "you can always get a table midweek".*
/ 10.45 pm; set weekday L £29 (FP).

### E Pellicci E2 £10 ❸④❶

332 Bethnal Grn   7739 4873   1–2D

The listed Art Deco interior helps create a "great atmosphere" at this "old-fashioned" East End greasy spoon, which is something of a breakfast favourite. / L only; L only, closed Sun; no credit cards.

### The Pen SW6 £36 ❸❸❸

51 Parsons Green Ln   7371 8517   10–1B

Long one of the best options around Parson's Green, this ever-"trendy" first-floor dining room (over a bar) is a "relaxed" venue, that can still deliver some "good" cooking; overall, however, it doesn't attract quite the support it once did. / 11 pm; D only, closed Sun.

### Pengelley's SW1 NEW £48 ❸④④

164 Sloane St   7750 5000   5–1D

"Sleek" but "soulless", this much-hyped Knightsbridge newcomer has enjoyed a muted reception from reporters; many do hail its "stonkingly imaginative" dishes (from ex-E&O chef, Mr P), but there's also a feeling that "with so many places now doing the Asian-fusion thing, it needs to be better to justify these prices". / www.pengelleys.com; 11 pm; smoking in bar only; booking: max 12; set weekday L £30 (FP).

### The Penthouse WC2 NEW £52 ⑤⑤❷

1 Leicester Sq   7734 0900   4–4A

The "magnificent panorama" of Westminster adds drama to a visit to this 7th-floor West End nightclub newcomer; service is iffy, though, and the Asian-fusion fare is "vastly overpriced and mediocre". / 1 am; closed Sun D.

### The People's Palace
### Royal Festival Hall SE1 £44

South Bank Centre   7928 9999   2–3D

You can't enjoy the magnificent views from this first-floor dining chamber at present – it's closed until completion of the refit of the Royal Festival Hall, which is unlikely to be before January 2007. / www.peoplespalace.co.uk; 10.45 pm; smoking in bar only.

### The Pepper Tree SW4 £19 ❶❷❸

19 Clapham Common S'side   7622 1758   10–2D

"Fresh and tasty" food that's "quick, easy and reliable" – and "unbeatable at the price" – keeps on packing 'em in at this "squashed" refectory-style Clapham Thai; the former Earlsfield branch is no more. / 11 pm; no Amex; no smoking area; no booking at D.

### Perc%nto EC4 £42 ④④④

26 Ludgate Hill   7778 0010   9–2B

"Resting on its laurels", this City basement Italian takes a lot of flak for being "very average all round". / www.etruscarestaurants.com; 10 pm.

### Père Michel W2 £38 ❸❸④

11 Bathurst St   7723 5431   6–2D

A "very intimate" local near Lancaster Gate, with an ambience that feels a bit like "a suburb in the '70s"; its "time-warped" menu offers "straightforward" fish dishes in "good portions". / 11.30 pm; D only, closed Sun.

**Perla** £30 ④④❸

11 Charlotte St, W1   7436 1744   2–1C
28 Maiden Ln, WC2   7240 7400   4–4D
803 Fulham Rd, SW6   7471 4895   10–1B
*"It's too limited to be called 'real' Mexican", but the food at these
"friendly" drinking dens is "not too bad". / 10 pm-11 pm.*

**The Perseverance WC1** £40 ❸④❸

63 Lamb's Conduit St   7405 8278   2–1D
*A once-notable Holborn gastropub, whose cooking is only
"intermittently great" nowadays; some reporters prefer lunch
(when the bar is quiet) to the "noisy" evenings, when the upstairs
dining room is open. / 10 pm; closed Sun D; no Amex.*

**Pescador Too NW3** £32 ❸❷❸

108 Heath St   7443 9500   8–1A
*A "very good" and "friendly" Portuguese fish and seafood
restaurant, regarded by some reporters as "Hampstead's bright
point". / 10.30 pm.*

**Petersham Nurseries TW10** £54 ❸④❶

Off Petersham Rd   8940 5230   1–4A
*"An old glasshouse" surrounded by trees is the wonderful setting
for this quirky venture – in a posh garden centre near Ham
House – which serves a "short" menu of "high-quality" dishes;
prices are steep, though (and "seem to go up weekly"),
and service can be weak; book ahead in summer. / 2.45 pm;
Thu-Sun D only, closed Mon-Wed; no Amex; no smoking; booking essential.*

**Petit Auberge N1** £28 ❸④❸

283 Upper St   7359 1046   8–2D
*"Cramped", but "cosy" and "fun", this Islington bistro, offers
"tasty" and "inexpensive" Gallic fare. / 11 pm.*

**Le Petit Max SW11** £34 ❷❷❸

Riverside Plaza, Chatfield Rd   7223 0999   10–2B
*Those in search of "a superb French bistro experience" will find
it "worth discovering" this "out-of-the-way" Battersea riverside
spot, where "good, old-fashioned, well-priced" food is set off
by Max Renzland's "welcoming" (and perhaps slightly "OTT")
service. / 10.30 pm; closed Sun D; no Amex; smoking in bar only.*

**Le Petit Prince NW5** £24 ❸❸❸

5 Holmes Rd   7267 3789   8–2B
*"Like eating in a Frenchman's kitchen", this scruffy Kentish Town
veteran offers some "good", simple cooking at reasonable prices;
"very decent couscous" is the highlight.*
*/ www.lepetitprincerestaurant.com; 10.30 pm; closed Mon, Sat L & Sun;
no Amex.*

## PÉTRUS
### THE BERKELEY SW1 £84 ❷❷❷
Wilton Pl 7235 1200 5–1D
Marcus Wareing is now fully settled in to this "pampering" year-old Knightsbridge dining room, and his "stunning" cooking – served by "unhurried" staff – is "firing on all cylinders"; a "superlative" wine list ("on which not everything is wildly-priced") remains a stand-out attraction. / www.marcuswareing.com; 10.45 pm; closed Sat L & Sun; jacket required; no smoking; booking: max 10; set weekday L £44 (FP).

### Pham Sushie EC1 £22 ❶❷④
155 Whitecross St 7251 6336 9–1B
"The standard of the sushi is superb", at this "tiny", "bargain" café, near the Barbican (which relocated to this site a year or two ago). / 10 pm; closed Sat L & Sun; no smoking area.

### Philpotts Mezzaluna NW2 £38 ❸❸④
424 Finchley Rd 7794 0455 1–1B
David Philpott's cooking can be "delicious", and service at this "suburban" Italian – "an oasis" in Child's Hill – is usually "very friendly", too; declining ratings, though, support those who fear that the "sparkle has been missing" of late.
/ www.philpotts-mezzaluna.com; 11 pm; closed Mon & Sat L; no Amex.

### The Phoenix SW3 £34 ④❸❷
23 Smith St 7730 9182 5–2D
"Nosh up and kick off a hangover" – "or work up a new one" – at this "lively" gastropub, just off the King's Road.
/ www.geronimo-inns.co.uk; 9.45 pm; no Amex; no smoking area; need 6+ to book.

### Phoenix Bar & Grill SW15 £39 ❸❷❸
162-164 Lower Richmond Rd 8780 3131 10–1A
A new chef seems to have revitalised this Putney "favourite", where "lovely" staff serve some "splendid" Italian cooking.
/ www.sonnys.co.uk; 11 pm; no smoking area.

### Phoenix Palace NW1 £29 ❶❸❸
3-5 Glentworth St 7486 3515 2–1A
"Always full of Chinese families", this Cantonese two-year-old, "tucked-away near Baker Street", provides "high-quality" cooking, and notably "fabulous" dim sum. / 11.15 pm; no smoking area.

### Picasso SW3 £27 ④④❸
127 King's Rd 7352 4921 5–3C
"Staunchly loyal" regulars tend to bag the tables outside ("whatever the weather") at this Italian coffee shop – "one of the last survivors of '60s Chelsea"; it's primarily of interest as a breakfast destination. / www.dinos-restaurants.com.uk; 11.15 pm.

## PIED À TERRE W1 £77
34 Charlotte St 7636 1178 2–1C
As this guide goes to press, a total post-fire revamp of David Moore's hallowed Fitzrovian is nearing completion; Shane Osborne is an exceptional chef, so let's hope the new décor provides – at last! – the setting his cooking deserves.
/ www.pied.a.terre.co.uk; 11 pm; closed Sat L & Sun; no smoking area; booking: max 8; set weekday L £50 (FP).

**The Pig's Ear SW3** NEW  £36  ❸❷❷
35 Old Church St  7352 2908  5–3C
*"Good cooking" and an "intimate" (curiously Art Nouveau) style
are making a big hit of this new Chelsea gastropub (formerly the
Front Page, RIP); the food in the bar is just as good as the
restaurant upstairs.* / www.thepigsear.co.uk; 10.30 pm; closed
Mon & Sun D.

**The Pilot W4**  £28  ❸❸④
56 Wellesley Rd  8994 0828  7–2A
*"Consistent" cooking makes it worth knowing about this
gastropub south of Gunnersbury Park; the ambience "leaves
room for improvement" (but there's "a great rear courtyard
in summer").* / 10 pm.

**Ping Pong W1** NEW  £26  ❷❶❶
45 Gt Marlborough St  7851 6969  3–2C
*This friendly newcomer, near Liberty's, offers good-value dim sum
in a stylish and impressive setting, and was already deservedly
busy on an early visit in June 2005; a further site, in Bayswater,
has already been acquired – the first of many planned for the
next few years.* / Rated on Editors' visit; www.pingpongdimsum.com;
midnight, Sun 10.30 pm; no smoking.

**La Piragua N1**  £23  ❸④❷
176 Upper St  7354 2843  8–2D
*A "fantastic" Latino ambience and "huge, tasty steaks" keep
on packing the young crowd in at this "cheap" Islington cantina.*
/ www.lapiragua.co.uk; 10.50 pm; no Amex.

**El Pirata W1**  £31  ④❸❸
5-6 Down St  7491 3810  3–4B
*"Surprisingly good prices, for such a posh area" make this "noisy
and busy" tapas bar, not far from Hyde Park Corner, an ever-
handy stand-by.* / 11.30 pm; closed Sat L & Sun.

**Pissarro's W4**  £36  ④❸❶
Corney Reach Way  8994 3111  10–1A
*"Hidden-away, but worth the search", this riverside venture
in deepest Chiswick boasts a "great conservatory"
(with removable roof) and "excellent views"; the food is "fine",
too, if "quite pricey" for what it is.* / www.pissarro.co.uk; 10.30 pm;
no smoking area.

**Pizza Metro SW11**  £29  ❷❷❷
64 Battersea Rise  7228 3812  10–2C
*"It sure helps if you speak Italian", at this "immensely popular"
and "chaotic" Battersea pizza-by-the-metre spot; since
it enlarged, some regulars feel it's "not quite as good as it was",
but even so, many reporters still tip it as "the best pizza joint
in town".* / 11 pm; no Amex; no smoking area.

**Pizza on the Park SW1**  £35  ④④❷
11 Knightsbridge  7235 5273  5–1D
*This "large and airy" landmark, near Hyde Park Corner –
a PizzaExpress in disguise – serves "reliable" pizza and so on,
at fairly high prices; it has a "famous basement jazz venue"
(separate entry charge), where "the music's usually excellent".*
/ www.pizzaonthepark.co.uk; midnight; no smoking area.

### Ciro's Pizza Pomodoro £32 ④④❷

51 Beauchamp Pl, SW3   7589 1278   5–1C
7-8 Bishopsgate Churchyard, EC2   7920 9207   9–2D
*The atmosphere at these "late-night" thirtysomething party-pizzerias "really comes alive when the live music is playing"; the seedy Knightsbridge original is of much more interest than the City offshoot.* / SW3 1 am, EC2 midnight; EC2 closed Sun, SW3 D only; EC2 no smoking area at L.

### PizzaExpress £25 ④❸❸

Branches throughout London
*"A good old-faithful", or just "too predictable"? – the question mark remains over this benchmark group; legions of reporters still laud it as a "reliable" stand-by (and "a life-saver for families"), but this year's much-hyped menu-revamp has barely registered and – for the first time ever – PE was not the survey's most-mentioned chain.* / www.pizzaexpress.co.uk; 11.30 pm-midnight; most City branches closed all or part of weekend; no smoking area; no booking at most branches.

### Pizzeria Castello SE1 £27 ❸❷❸

20 Walworth Rd   7703 2556   1–3C
*"Down-to-earth" Elephant & Castle veteran, which remains a favourite pizzeria for some reporters thanks to its "fun" style and "reasonable prices"; (n.b. it's got no connection with the similarly-named – and quite similar – venture at 192 Jamaica Road, SE1).* / 11 pm, Fri & Sat 11.30 pm; closed Sun.

### Pizzeria Oregano N1 £29 ❸❸④

19 St Albans Pl   7288 1123   8–3D
*"Great pizzas" and a "friendly" attitude win praise for this Islington side street Italian; the setting, however, is "too like an ice cream parlour to be cosy".* / 10.45 pm; closed Mon; no Amex; no smoking area.

### PJ's SW3 £43 ④④❸

52 Fulham Rd   7581 0025   5–2C
*The food's "not so bad", according to fans of this "always-busy" bar/restaurant, in South Kensington; it's the "lovely" atmosphere, though – not the American cooking – which makes it "THE place for Sunday brunch with the local Euro-crowd".* / www.maxwellsrestaurants.co.uk; 11.45 pm.

### The Place Below EC2 £18 ❷④④

St Mary-le-Bow, Cheapside   7329 0789   9–2C
*In an atmospheric church crypt, one of the City's few decent "cheap and cheerful" options – a "reliable" self-service canteen, where the veggie fare is "never inspiring, but always well-executed".* / www.theplacebelow.co.uk; L only, closed Sat & Sun; no Amex; no smoking; need 15+ to book.

### Planet Hollywood W1 £41 ⑤④④

13 Coventry St   7287 1000   4–4A
*"Faded" Tinseltown-themed West End landmark – "kids love it, but adults hate its expensive and bad food".* / www.planethollywoodlondon.com; 1 am; no smoking area.

**Plateau E14**  £60  ④④❸

Canada Pl   7715 7100   11–1C

*"Tailor-made for expense-accounters", this "smart" fourth-floor yearling, with its impressive Canary Wharf views, is proclaimed as "a Conran that works" by some reporters; its "cooking-by-numbers" cuisine is "seriously overpriced", though (and "the grill offers better value than the restaurant"). / www.conran.com; 10 pm; closed Sat L & Sun D; set D £39 (FP).*

**Poissonnerie de l'Avenue SW3**  £53  ❷❷❸

82 Sloane Ave   7589 2457   5–2C

*"Professional" – if "old-fashioned" and "rather stuffy" – this Brompton Cross veteran particularly appeals to an "older clientèle", for whom its "top-quality" dishes "still set the standard in fish cooking". / www.poissonnerie.co.uk; 11.30 pm; closed Sun.*

**(Ognisko Polskie) The Polish Club SW7**  £37  ❸❷❷

55 Prince's Gate, Exhibition Rd   7589 4635   5–1C

*For "faded glory", it's hard to beat this "quiet" South Kensington émigrés' club dining room, with its "old-fashioned" service and its "robust" Polish cooking; in summer, you can "eat outside, overlooking the garden". / www.ognisko.com; 11 pm.*

**Polygon Bar & Grill SW4**  £35  ⑤⑤⑤

4 The Polygon   7622 1199   10–2D

*Perhaps the new chef can rescue this "uninspiring" Clapham brasserie – recent feedback has been very poor indeed. / www.thepolygon.co.uk; 11 pm; Mon-Thu closed L; smoking in bar only.*

**Pomegranates SW1**  £49  ④④❸

94 Grosvenor Rd   7828 6560   2–4C

*Patrick Gwynn-Jones's '70s-survivor, in a Pimlico basement, holds a "cosy and romantic" allure for (older) romantics; the eclectic cooking isn't bad at all, but the prices can sometimes seem "outrageous". / 11.15 pm; closed Sat L & Sun.*

**Pomino SW17**  NEW  £38  ⑤④④

25 Bellevue Rd   8672 5888   10–2C

*We enjoyed our trip to Christopher Gilmour's "cavernous" new Italian, by Wandsworth Common; reporters are adamant, however, that it needs "to get its act together", with too many finding it "overpriced" or "disappointing". / www.pomino.co.uk; 11 pm; set weekday L £17 (FP).*

**Il Pomodorino SW1**  £35  ⑤④④

4-12 Regent St   7321 2100   3–3D

*This "Roman import" – managed and provisioned directly from the Eternal City – has been a remarkable West End flop; it has the occasional fan, but most reports are very negative. / www.pomodorino.co.uk; 10.45 pm; closed Sun; no Amex; no smoking area.*

**Le Pont de la Tour SE1**  £60  ④④❸

36d Shad Thames   7403 8403   9–4D

*An "unbeatable location" (near Tower Bridge) and an "incredible" wine list draw expense-accounters in droves to Conran's riverside flagship; perhaps that's why – with its "run-of-the-mill cooking, indifferent service and eye-watering bills" – it can seem "astoundingly complacent". / www.conran.com; 11 pm; closed Sat L.*

### Le Pont de la Tour Bar & Grill SE1 £46 ④④❸
36d Shad Thames 7403 8403 9–4D
*"Much more relaxed than the main restaurant", the neighbouring grill offers similar advantages on the location, view and alfresco fronts, at (somewhat) more moderate cost.* / www.conran.com; 11 pm; no booking; set weekday L & pre-theatre £30 (FP).

### Poons WC2 £22 ④④④
4 Leicester St 7437 1528 4–3A
*Standards at this once-famous Cantonese canteen, just off Leicester Square, are a bit, er, "standard" these days, but fans still feel it offers "good value" for the West End.* / 11.30 pm; no smoking area.

### Popeseye £40 ❷❸⑤
108 Blythe Rd, W14 7610 4578 7–1C
277 Upper Richmond Rd, SW15 8788 7733 10–2A
*"Fantastic" steaks – plus a "very good selection of red wines" – maintain the popularity of these "cramped" and decidedly "basic" steak-bistros, in Olympia and Putney.* / 10.30 pm; D only, closed Sun; no credit cards.

### La Porchetta Pizzeria £23 ❸❸❸
33 Boswell St, WC1 7242 2434 2–1D
141-142 Upper St, N1 7288 2488 8–2D
147 Stroud Green Rd, N4 7281 2892 8–1D
74-77 Chalk Farm Rd, NW1 7267 6822 8–2B NEW
84-86 Rosebery Ave, EC1 7837 6060 9–1A
*"They can hardly find plates big enough", for the "massive" pizzas at these "noisy" and "brightly-lit", family-run Italians; "it's hard to spend a lot of money", and "there's often a queue", especially at the Finsbury Park original.* / midnight, WC1 10.30 pm; WC1 closed Sat L & Sun, N1 Mon-Thu closed L, N4 closed weekday L, EC1 closed Sat L; no Amex; no smoking area; need 5+ to book.

### Portal EC1 NEW £40
88 St John St 7253 6950 9–1B
*An ambitious new restaurant on an intriguing Clerkenwell site (that was until recently an attractive branch of Café Lazeez); we didn't have an opportunity to visit before our press date, but the chefs' CVs are impressive.* / www.portalrestaurant.com; 10.30 pm; closed Sat L & Sun; no Amex; no smoking area.

### La Porte des Indes W1 £50 ❸④❷
32 Bryanston St 7224 0055 2–2A
*"Hidden behind a narrow entrance", near Marble Arch, this large and "lavish" Indian basement comes "complete with waterfall and palm trees"; fans say its "interesting French-influenced" cuisine can be "second to none" (but occasions when it "misses the mark" are not unknown).* / www.pilondon.net; 11.30 pm; closed Sat L; set weekday L £30 (FP).

### Porters English Restaurant WC2 £28 ⑤④⑤
17 Henrietta St 7836 6466 4–3D
*Fans continue to insist that you get "good English cooking" at this heritage-themed Covent Garden stalwart; for doubters, though, it's just a "rip-off" – "if tourists think this is our British standard, they are misled".* / www.porters-restaurant.com; 11.30 pm; no Amex; no smoking area.

**Il Portico W8** £42 ❸❶❸

277 Kensington High St   7602 6262   7–1D
*"An old-fashioned, family-run gem", by the Kensington Odeon;
the Italian food "has its ups and downs", but fans insist
"it's currently on an up". /* www.ilportico.co.uk; *11.15 pm; closed
Sun, & Bank Holidays; mainly non-smoking.*

**The Portrait
National Portrait Gallery WC2** £45 ④④❷

St Martin's Pl   7312 2490   4–4B
*It may have a "wonderful" view, but – with its "poor" food and
"dispiriting" service – this rooftop West End dining room is ever
more a "wasted opportunity". /* www.searcys.co.uk; *8.30 pm; Sat-Wed
closed D; no smoking; set pre-theatre £30 (FP).*

**Potemkin EC1** £36 ❸❷④

144 Clerkenwell Rd   7278 6661   9–1A
*The "fantastic selection of vodkas" tends to overshadow the
"good" cooking at this would-be trendy Clerkenwell Russian;
the basement restaurant can be romantic, too ("as long as they
don't have any parties in"). /* www.potemkin.co.uk; *10.30 pm; closed
Sat L & Sun; no smoking.*

**LA POULE AU POT SW1** £43 ❸❷❶

231 Ebury St   7730 7763   5–2D
*"For lovers and Francophiles", nowhere beats this "timeless"
Pimlico survivor – yet again reporters' romantic No 1 destination
– where "authentic" bourgeois cuisine is delivered
by "nonchalantly Gallic" staff in a "dark" and "rustic" setting
that's "ever so slightly louche". /* 11 pm; set weekday L £29 (FP).*

**Prego TW9** £37 ❸④❸

106 Kew Rd   8948 8508   1–4A
*A "casual" Richmond Italian of long standing, which maintains
a dedicated local fan club. /* www.pregorestaurants.com; *11 pm;
no smoking area.*

**Pret A Manger** £9 ❸❷④

Branches throughout London
*"Always reliable, always round the corner", this "peerless" chain
is still London's default snack choice, thanks to the "freshness"
of its food and – not least – to the "implausible friendliness"
of its staff. /* www.pret.com; *4 pm-6 pm, Trafalgar Sq 9 pm, St. Martin's
Ln 10 pm; closed Sun (except some West End branches), City branches closed
Sat & Sun; no credit cards; no smoking; no booking.*

**The Prince Bonaparte W2** £27 ❷④❸

80 Chepstow Rd   7313 9491   6–1B
*"Guaranteed to be lively", this "Notting Hill staple" – actually
in Bayswater – offers an "interesting and ever-changing"
gastropub menu. /* 10 pm; no smoking; no booking.*

**The Princess EC2** NEW £34

76 Paul St   7729 9270   9–1C
*We haven't had the opportunity to visit this new Shoreditch
gastropub, which opened shortly before this guide went to press;
it's from the same Antipodean team as Farringdon's
commendable Easton, and newspaper reports suggest that the
newcomer measures up. /* 10.30 pm; closed Sat L.*

**Princess Garden W1**  £54  ❷❷④

8 North Audley St   7493 3223   3–2A

*This rather "inscrutable" Mayfair oriental is, as ever, hailed by its small fan club as "London's best smart Chinese"; partly because it's so "expensive", though, it leaves sceptics stone cold.* / www.princessgardenofmayfair.com; 11.30 pm.

**Prism EC3**  £62  ④④④

147 Leadenhall St   7256 3888   9–2D

*For fans, Harvey Nic's City outpost (in a "high-ceilinged" former banking hall) is a "slick" and "business-like" operation with "good food and service"; it has a fair few detractors, though, who say it's a "noisy" place, with prices that "can't be justified".* / www.harveynichols.com; 10 pm; closed Sat & Sun; booking: max 8.

**The Providores W1**  £56  ❸④④

109 Marylebone High St   7935 6175   2–1A

*"Scintillating" cooking and "a great list of NZ wine" make this small first-floor Marylebone venture "the discovery of the year", for some reporters; it's sometimes "quiet", though, and the occasional reporter feels it "doesn't justify the premium over the Tapa Room, downstairs".* / www.theprovidores.co.uk; 10.30 pm; no smoking; booking: max 12.

**(Tapa Room)**
**The Providores W1**  £32  ❷❷❷

109 Marylebone High St   7935 6175   2–1A

*You may have to queue to enjoy "the best light lunch in town", at this "interesting" Marylebone café/bar – its "terrific" weekend brunches have a particular following.* / www.theprovidores.co.uk; 10.30 pm; no smoking.

**Pucci Pizza SW3** NEW  £29  ❷④❷

315 King's Rd   7352 0091   5–3C

*"In the nicest way, more a social club than a restaurant" – this rather scruffy, younger-scene Chelsea hang-out seems to be putting down firm roots in its new location (further along the King's Road), aided by its "great" pizza.* / midnight.

**The Pumphouse N8** NEW  £31

1 New River Ave   8340 0400   1–1C

*The latest outlet from the deservedly successful Mosaica Restaurants group opened shortly before this guide went to press in a strikingly-scaled former pumping station, in Hornsey; newspaper reviews have been full of praise.* / 9.45 pm; no smoking area.

**Putney Station SW15** NEW  £26  ④④④

94-98 Upper Richmond Rd   8780 0242   10–2B

*A "lively" and "smoky" new addition to John Brinkley's empire, where, his trademark "interesting" wine list comes at extremely reasonable prices; the food, as always, is an afterthought.* / www.brinkleys.com; 11 pm; no Amex; no smoking area.

**sign up for the survey at www.hardens.com**

**Quadrato**
**Four Seasons Hotel E14**　　　　　£61　　　❸❷④

Westferry Circus　7510 1857　11–1B
*"Confident" service and "very sound" cuisine help offset the*
*"corporate" ambience at this luxury hotel dining room in Canary*
*Wharf; fans insist it's unfairly "under-used", tipping it for brunch*
*as well as business.* / www.fourseasons.com; 10.30 pm; no smoking area.

**Quaglino's SW1**　　　　　　　£51　　　⑤⑤⑤

16 Bury St　7930 6767　3–3D
*Even by Conran standards, this "loud" and "tawdry" St James's*
*mega-brasserie is "outrageously bad" – it offers "all the*
*enjoyment of eating ready meals in an aircraft hangar"*
*(and expensively, too).* / www.conran.com; midnight, Fri & Sat 1 am;
set weekday L & pre-theatre £32 (FP).

**The Quality Chop House EC1**　　　£38　　　❸❸❸

94 Farringdon Rd　7837 5093　9–1A
*Refurbishment "has helped the ambience" of Clerkenwell's*
*agreeably "unfancy" 'working class caterer' (where some of the*
*infamously bum-numbing seats now even have cushions!);*
*a "relaxing" spot, it serves "classic" British dishes.*
/ www.qualitychophouse.co.uk; 11 pm; closed Sat L; set weekday L &
pre-theatre £25 (FP).

**Queen's Head W6**　　　　　　　£25　　　④❸❸

13 Brook Grn　7603 3174　7–1C
*"Invaluable in summer" – it's the vast garden which is the*
*highlight of this big, quaint tavern on Brook Green; it serves*
*a "wide menu", done to an "OK" standard.* / 10 pm; no smoking
area; no booking.

**Queen's Head & Artichoke NW1**　£36　　　❸❷❸

30-32 Albany St　7916 6206　8–4B
*"A very good and fresh tapas selection" helps win a consistent*
*thumbs-up for this "friendly" boozer, near Regent's Park.*
/ www.theartichoke.net; 10.15 pm; no smoking area.

**Queen's Pub & Dining Rm NW1**　£36　　　④❸④

49 Regents Park Rd　7586 0408　8–3B
*Landmark Primrose Hill tavern, with a small first-floor dining*
*room, serving food that's "sometimes lovely, sometimes very dull".*
/ www.geronimo-inns.co.uk; 10 pm; no Amex; booking: max 10.

**Quilon SW1**　　　　　　　　　£45　　　❷❷❸

41 Buckingham Gate　7821 1899　2–4B
*"A mainly business clientèle" frequents this smart dining room,*
*off Victoria Street; it wins high praise for its "extremely helpful"*
*staff and for its "haute-cuisine, Indian-style".*
/ www.thequilonrestaurant.com; 11 pm; closed Sat L & Sun; no smoking area;
set weekday L £26 (FP).

**Quirinale SW1**　　　　　　　　£46　　　❶❶❸

North Ct, 1 Gt Peter St　7222 7080　2–4C
*"Streets ahead of anything else in Westminster", this rather*
*"serious" basement operation offers "some of the best high-end*
*Italian food in town"; service is notably "attentive", too.* / 10.30 pm;
closed Sat L & Sun.

### Quo Vadis W1 £50 ④④④
26-29 Dean St 7437 9585 4–2A
*Some "solid" performances are still reported at this Soho old-timer, which was revamped by Marco Pierre White in the late-'90s; overall, however, the verdict is that it's "really gone downhill". / www.whitestarline.org.uk; 10.45 pm; closed Sat L & Sun; no smoking area.*

### Quod SW1 £36 ⑤④④
57 Haymarket 7925 1234 4–4A
*A large and "bland" West End Italian; it can be "good pre-theatre"... if you succeed in avoiding the occasions when service is "desperately slow". / www.quod-london.co.uk; 11 pm; closed Sun L; no smoking area.*

### Racine SW3 £44 ❷❶❸
239 Brompton Rd 7584 4477 5–2C
*Henry Harris delivers "no culinary fireworks" – just cooking that's "robust and bursting with flavour" – at this "very Parisian" brasserie, in Knightsbridge; its huge success also owes much to its "incredibly smooth and professional" service. / 10.30 pm; no smoking area; set weekday L & pre-theatre £30 (FP).*

### Ragam W1 £30 ❶❶⑤
57 Cleveland St 7636 9098 2–1B
*"Still superb after all these years", this south Indian restaurant, by the Telecom Tower, serves "remarkable-value" dishes "to die for"; the setting is "pretty awful", though ("but not so much as to put you off"). / www.mcdosa.com; 11 pm; set weekday L £16 (FP).*

### Rainforest Café W1 £33 ⑤⑤④
20 Shaftesbury Ave 7434 3111 3–3D
*"Kids love it", but the best advice to parents on this "expensive and dire" West End theme palace is: "eat before you go". / www.therainforestcafe.co.uk; 10 pm, Thu-Sat 7.30 pm; no smoking.*

### Rajasthan EC3 £28 ❷❷④
49 Monument St 7626 1920 9–3C
*"The best curry in the Square Mile" helps ensure that this City Indian is "always busy"; "very good service", too. / www.rajasthan.co.uk; 11 pm; closed Sat & Sun.*

### Randall & Aubin £34 ❷❷❶
16 Brewer St, W1 7287 4447 3–2D
329-331 Fulham Rd, SW10 7823 3515 5–3B
*"A haven in the sex quartier" – the "cramped" stools at the "always-buzzing" Soho original of this mini-chain provide prime people-watching, as well as "excellent" seafood snacks; the "fun" but less funky Chelsea brasserie offers a more standard "staples" menu. / www.randallandaubin.co.uk; 11 pm; SW10 no smoking area; W1 no booking.*

### Rani N3 £24 ❷❷❸
7 Long Ln 8349 4386 1–1B
*"A good-value buffet" and some "unusual" dishes contribute to the ongoing success of this "nice" and "utterly reliable" Gujarati vegetarian, in North Finchley. / www.raniuk.com; 10 pm; D only, ex Sun open L & D; no smoking.*

**sign up for the survey at www.hardens.com**

**Ranoush**                    £25        ❷④④
22 Brompton Rd, SW1   7235 6999   5–1D
338 Kings Rd, SW3   7352 0044   5–3C
43 Edgware Rd, W2   7723 5929   6–1D
86 Kensington High St, W8   7938 2234   5–1A   **NEW**
*"Good food at amazingly low prices" – not least "fantastic shwarmas" and "fresh juices to die for" – make these "crowded" Lebanese cafés brilliant stand-bys, especially "for a late-night snack". / www.maroush.com; midnight-2.30 am; no credit cards.*

**Ransome's Dock SW11**             £44        ❸❷❸
35 Parkgate Rd   7223 1611   5–4C
*The "encyclopaedic but unintimidating" wine list crops up in over half of the many reports on Martin Lam's "casual" but "well-managed" Battersea fixture; "consistent" cooking and "wonderful" outdoor tables play respectable supporting rôles. / www.ransomesdock.co.uk; 11 pm; closed Sun D; no smoking area.*

**Raoul's Café W9**                £32        ❸⑤❸
13 Clifton Rd   7289 7313   8–4A
*"You battle for a table" – especially for the legendary brunch – at this "really buzzy" Maida Vale pâtisserie; service, though, seems "increasingly unhelpful". / 10.15 pm; no smoking; no booking at L.*

**Rapscallion SW4**                £37        ❸❸❷
75 Venn St   7787 6555   10–2D
*"Inventive" cooking and an "interesting" cocktail menu make this "buzzy" Clapham bar a leading local destination of its type; it's also popular for breakfast. / www.therapscalliononline.com; 10.30 pm, Fri & Sat 11 pm; booking: max 6.*

**Rasa N16**                    £20        ❶❷❷
55 Stoke Newington Church St   7249 0344   1–1C
*"Worth the trip to Stokey!" – the "intriguing" south Indian veggie dishes on offer at the "cramped" but "friendly" cradle of the Rasa empire offer "a new taste experience". / 10.30 pm, Fri & Sat 11 pm; closed weekday L; no smoking area.*

**Rasa**                        £35        ❶❷❸
5 Charlotte St, W1   7637 0222   2–1C
6 Dering St, W1   7629 1346   3–2B
Holiday Inn, 1 Kings Cross, WC1   7833 9787   8–3D   **NEW**
56 Stoke Newington Church St, N16   7249 1340   1–1C
*The "plate-lickingly good" Keralan cuisine at these spin-off ventures is impressively faithful to that at the famed Stoke Newington original (see also); Dering Street and N16 (Travancore) serve meat, while Charlotte Street (Samudra) also offers some "gorgeous" seafood dishes. / www.rasarestaurants.com; 10.45 pm; N16 Mon-Thu closed L, W1 closed Sun L; N16 no smoking area.*

**RASOI VINEET BHATIA SW3**       £70        ❶❷❸
10 Lincoln St   7225 1881   5–2D
*An "extraordinary range of subtle flavours" leads reporters on a "rare journey of gastronomic discovery" when they visit Vineet Bhatia's "haute Indian" yearling, in a Chelsea townhouse; the high prices make it "a rare treat", though, and the setting is on the "cramped" side. / www.vineetbhatia.com; 10.30 pm; closed Sat L & Sun; no smoking.*

**Real Burger World SW11** NEW £11 ②③⑤
252 Lavender Hill 7738 1500 10–2C
*This Battersea diner gets "10/10 for effort", for its "really tasty"
burgers and its "fabulous" shakes; nul points, though, for its
bright cafeteria premises. / 11.30 pm; no credit cards; no smoking.*

**The Real Greek N1** £38 ④⑤④
15 Hoxton Market 7739 8212 9–1D
*Many reporters perceive an ongoing "slacking-off" at this "lively"
Hoxton fixture – the "Greek-with-a-twist" cooking here was once
outstanding, but now it's just "dull", and service is so-so in the
extreme. / www.therealgreek.com; 10.30 pm; closed Sun; no Amex.*

**The Real Greek Souvlaki & Bar** £25 ⑤⑤④
1-2 Riverside Hs, Southwark Br Rd, SE1 7620 0162 9–3B
140-142 St John St, EC1 7253 7234 9–1A
*In a pattern echoing that of his first venture (Livebait), ratings
at Theodore Kyriakou's souvlaki-based chain have 'cratered' now
he's done his 'exit' deal; its branches can now just seem like
"jumped-up kebab shops", with a "cold" ambience, "appalling"
service and "rip-off" prices. / www.therealgreek.co.uk; 11 pm; EC1 closed
Sun; no Amex.*

**Rebato's SW8** £27 ②①①
169 South Lambeth Rd 7735 6388 10–1D
*"Magic, such a find"; this "Vauxhall stalwart" offers "a great
buzzing atmosphere" and "unbeatably friendly service",
plus "real" Spanish food – both in the tapas bar, and the
amusingly cheesy restaurant. / www.rebatos.com; 10.45 pm; closed
Sat L & Sun.*

**Red Fort W1** £47 ②③③
77 Dean St 7437 2525 4–2A
*"Modern minimalist decor, a water feature and a groovy
basement bar" set the tone at this Soho subcontinental veteran,
which was revamped a couple of years ago; its "delicious"
cooking is currently on a high, but even fans find it "fully priced".
/ www.redfort.co.uk; 11 pm; closed Sat L & Sun L.*

**The Red Pepper W9** £32 ③④④
8 Formosa St 7266 2708 8–4A
*"Excellent" pizzas help make it "worth the crush", when you visit
this "lively" Maida Vale veteran; "slow" and "arrogant" service,
though, can make a trip "disappointing".
/ www.theredpeppergroup.com; 11 pm; closed weekday L; no Amex.*

**Red Veg W1** £9 ③⑤⑤
95 Dean St 7437 3109 3–1D
*"Tasty and fresh" vegan/veggie burgers are the star attraction
at this "reliable" Soho "fast food" café – you'd never know they
were meat-free! / www.redveg.com; 10 pm; no credit cards; no smoking;
no booking.*

**Redmond's SW14**                £45        ❷❶④
170 Upper Richmond Rd West   8878 1922   10–2A
*"Courteous and friendly service" is a hallmark of this "slightly old-fashioned" East Sheen "favourite"; other attractions include "consistently high-quality" food and a "short but fine" selection of wines.* / www.redmonds.org.uk; 10 pm; D only, ex Sun L only; no Amex; no smoking; set pre-theatre £27 (FP).

**Refettorio**
**The Crowne Plaza Hotel EC4**    £52       ❸④④
19 New Bridge St   7438 8052   9–3A
*"Delicious cheeses and salami platters" are the culinary highlight of a visit to this slightly odd City Italian yearling; it's a well-spaced place, and undoubtedly "useful for an informal business lunch" – at other times it can be "quiet".* / www.tableinthecity.com; 10.30 pm; closed Sat L & Sun; booking: max 8.

**Refuel**
**Soho Hotel W1**                 £58       ⑤④④
4 Richmond Mews   7559 3007   3–2D
*It may be "buzzy", "trendy" and "full of meedjah types and fashionistas", but this "beautifully-decorated" Soho spot offers "very average" food and "casual" service, at prices which are "well over the top".* / www.sohohotel.com; 11 pm; closed Sat L; set weekday L, Sun L & pre-theatre £37 (FP).

**Relais de Paris SW3** NEW       £36       ④④④
101-103 Walton St   7052 9333   5–1A
*Resembling a Parisian 'formule' restaurant, this comfortable new Brompton Cross spot can make a handy stand-by for a steak 'n' salad; it can seem "overpriced", though, and doubters dismiss it as a "simple concept, poorly executed".* / 11 pm.

**Le Relais de Venise**
**'L'Entrecôte' W1** NEW          £28
120 Marylebone Ln   7486 0878   2–1A
*Opening in late-2005, this Marylebone newcomer aims to be an 'exact replica' of a celebrated Parisian steakhouse (whose menu is restricted to a green salad with walnuts, sirloin steak and chips – plus a secret special sauce – and dessert); if the realisation of the concept lives up to the sourcing – pâtisserie from Paris's Ladurée, for example – it could be a hit.*

**Le Rendezvous du Café EC1**     £37       ❸❸④
22 Charterhouse Sq   7336 8836   9–1B
*"Good steak/frites, reasonably-priced" is the sort of dish that makes the Café du Marché's authentic-looking bistro offshoot a handy Smithfield stand-by.* / 10 pm; closed Sat L & Sun; no Amex.

**Reubens W1**                    £41       ④④❸
79 Baker St   7486 0035   2–1A
*The ground-floor deli of this Marylebone fixture dishes up "wholesome" kosher snacks; the pricier basement restaurant is little commented-on.* / www.reubensrestaurant.com; 10 pm; closed Fri D & Sat; no Amex or Maestro; no smoking.

### Rhodes 24 EC2 £59 ❷❷❷
25 Old Broad St   7877 7703   9–2C
*"Stunning" views and "wonderful" British classic dishes (from a "short" menu) make Gary Rhodes's City eyrie "more than just a business haunt"; rents can't be cheap up on the 24th floor, so it's all the more pleasing how "well-spaced" the tables are.*
/ www.garyrhodes.co.uk; 9 pm; closed Sat & Sun; booking essential.

### Rhodes W1 NEW
### Cumberland Hotel W1 £47
Gt Cumberland Pl   7479 3838   2–2A
*Gary Rhodes's new 'diffusion' outlet – in a minimalistically revamped hotel, by Marble Arch – offers the opportunity to check out the cuisine of one of the most 'British' of chefs at relatively reasonable cost, and early press reports are encouraging; a Rhodes fine dining restaurant is also set to open here in late-2005.* / 9.45 pm; no smoking area.

### Rib Room & Oyster Bar
### Carlton Tower Hotel SW1 £75 ④④④
2 Cadogan Pl   7858 7053   5–1D
*This "traditional", "comfortable" and "calm" Belgravia dining room, aims to offer "plain, simple and superb" fare (not least "first-class" beef); even those who "expect high prices in a place like this", however, can find the bill "ridiculous".*
/ www.carltontower.com; 10.30 pm.

### RIBA Café
### Royal Ass'n of Brit' Architects W1 £33 ④❸❶
66 Portland Pl   7631 0467   2–1B
*In summer, "you can eat outside in peace" on the "terrific" terrace of this "fabulous" Art Deco building – in winter the interior is "splendid" too (if a little 'dry'); the food is fine for business, or "a lazy brunch".* / L & afternoon tea only; L only, closed Sun; no smoking.

### Riccardo's SW3 £33 ❸❸❷
126 Fulham Rd   7370 6656   5–3B
*It's "always fun", at this "cheerful" Chelsea fixture, whose Italian 'tapas' formula helps make it a favourite for a "relaxed meal with friends".* / 11.30 pm.

### Richoux £33 ④④❸
172 Piccadilly, W1   7493 2204   3–3C
41a South Audley St, W1   7629 5228   3–3A
86 Brompton Rd, SW3   7584 8300   5–1C
3 Circus Rd, NW8   7483 4001   8–3A
*These tourist-friendly 'period' cafés may do "great afternoon teas" and "an OK breakfast", but – especially for more substantial fare – they can seem "expensive" and "disappointing".* / 10.30 pm, SW3 7.30 pm, W1 Sat 11 pm; no smoking area; W1 no booking Sat & Sun.

**Rick's Café SW17** £31 ❷❷❷

122 Mitcham Rd   8767 5219   10–2C

*"Just what you want from a local" – this "busy and cramped" outfit ("Tooting's top place!", say fans) is always "buzzing", and serves an "adventurous" menu prepared to a "surprisingly good" standard. / 11 pm; no Amex; no smoking area.*

**The Ritz W1** £89 ④❷❶

150 Piccadilly   7493 8181   3–4C

*Promoters of this "staggeringly beautiful" Louis XVI chamber say new chef John Williams is leading an "inspirational revolution" there; service is certainly more "motivated" these days, but the "traditional" cuisine still has a way to go to banish recollections of the "tragic" standards of former years. / www.theritzlondon.com; 11.30 pm; jacket & tie required; no smoking; set weekday L & pre-theatre £60 (FP).*

**Riva SW13** £45 ❸❸④

169 Church Rd   8748 0434   10–1A

*As usual, Andreas Riva's very "individual" Barnes foodie-favourite wins praise for its "classic" Italian cooking and "knowledgeable" service; a minority of reporters, however, has always found the place "serially disappointing", and these doubters gained ground this year. / 11.30 pm, Sun 9.30 pm; closed Sat L.*

**The River Café W6** £60 ❷❸❸

Thames Wharf, Rainville Rd   7386 4200   7–2C

*This Thames-side legend, in the backstreets of Hammersmith (and with a "beautiful" summer terrace), achieved renewed acclaim this year for its "flavour-packed" Italian cooking, using "the finest seasonal ingredients"; the question remains, though: "how do they get away with such mind-blowing prices?" / www.rivercafe.co.uk; 9 pm; closed Sun D; no smoking.*

**Riviera**
**Gabriels Wharf SE1** £37 ④④❸

56 Upper Ground   7401 7314   9–3A

*"Lovely views" are the main draw to this South Bank Mediterranean; it's "good value pre-theatre", too. / 11.30 pm; no smoking area; set weekday L £23 (FP).*

**The Rivington Grill Bar Deli EC2** £44 ❷❸❸

28-30 Rivington St   7729 7053   9–1C

*A "cool place in cool Shoreditch", where the "British classic" fare – including pies and fish-fingers – is "not cheap" but "fulfills its promise". / www.rivingtongrill.co.uk; 11 pm.*

**Roast** NEW
**The Floral Hall SE1**

Stoney St   7872 5625   9–4C

*'Traditional' restaurants are amazingly thin-on-the-ground in London, so it's a joy to contemplate this late-2005 British newcomer, which aims to showcase native pies, puddings and rôtisserie dishes; needless to say, it's an entrepreneur of Indian extraction (Iqbal Wahhab of Cinnamon Club fame) who is driving this display of national pride. / www.roast-restaurant.com.*

### The Rocket W3 £35 ❸❸❸
11-13 Churchfield Rd   8993 6123   1–2A
This "lively" trendified Acton pub has a "classy" adjacent dining room, where "good" food is served at "reasonable" prices.
/ 10.15 pm; closed Mon L; no Amex.

### Rocket £30 ❸❸❶
4-6 Lancashire Ct, W1   7629 2889   3–2B
Putney Wharf, Brewhouse St, SW15   8789 7875   10–2B
It's hard not to be won over by these "very buzzy" joints, where you can "catch up with friends" over a drink or some "super" pizza or a "really nice salad"; Mayfair is "fairly-priced for somewhere so central" – Putney has "great Thames views".
/ www.rocketrestaurants.co.uk; 10.45 pm; W1 closed Sun; no smoking area.

### Rodizio Rico £30 ④④④
111 Westbourne Grove, W2   7792 4035   6–1B
77-78 Upper St, N1   7354 1076   8–3D   NEW
The "tightly-packed" Bayswater original of these Brazilian, all-you-can-eat BBQs now has an Islington sibling (which is a bit of a "barn"); as "a fun place to take hungry friends", they do have fans – to critics, though, they are soulless haunts where "you are intermittently fed rather average grilled meat and fish".
/ www.rodizio.co.uk; W2 11.30 pm, N1 midnight; closed weekday L; N1 no smoking area.

### Roka W1 £47 ❷④❸
37 Charlotte St   7580 6464   2–1C
Zuma's year-old offshoot, this "sophisticated" and "brightly-lit" Fitzrovia "goldfish bowl" serves some "interesting" Japanese cooking, much of it from a central 'robata' grill; service can "struggle", though, and the place has yet to live up to its parent's 'destination' status. / 11.15 pm; closed Sun L; no smoking.

### Rosemary Lane E1 £41 ❷❷④
61 Royal Mint St   7481 2602   11–1A
Though "cheerlessly-located", this East End pub-conversion is hailed by most (if not quite all) reporters as a "gem", where Christina Anghelescu's cooking shows "good attention to detail".
/ www.rosemarylane.btinternet.co.uk; 10 pm; closed Sat L & Sun.

### Rosmarino NW8 £43 ④④❸
1 Blenheim Terrace   7328 5014   8–3A
A "stylish" St John's Wood Italian, where the summer terrace is an undoubted "joy"; since it changed hands last year, however, its overall appeal has become less certain, and though it's still a "favourite" for some reporters, others fear it's "going off".
/ 10.30 pm; no smoking area.

### Rôtisserie Jules £23 ❸❷⑤
6-8 Bute St, SW7   7584 0600   5–2B
133 Notting Hill Gate, W11   7221 3331   6–2B
"Fresh and tasty chicken", but "not much atmosphere" – that's the package on offer at these bare BYO canteens. / 11 pm; W11 no smoking area.

## ROUSSILLON SW1 £62 ❶❶❸

16 St Barnabas St   7730 5550   5–2D

*Alexis Gauthier's "flamboyant but thoughtful" Gallic cuisine may be well and truly "in the top tier", but this Pimlico backstreet "gem" – with its "fantastic" wine and "wonderful" service – is still known mainly "by foodies, rather than the fashionable".* / www.roussillon.co.uk; 10.30 pm; closed Mon L, Sat L & Sun; no smoking area.

## Rowley's £49 ④④④

113 Jermyn St, SW1   7930 2707   3–3D
23 Conduit St, W1   7493 7050   3–2C   **NEW**

*As ever, views on this St James's stalwart – which now has a Mayfair sibling on the former site of Deca (RIP) – diverge dramatically; fans approve its "old-fashioned" style, "decent" steak and "unlimited chips" – critics deride its "silly" prices, "very moderate" food and "bland" décor.* / www.rowleys.co.uk; 11.30 pm.

## Royal Academy W1 £29 ④⑤④

Burlington Hs, Piccadilly   7300 5608   3–3C

*Some reporters find the RA's recently made-over basement café a "handy and convenient" spot for a "reasonably-priced meal in the West End"; it remains "noisy" and "disorganised", though, and service is often "frazzled".* / www.royalacademy.org.uk; 8.15 pm; L only, except Fri & Sat open L & D; no smoking; no booking at L.

## Royal China £37 ❶④④

24-26 Baker St, W1   7487 4688   2–1A
13 Queensway, W2   7221 2535   6–2C
68 Queen's Grove, NW8   7586 4280   8–3A
30 Westferry Circus, E14   7719 0888   11–1B

*"Epic" dim sum – "just like Hong Kong or Singapore" – ensures that this oriental chain is "still tops" ("'70s-disco decor" notwithstanding); the W2 branch is especially "busy" – "expect a wait at weekends".* / 10.45 pm, Fri & Sat 11.15 pm; E14 no bookings Sat & Sun L.

## Royal China SW15 £34 ❷❸④

3 Chelverton Rd   8788 0907   10–2B

*This Putney "legend" is "not quite as good as its Bayswater namesake" (to which it is unrelated), but it still offers "expert" Chinese fare, with "delicious" dim sum a speciality.* / 10.30 pm; only Amex.

## Royal Court Bar
## Royal Court Theatre SW1 £38 ⑤④❸

Sloane Sq   7565 5061   5–2D

*"Drink, don't eat", at this "buzzy" bunker beneath Sloane Square – the "great" location "fails to compensate" for its "poorly-executed" food.* / 10.30 pm; closed Sun; no smoking area.

## The Royal Exchange Grand Café
## The Royal Exchange EC3 £42 ④④❷

Cornhill   7618 2480   9–3C

*A "wonderful" location in the Royal Exchange's "grand" internal courtyard wins fans for this no-booking Conran seafood (and so on) bar; "the only really good thing is the building itself", though – the prices can seem "crazy".* / www.conran.com; 10.30 pm; closed Sat & Sun; no booking.

**RSJ SE1** £38 ❸❷⑤
33 Coin St  7928 4554  9–4A
*The "unbeatable" Loire wine list figures in most of the many
reports on this South Bank veteran (near the RNT);
the "consistent" cooking plays very much a supporting rôle –
more than can be said about the atmosphere, which is "almost
non-existent". / www.rsj.uk.com; 11 pm; closed Sat L & Sun.*

**Ruby Lounge & Sequoia Bar W11** NEW £31
6-8 All Saints Rd  7243 6363  6–1B
*On the former North Kensington site of Manor (RIP), this relaxed
summer 2005 newcomer offers a laid-back bar/restaurant
formula similar to those of a good number of the premises'
previous occupants; the location's 'form' suggests that it will major
as a weekend brunch destination. / www.ruby.uk.com; 11 pm.*

**Rudland Stubbs EC1** £40 ④④④
35-37 Greenhill Rents, Cowcross St  7253 0148  9–1A
*"Hardy perennial" Smithfield fish parlour, which has seldom
generated high enthusiasm amongst reporters – even fans
concede it's often "quiet". / 10.45 pm; closed Sat & Sun;
no smoking area.*

**La Rueda** £33 ④❸❸
102 Wigmore St, W1  7486 1718  3–1A
642 King's Rd, SW6  7384 2684  5–4A
66-68 Clapham High St, SW4  7627 2173  10–2D
*For a night of "cheesy live music and dancing", some reporters
still tip this "rowdy" tapas chain; it takes flak, though, for offering
"Brit-Spanish" food. / 11.30 pm, Sat & Sun midnight.*

**Rules WC2** £53 ❸❸❶
35 Maiden Ln  7836 5314  4–3D
*"Irresistible for entertaining foreign guests" – London's oldest
restaurant (1798) is a "unique" destination which generally
satisfies the natives too; the meaty English cuisine (with much
game) is "good", but it's the wonderful Victorian interior which
"really shines". / www.rules.co.uk; 11.30 pm; no smoking.*

**Running Horse W1** £25 ④❸④
50 Davies St  7493 1275  3–2A
*Tom Etridge's once-promising Mayfair gastropub still makes
a "reliable" stand-by for some reporters; scant feedback,
however, lends credence to those who feel its "trading on some
OK early reviews", and is now "disappointing".
/ www.therunninghorselondon.co.uk; 10.45 pm; closed Fri D, Sat D & Sun;
need 8+ to book.*

**Rusticana W1** £31 ❸❶❸
27 Frith St  7439 8900  4–3A
*"A good find in Soho" – a "great-value", family-run corner Italian,
with notably "friendly" service; it remains curiously little-known.
/ www.rusticanasoho.co.uk; 11.15 pm; no smoking area.*

**S & M Café** £22 ❸❸❸

268 Portobello Rd, W10  8968 8898  6–1A
4-6 Essex Rd, N1  7359 5361  8–3D
48 Brushfield St, E1  7247 2252  9–1D

"Sausage 'n' mash as it should be" (from a "huge variety
of speciality bangers") wins support for these very English cafés;
the "hugely popular" E1 branch, in particular, is a "godsend" for
brunch before a trip to Spitalfields market. / www.sandmcafe.co.uk;
10 pm-11 pm; no Amex.

**Sabai Sabai W6** £21 ❸❸⑤

270-272 King St  8748 7363  7–2B

"Consistently tasty Thai food at very reasonable prices" helps
make this ambience-free Hammersmith spot a "good stand-by".
/ www.come.to/sabai; 11.15 pm; closed Sat L & Sun L; no smoking area.

**Sabor N1** NEW £32 ❷①❷

108 Essex Rd  7226 5551  8–3D

It's hard not to be won over by the "very enthusiastic" and "well-
informed" service at this new Islington Latin American…
especially when it offers "interesting" food at "unfathomably low"
prices! / www.sabor.co.uk; 10.45 pm.

**Sabras NW10** £24 ❶④⑤

263 High Rd  8459 0340  1–1A

"Stunning" veggie food is served in "cafeteria-esque"
surroundings, at this family-run Willesden Green veteran, where
the cuisine is an "interesting mix" of Gujarati and south Indian
dishes. / www.sabras.co.uk; 10 pm; D only, closed Mon; no Amex; mainly
non-smoking.

**Le Sacré-Coeur N1** £27 ❸❸❸

18 Theberton St  7354 2618  8–3D

"Honest bistro fare, reasonably priced" maintains the appeal
of this "cramped" and "buzzy" Gallic spot, just off Islington's
Upper Street. / 11 pm.

**Sagar W6** £23 ❶❶④

157 King St  8741 8563  7–2C

"A surprise find" – even if it looks "sterile", this simple
Hammersmith café produces "wonderful, intensely-flavoured"
veggie dishes that are among the best south Indian food in town;
staff are "always charming", too. / 10.45 pm; no smoking area.

**ST JOHN EC1** £44 ❶❷❸

26 St John St  7251 0848  9–1B

Fergus Henderson is wooing ever more reporters to his "unique"
Smithfield ex-smokehouse – "a haven of British culinary lore" –
which serves "terrific" and unusual dishes (in which offal often
figures); the bright white interior is "beautifully utilitarian"
to some, but "cold and clinical" to others. / www.stjohnrestaurant.com;
11 pm; closed Sat L & Sun; no smoking area.

### St John Bread & Wine E1 £40 ❷❷❸
94-96 Commercial St 7247 8724 9–1D
"Apparently simple" English dishes from "truly outstanding"
ingredients can make it an "exciting culinary experience" to visit
this "canteen-like" Spitalfields spin-off from St John; "perfect
bacon sarnies" and "stunning Eccles cakes" rated particular
mention. / www.stjohnbreadandwine.com; 10.30 pm; closed Sun D; need 10+
to book.

### St Johns N19 £33 ❷❷❶
91 Junction Rd 7272 1587 8–1C
The "comfortably faded grandeur" of the "huge dining hall"
of this Archway gastropub can come as a "delightful surprise"
to first-timers – so can the "well-cooked" grub (from a "regularly-
changing blackboard menu") and the "incredibly welcoming"
staff. / 11 pm, Sun 9.30 pm; closed Mon L; booking: max 12.

### Le Saint Julien EC1 NEW £30 ❸❷❸
62-63 Long Ln 7796 4550 9–1B
It always astonishes us how few authentic and straightforward
Gallic brasseries there are in London, so let's hope for more
arrivals like this good all-round Smithfield newcomer (which would
make a useful destination for a low-key business lunch). / Rated
on Editors' visit; 10.15 pm; closed Sat L & Sun.

### St Moritz W1 £40 ❷❸❷
161 Wardour St 7734 3324 3–1D
It may look like a tourist trap, but this Soho veteran – with its
"homely" and "cosy" chalet décor – is a "romantic" spot, serving
sound Swiss cooking; highlights include the "great, if pricey,
fondue", and some "fantastic Swiss wines".
/ www.stmoritz-restaurant.co.uk; 11.30 pm; closed Sat L & Sun.

### Sakonis HA0 £18 ❶④⑤
129 Ealing Rd 8903 9601 1–1A
"Excellent" and "authentic" Indian snacks at dirt-cheap prices
justify the trek to this Wembley caff; "skip the buffet", though –
"the prepared food is much better". / 9.30 pm; no Amex; no smoking.

### Sakura W1 £25 ❷④④
9 Hanover St 7629 2961 3–2C
"Most of the clientèle are oriental", at this large Japanese,
off Hanover Square, which seems to get "busier and busier";
"you might want to take a friend who knows what they're doing",
as the menu – though "reasonably-priced" – is long,
and bewilderingly "authentic". / 10 pm.

### Sale e Pepe SW1 £45 ❸❷❸
9-15 Pavilion Rd 7235 0098 5–1D
"If you don't mind sitting in someone else's lap", this "real '70s
trattoria survivor", near Harrods, is "always a laugh"; the food
is "OK", too. / 11.30 pm; closed Sun.

### The Salisbury Tavern SW6 £33 ❸❷❸
21 Sherbrooke Rd 7381 4005 10–1B
This large, recently-improved boozer, in deepest Fulham, "really
stands out" locally, thanks to its attractive rear dining area and
"good comfort food"; like its sibling, the (Admiral) Cod', it too now
has a retractable roof. / www.thesalisbury.co.uk; 11 pm.

**Salloos SW1**      £38    ❶④④
62-64 Kinnerton St   7235 4444   5–1D
*"Subcontinental food doesn't come much better"* than at this
*"dingy"* Belgravia Pakistani (where Abdul Aziz celebrates three
decades at the stoves this year); spécialité de la maison –
*"the best lamb chops"*. / 11.15 pm; closed Sun.

**Salt Yard W1** NEW      £31    ❶❸❸
54 Goodge St   7637 0657   2–1B
*"Fantastic"* tapas (Italian, as well as Spanish) and *"interesting"*
wines – all at *"good-value"* prices – have helped make
an *"exciting"* start for this plain but *"buzzy"* Fitzrovia newcomer.
/ 11 pm; closed Sat L & Sun; no smoking.

**The Salusbury NW6**      £35    ❸❸❸
50-52 Salusbury Rd   7328 3286   1–2B
*"Back on form as a fine gastropub"*, this Queen's Park linchpin
is *"always packed"*; most reporters say its *"rustic Italian fare"*
is *"great"*, but some also feel that *"the pricing could be better"*.
/ 10.15 pm; closed Mon L; no Amex.

**Sam's Brasserie W4** NEW      £36
11 Barley Mow Pas   8987 0555   7–2A
A large new Chiswick bar/brasserie of some ambition, scheduled
to open around the publication date of this guide; run by
a protégé of Rick Stein, it will certainly not want for launch
publicity.

**San Carlo N6**      £39    ④❸❷
2 Highgate High St   8340 5823   8–1B
A *"timeless classic"*, or a *"throwback"*? – the modest feedback
on this *"expensive"* Highgate Italian is as sharply divided as ever.
/ 11 pm; closed Mon; no smoking area.

**San Daniele del Friuli N5**      £28    ❸❶❷
72 Highbury Park   7226 1609   8–1D
This *"bustling"* Highbury Italian wins praise for its *"lovely"*,
*"welcoming"* staff and *"authentic regional cooking"* (with game
a speciality); be warned, though – *"you can never get in on
Arsenal match days"*. / 10.30 pm; closed Mon L, Tue L, Sat L & Sun;
no Amex; no smoking area.

**San Frediano SW3** NEW      £42    ❸❷❸
62 Fulham Rd   7589 2232   5–2C
Now (yet) again trading under its once-famous original name,
this Chelsea Italian – recently known as Giá (RIP) – had already
settled into a comfortable stride when we visited in May 2005;
it is well-spaced to a degree not often seen nowadays. / Rated
on Editors' visit; 11 pm; no smoking area.

**San Lorenzo SW3**      £52    ④④❸
22 Beauchamp Pl   7584 1074   5–1C
Many reporters are perplexed by the ongoing celebrity of this
*"overhyped"* and *"average"* Knightsbridge trattoria; as a
*"sanctuary for surreptitious gawping"*, however, it still has its fans.
/ www.sanlorenzo.com; 11.30 pm; closed Sun; no credit cards.

**San Lorenzo Fuoriporta SW19**          £43          ❸④④

38 Worple Road Mews   8946 8463   10–2B

*"A little pricey, but a reliably enjoyable experience" –*
this Wimbledon Town 'country cousin' of the famed Knightsbridge
trattoria serves "well-cooked" Italian fare in a '70s setting which
is akin to a grand PizzaExpress. / www.sanlorenzo.com; 10.45 pm.

**Santa Lucia SW10**          £32          ❸⑤④

2 Hollywood Rd   7352 8484   5–3B

You get "genuine cooking" – not least, "good pizza" – at this
family-run Chelsea-fringe Italian; service, however, is "chaotic,
and often bad". / 11.15 pm; closed weekday L; no Amex; no smoking area.

**Santa Maria de Buen Ayre E8** NEW   £29          ❸❷④

50 Broadway Mkt   7275 9900   1–2D

A smash hit with East End carnivores, this basic, buzzy and very
cramped new Argentinian was packing 'em in on our visit in May
2005; early reporters confirm our feeling that, compared to the
"undoubtedly high-quality steaks", other dishes can be rather
a "let-down". / www.buenayre.co.uk; 10.30 pm; closed Mon, Tue-Fri D only,
Sat & Sun open L & D; no Amex; no smoking.

**Santini SW1**          £60          ④④④

29 Ebury St   7730 4094   2–4B

"They really push it on the prices", at this somewhat glamorous,
but now "dated", Italian; its handy Belgravia location (a stone's
throw from Victoria), however, makes it a useful business
rendezvous. / www.santini-restaurant.co.uk; 11 pm; closed Sat L & Sun L;
set weekday L £36 (FP).

**Sapori WC2**          £30          ④❸❷

43 Drury Ln   7836 8296   4–2D

"Friendly", "fun" and "not expensive" – this "simple" and
"authentic" Italian, two minutes' walk from the Royal Opera
House, makes "a great stand-by"; the odd reporter, however,
scents "decline" – hopefully just a blip. / 11.30 pm.

**Sarastro WC2**          £39          ⑤⑤❶

126 Drury Ln   7836 0101   2–2D

"Flamboyant" décor, loud opera music and "dire" Middle Eastern
food are the cornerstones of this "strange" Covent Garden
"experience"; supporters praise its "sheer ebullience and joy",
but, for a fair proportion of reporters, it's just a "monstrous
horror story". / www.sarastro-restaurant.com; 11.30 pm.

**Sardo W1**          £43          ❷❸❸

45 Grafton Way   7387 2521   2–1B

"Great" and "gutsy" Sardinian fare is helping to win growing
acclaim for this "delightful family-run restaurant, tucked-away
in north Fitzrovia"; it's usually "full of doctors from UCH, plotting
against the management". / www.sardo-restaurant.com; 11 pm; closed
Sat L & Sun; no smoking area.

**Sardo Canale NW1**　　　　　　£40　　❸❷❸
42 Gloucester Ave　7722 2800　8–3B
Sardinian cooking "with gusto" has won instant applause for this
"airy", year-old Primrose Hill sibling to Sardo; it still doesn't
impress everyone, though, with "small" portions attracting
particular flak. / www.sardocanale.com; 10 pm; closed Mon L;
no smoking area.

**Sargasso Sea N21**　　　　　　£45　　❷❷❷
10 Station Rd　8360 0990　1–1C
"West End ambience and quality" have made this suburban five-
year-old world-famous in Winchmore Hill; it serves "excellent"
(if quite "pricey") seafood in a "contemporary" setting;
"book early". / www.sargassosea.co.uk; 10.30 pm; closed Mon, Tue L,
Wed L, Sat L & Sun D; set weekday L £23 (FP), set Sun L £30 (FP).

**Sarkhel's**　　　　　　　　£28　　❷❷❸
199 Up' Rich'nd Rd West, SW14　8876 6220　10–2B　NEW
199 Replingham Rd, SW18　8870 1483　10–2B
Udit Sarkhel's "stunning" food (and his "friendly" staff) have won
a London-wide reputation for his Southfields curry house; a new
more "intimate" branch opened in East Sheen last winter –
one early reporter found it "still with some shaking down to do".
/ www.sarkhels.com; 10.30 pm; closed Mon; no Amex.

**Sarracino NW6**　　　　　　£32　　❷❷❸
186 Broadhurst Gdns　7372 5889　1–1B
A "lovely" West Hampstead Italian, applauded for its "tasty"
pasta and "fabulous" pizzas. / 11 pm; closed weekday L;
no smoking area.

**Sartoria W1**　　　　　　　£55　　⑤⑤⑤
20 Savile Row　7534 7000　3–2C
Conran's tailoring-themed Mayfair Italian is often dismissed
by reporters nowadays as "pretentious", "poor" and seriously
"overpriced"; when it attracts support, it tends to be as a location
for business. / www.conran.com; 11.15 pm; closed Sun L; set weekday L
£35 (FP).

**Satsuma W1**　　　　　　　£27　　❸❷④
56 Wardour St　7437 8338　3–2D
"For a tasty and cheap 30-minute fill-up", this "bustling Soho
canteen" – with its "reliable noodles and good sushi" – offers
an experience "one up from Wagamama"; the "loud" ambience
"can be lacking", though ("especially downstairs").
/ www.osatsuma.com; 10.30 pm, Fri & Sat midnight; no smoking; no booking.

**Satu Bar & Kitchen EC2**　　　£29　　❸④❷
10 Cutlers Gardens Arc, Devonshire Sq　7283 7888　9–2D
"Not too pricey, considering the location, and with reasonable
food, too" – this large, stylish and "cheerful" basement oriental
makes a handy City stand-by, and remains surprisingly little-
known. / www.satu-bar-kitchen.co.uk; 10.30 pm; closed Sat & Sun.

### Savarona EC2 [NEW] £31 ❸❸❸
66 Gt Eastern St 7739 2500 9–1D
*On the fringe of Hoxton, this fairly 'standard' Turkish venture occupies a large and comfy basement and offers "tasty" "home-cooking"; the ground-floor bar is rather funkier. / www.savarona.co.uk; 11 pm; closed Sun L; no smoking area.*

### (Banquette)
### Savoy Hotel WC2 £47 ④④⑤
Strand 7420 2392 4–3D
*A "disappointing" Ramsay-group revamp of the former Savoy Upstairs; it offers "simple" but "variable" food at pushy prices, in a "sterile" setting that supposedly evokes an American diner – call that a diner? / www.marcuswareing.com; midnight; no smoking; booking: max 8.*

### Savoy Grill
### Savoy Hotel WC2 £77 ❸❷❸
Strand 7592 1600 4–3D
*Marcus Wareing "has improved the food", at this famous power scene, making it again a "perfect all-rounder for business"; ratings waned this year, though, putting the place in line with the good-but-no-more standards which now characterise most of the Ramsay empire. / www.marcuswareing.com; 11 pm; jacket required; no smoking; booking: max 12; set weekday L & pre-theatre £50 (FP), set Sun L £44 (FP).*

### Scalini SW3 £54 ❷❷❷
1-3 Walton St 7225 2301 5–2C
*"Bellissimo" – this "loud", "lively" and "cosmopolitan" Knightsbridge spot is "your classic, full-on Italian job"; with its "happy" and "consistent" charms, it is – for many reporters – simply "the best". / 11.45 pm.*

### The Scarsdale W8 £32 ④❸❶
23a Edwardes Sq 7937 1811 7–1D
*This "perfect little inn" – which has "retained its pubby character" – has a "lovely, quiet Kensington location" (and a "beautiful, sunny-day terrace"); it offers "down-to-earth" grub – "the challenge is finding a place to eat it". / 10 pm; no smoking area.*

### Scoffers SW11 £33 ④❸❷
6 Battersea Rise 7978 5542 10–2C
*"The tree in the centre" adds much to the ambience, which is the key strength of this "romantic" Battersea spot; it's especially popular "for a lazy brunch". / 11 pm.*

### Scuzi £30 ④⑤❸
West India Quay, E14 7001 0991 11–1C
2 Creechurch Ln, EC3 7623 3444 9–2D
*"Scuzi if I don't come back"; while some reporters find these this pizzeria-chain "reasonably-priced", others just consider it a "waste of time" – "not even the pleasant setting (at West India Quay) could make up for the dire food". / www.scuzi.co.uk; midnight; EC3 closed Sat & Sun; no smoking area.*

### The Sea Cow £23 ❷❸④

37 Lordship Ln, SE22   8693 3111   1–4D
57 Clapham High St, SW4   7622 1537   10–2D   **NEW**
*"Very fresh fish and excellent chips"* – not to mention *"fabulous minty mushy peas"* – are putting this refectory-style south London mini-chain on the map; in fact, they can already get *"too busy"*. / www.theseacow.co.uk; 10.30 pm, Sun 8.30 pm; SW4 closed Mon; no smoking.

### Seafresh SW1 £26

80-81 Wilton Rd   7828 0747   2–4B
*After a total refurbishment in the summer of 2005, this age-old Pimlico chippie now has a bright new look; let's hope it's not just the ambience they refurbished!* / 10.30 pm; closed Sun.

### Searcy's Brasserie EC2 £41 ④❸④

Level 2, Barbican Centre   7588 3008   9–1B
*The "very good pre- or post-concert menu" and a "nice outlook" (over the Barbican) are highlights at this smart but "unatmospheric" brasserie; reporters tussle as to whether its cooking is "imaginative", or "underpowered and overpriced".* / www.barbican.org.uk; 10.30 pm; closed Sat L & Sun; no smoking area.

### Seashell NW1 £32 ❸④⑤

49 Lisson Grove   7224 9000   8–4A
*"Past its prime, but still my favourite"* – this *"major tourist stop"*, in Marylebone, was once renowned for London's best fish 'n' chips; its *"reliably fresh"* dishes still have a loyal following, but the décor is naff as hell. / www.seashellrestaurant.co.uk; 10.30 pm; closed Sun; no smoking area.

### Sedir N1 £27 ❸❸④

4 Theberton St   7226 5489   8–3D
*Just off Islington's Upper Street, this "friendly" Turkish restaurant is "a good spot for a cheap and reasonably consistent meal".* / 11.30 pm.

### The Sequel SW4 £37 ④❸❸

75 Venn St   7622 4222   10–2D
*A fairly precise market segment* – locals aged 26-33, if our survey is anything to go by – is served by this quirky but *"friendly"* Clapham fixture, which features a big screen showing old movies, and is tipped as *"a great place for brunch"*. / www.thesequelonline.com; 11 pm; closed Mon, Tue-Fri D only, Sat & Sun open L & D.

### Serafino W1 £48 ❸❷④

8 Mount St   7629 0544   3–3B
*An old-fashioned Mayfair Italian, with "good" cooking and "speedy" service; downstairs, the snack bar* – which does *"great pasta, soup and sandwiches"* – is *"hard to beat for value".* / 10.45 pm; closed Sat L & Sun.

### Settle Inn SW11 £29 ❸❸❸

186 Battersea Bridge Rd   7228 0395   10–1C
*"Sociable"* (*"particularly for rugby fans"*) Battersea boozer, where the small garden is *"a great sun-trap"*; *"huge Sunday roasts, which you carve yourself, are legendary"* – other fare, though, can be very ordinary. / 11 pm.

### Seven Stars W12 £32 ④❸❷
243 Goldhawk Rd 8748 0229 7–1B
*An awkward position (on a mini-roundabout) limits the appeal of this large and stylishly-converted Shepherd's Bush boozer – it's worth considering, though, in a thin area.*
/ www.sevenstarsdining.co.uk; 10.30 pm; no Amex; no smoking area.

### Shakespeare's Globe SE1 £32 ⑤④❷
New Globe Walk 7928 9444 9–3B
*"A spectacular view over the river" is the top attraction of this South Bank dining room, on the first floor of the theatre; it reminded one reporter of "the sort of 'British Restaurants' we had in WWII" – "if you don't remember them, you're lucky!"*
/ www.shakespeares-globe.org; 10.45 pm; no smoking.

### Shampers W1 £34 ❸❶❷
4 Kingly St 7437 1692 3–2D
*"Always welcoming", this "dependable" Soho-fringe wine bar "still has the same old '70s atmosphere", and still dishes up fare that's "simple", but generally "well-executed". / 10.45 pm; closed Sun (& Sat in Aug).*

### Shanghai E8 £26 ❷❷❸
41 Kingsland High St 7254 2878 1–1D
*This striking former Dalston pie & eel shop has been "lovingly restored" and turned into this "pretty good" oriental (where dim sum is a speciality); "other than sometimes ear-splitting Karaoke, it's a perfect local". / www.wengwahgroup.com; 10.45 pm.*

### Shanghai Blues WC1 NEW £35 ④④❷
193-197 High Holborn 7404 1668 4–1D
*Views on this "slick" Chinese newcomer, in the old Holborn Town Hall, differ wildly; our experience chimed with those who found "really superior" food (especially dim sum) – many meals, though, have been "uninspiring". / www.shanghaiblues.co.uk.*

### J SHEEKEY WC2 £55 ❶❷❷
28-32 St Martin's Ct 7240 2565 4–3B
*This "olde-worlde" star-magnet once again inspired more commentary than anywhere else in town, thanks to its "divine" fish, and the "exciting buzz" that permeates its "snug" Theatreland premises – "the only problem is getting in".*
/ www.caprice-holdings.co.uk; midnight.

### Shepherd's SW1 £43 ④❷❷
Marsham Ct, Marsham St 7834 9552 2–4C
*"Great for conspiratorial dinners", this clubby Westminster veteran has long been viewed as just a politicos' canteen; a recent wind of change, though – perhaps inspired by a press review so scathing legal action was threatened – has heralded "improved" cooking, and often-"fantastic" service.*
/ www.langansrestaurants.co.uk; 11 pm; closed Sat & Sun; no smoking area.

### Shikara SW3 NEW £26 ❸❸④
87 Sloane Ave 7581 6555 5–2C
*In chichi Brompton Cross, it's hard not to warm to this unpretentious (if sometimes slow) new Indian, which offers no-nonsense cuisine at reasonable prices. / 11.30 pm; no smoking area.*

**The Ship SW18**                                      £32        ④⑤❷
4l Jews Row    8870 9667    10–2B
This riverside pub by Wandsworth Bridge has a great "buzzing"
atmosphere; outside, it does a "super summer BBQ" – inside,
in the dining annex, "the food is not far above standard pub
fayre". / www.theship.co.uk; 10.30 pm; no booking, Sun L.

**Shish**                                              £22        ④❷❸
75 Bishops Bridge Rd, W2    7229 7300    6–1C    NEW
2-6 Station Pde, NW2    8208 9290    1–1A
313 Old St, EC1    7749 0990    9–1D
"The clandestine late-night-feed experience, made socially
acceptable" – that's the genius of this "brilliant concept", where
"posh kebabs" are served in a cool modern setting; the Willesden
Green original enjoys 'local hero' status. / www.shish.com; 11.30 pm;
no smoking; need 8+ to book.

**Shogun W1**                                          £50        ❶❷④
Adam's Row    7493 1255    3–3A
"One of the better-priced top Japanese" – this estimable Mayfair
basement "gem" still offers "excellent" food, and retains its "loyal
expat following". / 11 pm; D only, closed Mon.

**Signor Sassi SW1**                                   £50        ❸❷❷
14 Knightsbridge Grn    7584 2277    5–1D
"Entertaining" staff help create a "memorable" experience
at this "buzzy" Knightsbridge Italian; the food is not the main
thing, but is consistently good nonetheless. / 11.30 pm; closed Sun.

**Signor Zilli W1**                                    £44        ❸❸❸
41 Dean St    7734 3924    4–2A
Aldo Zilli's original Soho venture has been eclipsed by his newer
openings in recent years, but offers dependable food, in a "busy"
and "upbeat" setting. / www.zillialdo.com; 11.30 pm; closed Sat L & Sun.

**Silk**  NEW
**Courthouse Hotel Kempinski W1**        £60
19-21 Gt Marlborough St    7297 5555    3–1C
Although it has received many newspaper reviews – aided by the
good CV of chef Elisha Carter – not a single reporter bothered
to comment on this ambitious new Silk Route-inspired hotel
dining room (housed in a former Soho law court), hence we've
left it un-rated. / www.courthouse-hotel.com.

**Silka SE1**                                          £29        ❸④④
6-8 Southwark St    7378 6161    9–4C
This "different" basement Indian, in Borough Market, seems very
temperamental for a place founded on the calming principles
of Ayurveda – at its best, it does offer "delicious" and "healthy"
cuisine, but reports are by no means consistent. / 11.30 pm; closed
Sun; no smoking.

**Silks & Spice** £30 ❸❸❸
95 Chiswick High Rd, W4   8995 7991   7–2B
28 Chalk Farm Rd, NW1   7482 2228   8–2B
Temple Ct, 11 Queen Victoria St, EC4   7248 7878   9–2C
"Reliable and inexpensive" grub and "great décor" help carve out
a niche for this "cheap and cheerful" Thai chain.
/ www.silksandspice.net; 11 pm; EC4 closed Sat & Sun; no Amex;
no smoking area.

**Simpson's Tavern EC3** £24 ④❸❶
38 1/2 Ball Ct, Cornhill   7626 9985   9–2C
"Traditional English fayre" – of the "school dinners" variety –
sustains this wonderfully Dickensian (literally) chop-house, in the
heart of the City; the waitresses "have been there for years,
and treat everyone like friends". / www.simponsofmayfair.com; L only,
closed Sat & Sun.

**Simpsons-in-the-Strand WC2** £56 ④❸❸
100 Strand   7836 9112   4–3D
For "classic British old style", this roast beef "bastion" may
be unrivalled, but – aside from the "wonderful, full-works
breakfast" – its lacklustre cooking has caused it to fall into
relative obscurity in recent years; new management (Fairmont
Hotels) took over in 2005, though, so let's hope that change
is afoot... / www.simpsons-in-the-strand.com; 10.45 pm; Sun 9 pm; no jeans
or trainers; set always available £37 (FP).

**Singapore Garden NW6** £33 ❸❷❸
83-83a Fairfax Rd   7328 5314   8–2A
A long-time reputation for "authentic" Singaporean/Malay cuisine
ensures that this "suburban"-style Swiss Cottage spot is usually
"packed"; declining ratings, however, support those who feel
it "has deteriorated" in recent times. / 10.45 pm; set weekday L
£20 (FP).

**Singapura** £34 ④❸❸
31 Broadgate Circle, EC2   7256 5045   9–2D
78-79 Leadenhall St, EC3   7929 0089   9–2D
1-2 Limeburner Ln, EC4   7329 1133   9–2A
"Good when you need a quick City lunch" – these "efficient"
orientals serve "attractively-priced" cooking in a "swift but
unhurried" manner. / www.singapuras.co.uk; 10.30 pm; closed Sat & Sun,
EC3 L only; no smoking area.

**606 Club SW10** £35 ⑤④❶
90 Lots Rd   7352 5953   5–4B
The food (compulsory for non-members) at this hidden-away jazz
club, near Lot's Road Power Station, strikes some reporters
as "a pricey disgrace" – fortunately, however, "a bottle of wine
and the sublime music eradicate all memory of it".
/ www.606club.co.uk; 12.30 am-1.30 am, Sun 11 pm; D only; no Amex.

**06 St Chad's Place WC1** £31 ❷❸❸
6 St Chad's Pl   7278 3355   8–3D
It's still little-known, but this year-old venture – a smartly-
converted shed, by a railway line, down a King's Cross alleyway –
is a handy destination for a stylish snack in a thin area.
/ www.6stchadsplace.com; 9.15 pm; closed Sat & Sun; no Amex.

**Six-13 W1**　　　　　　　　　£53　　③④④
19 Wigmore St　7629 6133　3–1B
*Most reporters praise this (rare) West End kosher venture for its*
*"high standard" of cuisine and its suitability for business; prices*
*are also "high", though, and there's a disgruntled minority who*
*think the place a "wasted opportunity". / www.six13.com; 10.15 pm;*
*closed Sat L (also Fri D in winter, Sat D in summer).*

**(Gallery)**
**Sketch W1**　　　　　　　　　£60　　　⑤⑤④
9 Conduit St　0870 777 4488　3–2C
*"Go to be seen, not to eat" and you may enjoy a visit to this*
*"'70s"-sci-fi-style "scene", in Mayfair; prices for the "poncy" food,*
*though, are "from another planet", and the service*
*is "from Mars". / www.sketch.uk.com; 10.30 pm; D only, closed Sun;*
*booking: max 12.*

**(Lecture Room)**
**Sketch W1**　　　　　　　　　£133　　⑤⑤④
9 Conduit St　0870 777 4488　3–2C
*Some foodies opine that the "incredible creations" at Mourad*
*Mazouz's wonderfully opulent Mayfair dining room sort-of-justify*
*the "silly" prices; for the great majority of reporters, though,*
*this place is just a "vacuous circus", aimed at those "with more*
*money than sense". / www.sketch.uk.com; 10.30 pm; closed Mon,*
*Sat L & Sun; no smoking area; set weekday L £55 (FP), set D £88 (FP).*

**(Parlour)**
**Sketch W1**　　　　　　　　　£39　　④④③
9 Conduit St　0870 777 4488　3–2C
*"Perfect for a break from a busy shopping session",*
*this "gorgeous girlie boudoir", in the heart of Mayfair, offers*
*a "lovely" setting "for a delicious lunch, or some elegant*
*pâtisserie"; by night, it becomes the establishment's (new) main*
*bar. / www.sketch.uk.com; L & afternoon tea only; closed Sun; no smoking;*
*booking: max 6.*

**(Glade)** NEW
**Sketch W1**　　　　　　　　　£38
9 Conduit St　0870 777 4488　3–2C
*As part of a late-2005 rejig, a section of the ground floor*
*of Momo's ever-evolving Mayfair palazzo will be converted into*
*an 'entry-level' (in every sense) lunchtime-only spot; the name*
*apparently derives from the restful colour scheme.*
*/ www.sketch.uk.com.*

**(Ground Floor)**
**Smiths of Smithfield EC1**　　　£23　　④④②
67-77 Charterhouse St　7251 7997　9–1A
*"What better place for a hazy start to Sunday morning" than this*
*large and "buzzing" bar, which is renowned for its "bacon*
*butties" and other "perfect" breakfast fare; service, though,*
*is sometimes "really terrible" (and the non-breakfast fare is much*
*less of an attraction). / www.smithsofsmithfield.co.uk; L only.*

### (Dining Room)
### Smiths of Smithfield EC1     £35     ❸④❸

67-77 Charterhouse St   7251 7997   9–1A

*"There's always a buzzy feel" to this "reliable" brasserie on the second floor of a former Smithfield warehouse; "fabulous burgers" and "quality steaks" are highlights of a "fairly basic" menu.* / www.smithsofsmithfield.co.uk; 10.45 pm; closed Sat L & Sun.

### (Top Floor)
### Smiths of Smithfield EC1     £56     ❸❸❷

67-77 Charterhouse St   7251 7950   9–1A

*"The best steak in London" and "spectacular City views" – plus, in summer, a "great" terrace – make this top-floor Smithfield dining room an "impressive place to take clients"; those paying their own way, however, can find it "very expensive" for what it is.* / www.smithsofsmithfield.co.uk; 10.45 pm; closed Sat L; booking: max 10; set Sun L £40 (FP).

### Smithy's WC1     £28     ④❸④

15-17 Leeke St   7278 5949   8–3D

*Worth knowing given the dearth of respectable rendezvous near King's Cross – a wine bar offering a good list by the glass, and OK food to go with it.* / www.capitalpubcompany.com; 10 pm; closed Sat & Sun.

### Smollensky's     £34     ⑤⑤④

105 Strand, WC2   7497 2101   4–3D
Bradmore Hs, Ham'smith B'way, W6   8741 8124   7–2C
22-24 York St, TW1   8891 5200   1–4A
Reuters Plaza, Canary Wharf, E14   7719 0101   11–1C
22 Wapping High St, E1   7680 1818   11–1A

*"Great in a group" or for "a fun time with kids", say its supporters – otherwise, this witless American chain is often thought "a general let-down".* / www.smollenskys.co.uk; 10.30 pm; W6 closed Sat L & Sun, E14 closed Sun; WC2 no smoking area; set pre-theatre £22 (FP).

### Snows on the Green W6     £36     ❸❷❸

166 Shepherd's Bush Rd   7603 2142   7–1C

*"For unpretentious food at reasonable prices", Sebastian Snow's Brook Green fixture (est. 1991) offers "all you could want from a local"; it's quite "kind on the wallet", too.* / www.snowsonthegreen.co.uk; 10.45 pm; closed Sat L & Sun.

### Sofra     £29     ④❸④

1 St Christopher's Pl, W1   7224 4080   3–1A
18 Shepherd St, W1   7493 3320   3–4B
36 Tavistock St, WC2   7240 3773   4–3D
11 Circus Rd, NW8   7586 9889   8–3A
21 Exmouth Mkt, EC1   7833 1111   9–1A

*"Good food at sensible prices" commends these "formulaic" Turkish canteens to most reporter, even if standards aren't consistent and service can be "dreadfully slow".* / www.sofra.co.uk; midnight.

### Soho Spice W1 £34 ④④④
124-126 Wardour St 7434 0808 3–1D
It's hard not to feel a bit let down by this relaunched (under new ownership) Soho Indian – especially compared to its siblings (Mela and Chowki), it's a "dull" operation, with a "sterile" setting and "slow" service. / www.sohospice.co.uk; Mon-Tue midnight, Wed-Sat 2 am, Sun 10.30 pm; no smoking; need 4+ to book at L, 6+ at D.

### Solly's Exclusive NW11 £30 ④④❸
148 Golders Green Rd 8455 0004 1–1B
"Well OTT" décor is part of the 'charm' of this "buzzy" Golder's Green Israeli – less so the food, which is often proclaimed a "let-down"; (downstairs, they've refurbished the cheaper café/take-away, which does "good grills"). / 10.30 pm; closed Fri D & Sat; no Amex; no smoking.

### Sông Quê E2 £25 ❶④⑤
134 Kingsland Rd 7613 3222 1–2D
"Despite newer competition nearby", you "still get the best Vietnamese food in town" at this "always-busy" Shoreditch café; the setting may be "utterly lacking", but it is enlivened by "trendy regulars". / 11 pm; no smoking area.

### Sonny's SW13 £42 ❸❸❸
94 Church Rd 8748 0393 10–1A
This "bustling" Barnes brasserie has long been hailed as "a match for central London favourites"; its ratings waned this year, however, and even some fans note that "it doesn't quite have its old shine". / www.sonnys.co.uk; 11.45 pm; closed Sun D; no smoking area; set weekday L £29 (FP).

### Sophie's Steakhouse SW10 £34 ❸❸❶
311-313 Fulham Rd 7352 0088 5–3B
"The bar is a lively place to wait for a table" – there are no reservations – at this "young" and "always-overcrowded" joint on the Chelsea 'Beach', which serves up "good-value" grills and burgers, in a "party" atmosphere. / www.sophiessteakhouse.com; 11.45 pm; no booking; set weekday L £23 (FP).

### Sotheby's Café W1 £39 ❷❶❷
34 New Bond St 7293 5077 3–2C
"For a quick and delicious lunch" in Mayfair, this "elegant", small café – off the foyer of the auction house – is hard to beat; it offers "simple" but "interesting" dishes, and "good people-watching", too. / www.sothebys.com; L only, closed Sat & Sun; no smoking.

### Le Soufflé
### Inter-Continental Hotel W1 £68 ❷❶❸
1 Hamilton Pl 7318 8577 3–4A
Jeff Haviland's "outstanding modern cuisine" is really beginning to "find its way", say fans of this "comfortable" Mayfair "haven", which deserves to be better known; service is "exemplary", too. / www.london.interconti.com; 10.30 pm, Sat 11.15 pm; closed Mon, Sat L & Sun; no smoking area; booking: max 12; set weekday L £44 (FP).

### Souk WC2 £24 ⑤⑤❷
27 Litchfield St 7240 1796 4–3B
*"Low tables, cushions and candles whisk you to the Kasbah!",
at this budget, "souk-style" basement, near the Ivy; "the joy can
soon wear off", though, due to the "very bland" North African
dishes, and "very slow" service. / www.soukrestaurant.net; midnight;
no smoking area.*

### South EC2 £34 ❷❷④
128 Curtain Rd 7729 4452 9–1D
*"Simple French dishes, expertly prepared" make this Shoreditch
bistro well worth remembering (especially at lunchtime); if only
they could sort out the "cold" ambience... / 10.30 pm; closed Sun;
no Amex; no smoking area.*

### Spago SW7 £27 ❸④❸
6 Glendower Pl 7225 2407 5–2B
*"Entertaining" staff add to the "fun" of a visit to this "cheap and
cheerful" pizzeria – an ever-handy stand-by in pricey South
Kensington. / 11.30 pm; no credit cards.*

### La Spiga W1 £33 ❸④④
84-86 Wardour St 7734 3444 3–2D
*Now bereft of its Chelsea sibling, this "classy" but "cramped" and
"hectic" Soho Italian is consistently praised for its "proper thin-
crust pizza". / 11 pm, Wed-Sat midnight.*

### La Spighetta W1 £35
43 Blandford St 7486 7340 2–1A
*A recent change of ownership makes it impossible to pronounce
authoritatively on this clattery Marylebone basement pizzeria –
we've therefore left it unrated until next year's survey. / 10.30 pm;
no smoking area.*

### Spoon at Sanderson
### Sanderson W1 £77 ⑤⑤④
50 Berners St 7300 1444 3–1D
*"A triumph of pricing over sanity"; although the menu "sounds
interesting", the "bite-sized" dishes on offer at this "up-itself"
Fitzrovia design-hotel dining room often "fail to meet
expectations". / www.spoon-restaurant.com; 11 pm; no smoking area.*

### Sporting Page SW10 £27 ❸❸❷
6 Camera Pl 7349 0455 5–3B
*A rather superior Chelsea boozer, where lunch might be "washed
down with Berry Bros' claret" as readily as with a pint; "avoid
on Stamford Bridge match days". / www.frontpagepubs.com; 10 pm,
Sat & Sun 6 pm; closed Sat D & Sun D.*

### Spread Eagle SE10 £44 ❸❷❷
1-2 Stockwell St 8853 2333 1–3D
*"So cosy and romantic", this "beautiful" old Greenwich inn offers
"rather rich" Gallic cooking in a "professional" ("old-fashioned")
manner. / www.spreadeagle.org; 10.30 pm; no Amex; no smoking area.*

**THE SQUARE W1**  £76  ❷❷④

6-10 Bruton St  7495 7100  3–2C

Philip Howard realises his "creative" cooking "with aplomb",
at this "polished" Mayfair business-favourite (and the
"substantial" wine list would gladden the heart of any wine buff);
the place looks rather like a "swanky conference room" (but a
'new look' is apparently on the cards). / www.squarerestaurant.com;
10.45 pm; closed Sat L & Sun L.

**Sree Krishna SW17**  £19  ❶❷④

192-194 Tooting High St  8672 4250  10–2C

"Still excellent after all these years", this "dreary"-looking Tooting
veteran is well worth seeking out for its "wonderful, fresh and
inventive" south Indian cooking (including meat dishes). / 10.45 pm,
Fri & Sat midnight; no smoking area.

**Sri Siam City EC2**  £37  ❸❷④

85 London Wall  7628 5772  9–2C

"An efficient, tasty and reliable City basement Thai"; it makes
a popular option for a "relaxed business lunch".
/ www.orientalrestaurantgroup.co.uk; 10.30 pm; closed Sat & Sun; smoking
in bar only.

**Sri Thai EC4**  £33  ❸❷❷

3 Queen Victoria St  7827 0202  9–3C

The style may be "formulaic", but "extremely helpful" staff,
and sometimes "delicious" Thai cooking help make this City
"shed" a "fun" option for an informal get-together.
/ www.orientalrestaurantclub.co.uk; 10.30 pm; closed Sat & Sun; smoking
in bar only.

**Sri Thai Soho W1**  £37  ❷❷❸

16 Old Compton St  7434 3544  4–2A

A handy location ("at the less cruisy end of Old Compton Street")
contributes to the charm of this long-established Soho Thai,
and its "above-average" cuisine offers some "fabulous" flavours.
/ www.orientalrestaurantgroup.co.uk; 11 pm; closed Sun L; no smoking area.

**Standard Tandoori W2**  £22  ❸④④

21-23 Westbourne Grove  7229 0600  6–1C

"Just as the name implies", this Bayswater veteran goes on and
on; the recent "slight make-over" however, seems to have shaken
standards somewhat – let's hope it's a blip. / 11.45 pm;
no smoking area.

**Star Café W1**  £22  ❸❸❸

22 Gt Chapel St  7437 8778  3–1D

"A proper old-style Italian café" (and also a "media haunt") –
this "venerable Soho stand-by" offers "cheap" and "home-
cooked" fare (and breakfasts that are "the real McCoy").
/ www.thestarcafesoho.co.uk; L only, closed Sat & Sun; no smoking area.

**Star of India SW5**  £35  ❷❸④

154 Old Brompton Rd  7373 2901  5–2B

"Camp" décor and a "wonderfully eccentric" owner help make
this South Kensington curry house of 50 years standing "a little
bit different"; its cooking is "light and delicious", too.
/ www.starofindia.co.uk; 11.45 pm.

**Starbucks**                                    £11        ④❸④

Branches throughout London

*"Hate the concept, but horribly addicted to their lattes" – typical of the ambivalent feedback on this "American plague"; it's an "expensive" destination, especially for snacks, and its ratings slipped across the board this year.* / www.starbucks.com; 6.30 pm-11 pm; most City branches closed all or part of weekend; no smoking; no booking.

**Stick & Bowl W8**                              £16        ❸❸⑤

31 Kensington High St   7937 2778   5–1A

*"Many Chinese people eating" is "a good sign", at this "bustling" and very "basic" Kensington canteen – the sort of place were you "perch on stools" for "a fast mid-shopping feed".* / 11 pm; no credit cards; no booking.

**Sticky Fingers W8**                            £37        ④④④

1a Phillimore Gdns   7938 5338   5–1A

*This once-favourite Kensington burger joint seems "stuck in the '80s"; it still has fans, especially for a family meal, but critics find its food "ordinary" and "pricey", and say service can be "offhand".* / www.stickyfingers.co.uk; 10.45 pm.

**Stock Pot**                                    £15        ④④④

40 Panton St, SW1   7839 5142   4–4A
18 Old Compton St, W1   7287 1066   4–2A
273 King's Rd, SW3   7823 3175   5–3C

*"It's hard to find cheaper" than these "basic" canteens, which serve "quick and sustaining" light meals that are, at least, "edible".* / 11 pm-midnight; W1 no credit cards, SW3 no Amex; SW1 & SW3 no smoking area; some booking restrictions apply.

**Stone Mason's Arms W6**                        £29        ❸❸❷

54 Cambridge Grove   8748 1397   7–2C

*A "chilled-out" gastropub that overcomes its trafficky Hammersmith location to provide "a low-key but classy place to eat good, simple food".* / 9.45 pm.

**Story Deli**
**The Old Truman Brewery E1**                    £15        ❶④❷

3 Dray Walk   7247 3137   1–2D

*"Fantastic light and crispy pizzas" (in particular) help draw crowds of young East End fashionistas to the communal tables at this Brick Lane operation, in a "lovely" converted brewery; it can get "chaotic", though.* / L only; no smoking.

**Strada** £31 ④❸❸

15-16 New Burlington St, W1 7287 5967 3–2C
31 Marylebone High St, W1 7935 1004 2–1A
9-10 Market Pl, W1 7580 4644 3–1C
6 Gt Queen St, WC2 7405 6295 4–1D
237 Earl's Court Rd, SW5 7835 1180 5–2A
175 New King's Rd, SW6 7731 6404 10–1B
105-106 Upper St, N1 7276 9742 8–3D
4 South Grove, N6 8342 8686 8–1B
40-42 Parkway, NW1 7428 9653 8–3B
11-13 Battersea Rise, SW11 7801 0794 10–2C
375 Lonsdale Rd, SW13 8392 9216 10–1A
102-104 Clapham High St, SW4 7627 4847 10–2D
8-10 Exmouth Mkt, EC1 7278 0800 9–1A
Thanks to its "delicious, crispy-based pizza", many reporters
claim this "simple and stylish" Italian chain "knocks spots
of PizzaExpress"; complaints of "mediocre" cooking rose this
year, though, and its lead over its rival narrowed. / www.strada.co.uk;
11 pm; no smoking area; some booking restrictions apply.


**Stratford's W8** £38 ❷❶❸

7 Stratford Rd 7937 6388 5–2A
"A best-kept secret" – this "charmingly old-fashioned" Kensington
backwater seafood-specialist may have a slightly "quiet"
("teashop") ambience, but it offers "individual" service,
and "very good food at reasonable prices".
/ www.stratfords-restaurant.com; 11.30 pm; set D £25 (FP).


**Sugar Hut SW6** £43 ④❸❶

374 North End Rd 7386 8950 5–3A
The "dark" and "warm" ambience is the main selling point of this
"romantic" hide-away, near Fulham Broadway; "you're paying for
the trendiness", though – "you can get better Thai food a lot
cheaper elsewhere". / www.sugarhutfulham.com; 11.30 pm; D only.


**Sugar Reef W1** £37 ⑤⑤⑤

42-44 Gt Windmill St 7851 0800 3–2D
"Trendy surroundings don't make up for the bad, bad food"
at this Soho venue, which presumably owes its continued
existence to its attractions as a nite-club. / www.sugarreef.net; 11 pm;
closed Sun.


**Sumosan W1** £60 ❶❸④

26b Albemarle St 7495 5999 3–3C
Food "on a par with Nobu's" hasn't won this minimalist Mayfair
Japanese nearly the following it deserves; it would help if they
improved the "sterile" décor. / www.sumosan.com; 11.30 pm; closed
Sun L; no smoking area.


**The Sun & Doves SE5** £29 ❸④❷

61 Coldharbour Ln 7733 1525 1–4C
Residents of "trendy Camberwell" vaunt this "easy" café/bar for
its "good menu" and "relaxed" vibe – given that the area's so up-
and-coming, it's one of curiously few good options locally.
/ www.sunanddoves.co.uk; 10.30 pm; no Amex; no smoking area; need 10+
to book.


*for updates visit www.hardens.com*

**La Superba NW1** NEW £30 ❸❷❸

17 Princess Rd 7483 0192 8–3B
The "unpretentious" charms of the Primrose Hill Italian formerly
called Vegia Zena – with its "rustic" cuisine, and its "secluded"
garden – seem little changed by the adoption of a new name;
"the menu has a bit less choice, but the restaurant is as good
as ever". / 11 pm.

**Le Suquet SW3** £48 ❷④❸

104 Draycott Ave 7581 1785 5–2C
Chef Philippe Moron has recently celebrated 30 years at the
stoves of this "quintessentially Gallic" Chelsea corner,
long admired for its "genuine Côte d'Azur feeling", and "the best
fruits de mer". / 11.30 pm; set weekday L £28 (FP).

**Sushi-Hiro W5** £25 ❶❷④

1 Station Pde 8896 3175 1–3A
"Always chock full of Japanese expats", this small and "clinical"-
looking spot, near Ealing Common, is a real "rarity";
its "beautifully fresh sushi" (at "really cheap prices") are hailed –
by a number of oriental reporters – as arguably "the best
in London". / 9 pm; no credit cards.

**Sushi-Say NW2** £33 ❷❶⑤

33b Walm Ln 8459 7512 1–1A
"A wonderful little Japanese oasis in not very epicurean
Willesden" – this "authentic" ten-year-old offers "very fresh"
sushi and sashimi, with "charming" service that helps to enliven
the "basic" setting. / 10.30 pm; closed Mon, Tue-Fri D only, Sat & Sun
open L & D; no smoking.

**The Swag & Tails SW7** £39 ❸❸❷

10-11 Fairholt St 7584 6926 5–1C
It's "hard to believe that this 'village' pub is just two minutes' walk
from Harrods" – that's a big part of the charm, though, at this
"welcoming" spot, which serves "well-prepared" dishes
in "attractive" surroundings. / www.swagandtails.com; 11 pm; closed
Sat & Sun.

**The Swan W4** £33 ❷❷❷

119 Acton Ln 8994 8262 7–1A
"Great, if you're lucky enough to get a table" – this "excellent
little gastropub, on the Chiswick/Acton border" has "interesting"
food, "diverse" wine, and "service that stays on top of its game";
"the garden is heaven in summer". / 10.30 pm; closed weekday L;
no Amex; no booking.

**Sweetings EC4** £43 ❷❷❷

39 Queen Victoria St 7248 3062 9–3B
It may be "an anachronism" but "they've got the basics right",
at this "immortal" City "institution" – a "quaint" Victorian parlour
serving fish and seafood of "outstanding quality". / L only, closed
Sat & Sun; no booking.

### Taberna Etrusca EC4 £38 ④❸④
9 Bow Churchyard   7248 5552   9–2C
*"Nice staff"*, and outside tables in summer, help commend this
quietly-situated Italian to some City types; its food is somewhere
between *"reliable"* and *"below par"*. / www.etruscarestaurants.com;
L only, closed Sat & Sun.

### Talad Thai SW15 £25 ❷❷④
320 Upper Richmond Rd   8789 8084   10–2A
*"Great authentic Thai food"* – and *"at bargain prices"*, too –
makes this café-cum-supermarket a top Putney destination;
the queue, though, can be *"horrible"*. / 10.30 pm; no Amex;
no smoking.

### Taman gang W1 £71 ④④❶
141 Park Ln   7518 3160   2–2A
*"Sexy"* décor helps create an *"intimate but cool"* vibe at this
swanky Mayfair basement oriental; the food is *"better than you'd
expect"* for such a *"footballer-tastic"* venue, but it can also seem
*"incredibly pricey"* for what it is. / www.tamangang.com; 11.30 pm;
closed Sun; booking: max 6.

### Tamarind W1 £52 ❷❷❸
20 Queen St   7629 3561   3–3B
*"One of the first posh Indians"*, and still one of the best –
this *"sophisticated"* Mayfair basement has many fans, thanks
to Alfred Pasad's *"fantastic"* and *"sensitively-spiced"*
subcontinental dishes (with a *"twist"*). / www.tamarindrestaurant.com;
11.15 pm; closed Sat L; set weekday L & Sun L £33 (FP).

### Tandoori Lane SW6 £24 ④❸④
131a Munster Rd   7371 0440   10–1B
As a *"good, basic"* curry house, this deepest Fulham Indian still
wins local support; drifting ratings, though, support those who say
it's *"gone downhill"*. / 11.30 pm; no Amex.

### Tandoori Nights SE22 £25 ❶❶❷
73 Lordship Ln   8299 4077   1–4D
Local reporters in particular are unstinting in their praises for this
*"excellent"* and *"inexpensive"* East Dulwich curry house, where
the food is *"fresh"* and *"fabulous"*, and service *"friendly"* and
*"professional"*. / www.tandoorinights.co.uk; 11.30 pm; closed
weekday L & Sat L; no smoking area.

### Tapas Brindisa SE1 NEW £30 ❷❸❷
18-20 Southwark St   7357 8880   9–4C
This simple newcomer by Borough Market is run by the
eponymous Spanish food importers, and has won instant foodie
raves for its *"lovely"* tapas (using the *"outstanding"* ingredients
you'd hope for); it's *"not cheap"*, though, and *"tables are close"*.
/ 11 pm; closed Sun L; no Amex; no smoking in dining room.

**Taqueria W11** NEW £26 ❶④❸
139-143 Westbourne Grove 7229 4734 6–1B
*Our early (July 2005) visit to this new Notting Hill café (on the
site of Mandola, RIP) was a real breath of fresh air – never
before in London have we sampled such zesty Mexican fare
(comprising a selection of intriguing small dishes, plus some
interesting drinks). / Rated on Editors' visit; 11 pm; no Amex; no smoking;
no booking.*

**Taro** £20 ❸❸④
10 Old Compton St, W1 7439 2275 4–2B
61 Brewer St, W1 7734 5826 3–2D
*"Great Japanese food" – including "fresh sushi" and "huge bowls
of tasty ramen" – at "very cheap prices" makes Mr Taro's
"cramped" canteens very useful Soho stand-bys. / 10.30 pm;
no Amex; no smoking; no booking.*

**Tartine** £33 ❸❸❷
114 Draycott Ave, SW3 7589 4981 5–2C
24 Hill St, TW9 8940 4326 1–4A NEW
*"After a hard day's shopping", an "upmarket" toastie (made with
pain Poilâne) from this Brompton Cross snackery makes a very
handy pick-me-up; the similarly "stylish" new Richmond branch
has incited the odd "disappointing" report though.
/ www.tartine.co.uk; 10.30 pm; no smoking area; need 6+ to book at D (& L
in TW9).*

**Tas** £26 ❸❷❸
33 The Cut, SE1 7928 2111 9–4A
72 Borough High St, SE1 7403 7200 9–4C
*"Dependable" mezze and other dishes at "great-value" prices
make these "hustling and bustling" Turkish establishments
"invaluable" stand-bys; they're especially suited to large parties
on a budget. / www.tasrestaurant.com; 11.30 pm; no smoking area.*

**Tas Pide** £29 ❸❷❷
20-22 New Globe Walk, SE1 7928 3300 9–3B
37 Farringdon Rd, EC1 7430 9721 9–1A
*These notably "welcoming" and "cosy" Turkish restaurants dish
up "flavoursome" dishes at prices that represent "impressive
value-for-money"; they also feature "something different" –
pide is Anatolian flat-bread 'pizza'. / www.tasrestaurant.com; 11.30 pm.*

**La Tasca** £27 ⑤④❸
23-24 Maiden Ln, WC2 7240 9062 4–4C
404-406 Chiswick High Rd, W4 8994 4545 7–2A
18-19 The Mall, W5 8840 2041 1–2A
21 Essex Rd, N1 7226 3272 8–3D
West India Quay, E14 7531 9990 11–1C
15-17 Eldon St, EC2 7256 2381 9–2C NEW
*Perhaps it's true that no one ever lost money by under-estimating
the taste of the British public – these "loud" tapas bars are
hugely successful, commercially speaking, but many reporters
dismiss their product as plain "shoddy". / www.latasca.co.uk; 11 pm,
E14 10.45 pm; need 8+ to book.*

## Tate Britain SW1 £42 ④④❷
Millbank   7887 8825   2–4C
The 'old' Tate's "lovely" Whistler-muralled dining room is famed
as an oenophile's heaven (with food that's rather beside the
point) – it maintains a "thought-provoking" list, with many
"half bottle and by-the-glass options", but some reporters do feel
that it's "no bargain" nowadays. / www.tate.org.uk; L only; no smoking.

## (Café, Level 2)
## Tate Modern SE1 £32 ④④❸
Bankside   7401 5014   9–3B
The Tate's ground-floor café can be a "pleasant surprise" –
it may not have the views you get in the restaurant upstairs,
but it's easier to get into, and usually "OK". / www.tate.org.uk;
9.30 pm; L & tea only, except Fri & Sat open L&D; no smoking.

## (Restaurant, Level 7)
## Tate Modern SE1 £37 ④④❷
Bankside   7401 5020   9–3B
"You go for the sublime view" (one of the best in town), to this
museum café atop Tate Modern – not the "amateur" service
or "below-par" food. / www.tate.org.uk; 5.30 pm, Fri & Sat 9.30 pm;
Sat-Thu closed D; no smoking.

## Tatsuso EC2 £80 ❷❸④
32 Broadgate Circle   7638 5863   9–2D
"Make sure you're not paying", if you visit this "outstanding" –
but very "corporate" – City Japanese, where "the freshest and
best sushi and sashimi" and "top-quality" teppan-yaki come
at "absurd" prices; the basement is a bit "grim". / 9.45 pm; closed
Sat & Sun; no smoking area.

## Tawana W2 £29 ❷❷⑤
3 Westbourne Grove   7229 3785   6–1C
"Staple and authentic dishes" make this Bayswater Thai veteran
(near Queensway) a handy stand-by; it has "no atmosphere"
though. / www.tawana.co.uk; 11 pm.

## The Tea Palace W11  NEW £42 ④❸④
175 Westbourne Grove   7727 2600   6–1B
This brave new Notting Hill venture is a 'salon de thé de luxe'
of a sort barely known in England; however impressive the
infusions, though, we were struck by just how pricey a modest
Saturday lunch was on our June 2005 visit – this perhaps
explains why only two other tables were occupied. / Rated on Editors'
visit; www.teapalace.co.uk; 6.30 pm; L only; no smoking.

## Teca W1 £51 ❷❷④
54 Brooks Mews   7495 4774   3–2B
"Out-of-the-way" (by Mayfair standards), this "quiet", modern
Italian has never found the fame its "sophisticated" cooking,
distinctive wine list, and "polished" service deserve; its "anodyne"
interior doesn't help. / www.atozrestaurants.com; 10.30 pm; closed
Sat L & Sun.

**Ten Ten Tei W1**  £33  ❸❸⑤
56 Brewer St  7287 1738  3–2D
*"London's entire Asian student population (smokers to a man)" seems to crowd in to this "dull"-looking Soho veteran; dishes from the "wide menu" come in "generous" portions, and are "well-priced". / 10 pm; closed Sun; no Amex.*

**Tendido Cero SW5**  £28  ❷①❷
174 Old Brompton Rd  7370 3685  5–2B
*"Fabulous tapas, wonderful presentation and BYO… and all on the fringe of South Kensington!" – that's the deal at this "lively" and "intimate" sibling to Cambio de Tercio (opposite). / 11 pm; no credit cards.*

**Tentazioni SE1**  £49  ❷❷④
2 Mill St  7237 1100  11–2A
*"Tucked-away from the madding crowd", this quirky Italian (five minutes from Butler's Wharf) is winning renewed support as an "under-rated" location, with "excellent", genuine cooking, "interesting" wine and "enthusiastic" service; "the only thing lacking on occasion is diners". / www.tentazioni.co.uk; 10.45 pm; closed Mon L, Sat L & Sun.*

**The Tenth**
**Royal Garden Hotel W8**  £56  ④❷❷
Kensington High St  7361 1910  5–1A
*"Stunning" skyline views reward those who seek out this eyrie overlooking Kensington Gardens; generally, the cooking transcends the dreariness typical of rooms-with-a-view, but the odd meal was "a bit disappointing" this year. / www.royalgardenhotel.co.uk; 10.45 pm; closed Sat L & Sun; no smoking area.*

**Terminus**
**Great Eastern Hotel EC2**  £45  ④④⑤
40 Liverpool St  7618 7400  9–2D
*"Excellent fry-ups" are a staple feature of this "noisy" Conran group brasserie by Liverpool Street station – otherwise, it's "a yawn". / www.great-eastern-hotel.co.uk; 11 pm, Sat & Sun 10 pm; no smoking area.*

**Texas Embassy Cantina SW1**  £36  ④④❸
1 Cockspur St  7925 0077  2–2C
*"It's a bit of a tourist trap", but this Tex/Mex restaurant near Trafalgar Square can be "fun", especially "with kids"; the food "ranges from very good to absolutely awful". / www.texasembassy.com; 11 pm.*

**Texas Lone Star SW7**  £28  ④❸④
154 Gloucester Rd  7370 5625  5–2B
*Age-old, South Kensington Tex/Mex survivor, which serves "cheap" and "surprisingly fresh" dishes in a "cheerful" manner. / 11.30 pm.*

**TGI Friday's** £36 ⑤⑤⑤
25-29 Coventry St, W1  7839 6262  4–4A
6 Bedford St, WC2  7379 0585  4–4C
Fulham Broadway, SW6  7385 1660  5–4A  **NEW**
96-98 Bishops Bridge Rd, W2  7229 8600  6–1C
*"Kids love it" – otherwise reporters resolutely pan this "shocking"
and "overpriced" all-American chain (known for its "irritating
staff, with stupid badges"). / www.tgifridays.com; 11.30 pm, Fri & Sat
midnight; no smoking area.*

**The Thai SW7** £30 ❸❸④
93 Pelham St  7584 4788  5–2C
*A Brompton Cross oriental – "friendly" and "affordable",
if arguably rather "formulaic" . / 10.45 pm; no smoking area.*

**Thai Bistro W4** £25 ❸❷④
99 Chiswick High Rd  8995 5774  7–2B
*"Very reliable" standards figure in almost all reports on this
"good-value" Chiswick Thai, where you eat canteen-style
at shared benches. / 11 pm, Sun 10.30 pm; closed Tue L & Thu L;
no Amex; no smoking.*

**Thai Café SW1** £25 ❸④④
22 Charlwood St  7592 9584  2–4C
*A small Pimlico corner oriental serving "good-value", if rather
"unexciting", scoff, in a thin area. / 10.30 pm; closed Sat L & Sun L;
no smoking area.*

**Thai Corner Café SE22** £22 ❸❸❸
44 North Cross Rd  8299 4041  1–4D
*"There's little space between tables", at this "homely" East
Dulwich favourite; it's "always busy", thanks to its "good-value"
Thai fare, and the "appealing BYO option". / 10.30 pm; no credit
cards.*

**Thai Elephant TW10** £29 ❸❸❸
1 Wakefield Rd  8940 5114  1–4A
*An agreeable – if rather dated and pretentious – Richmond Thai,
worth knowing about in a thin area. / www.thaielephantrichmond.co.uk;
11 pm; no smoking area.*

**Thai Garden SW11** £24 ❸❸❸
58 Battersea Rise  7738 0380  10–2C
*This "consistently enjoyable" Battersea stand-by inspires only
positive reports, not least for its "attentive" staff.
/ www.thaigarden.co.uk; 11 pm, Fri & Sat 11.30 pm; D only.*

**Thai Noodle Bar SW10** £27 ❸❷❸
7 Park Walk  7352 7222  5–3B
*"Always a good bet" – this "friendly" and "efficient" Chelsea
canteen offers "well-executed" Thai fare. / 11.15 pm.*

**Thai on the River SW11** NEW £40 ❸❷❷
2 Lombard Rd   7924 6090   5–4B
*Part of the team from SW10's Thai on the River (RIP) has
crossed the Thames to the old Battersea premises of La Na Thai
(RIP); the new set-up offers "really good" (if "pricey") dishes in a
"beautiful" riverside setting; (n.b. a rival spin-off has also opened
under the same name, at 92-94 Waterford Road – no reports
as yet). / www.thaiontheriver.com; 11 pm.*

**Thai Pot WC2** £32 ❸❸④
1 Bedfordbury   7379 4580   4–4C
*"Enjoyable" nosh that's "well-priced" by West End standards
makes this "brisk" Thai fixture, behind the Coliseum, a useful
stand-by. / www.thaipot.co.uk; 11.15 pm; closed Sun; no smoking area.*

**Thai Square** £30 ④④❸
21-24 Cockspur St, SW1   7839 4000   2–3C
5 Princes St, W1   7499 3333   3–1C
148 Strand, WC2   7497 0904   2–2D
19 Exhibition Rd, SW7   7584 8359   5–2C
347-349 Upper St, N1   7704 2000   8–3D
224 Lower Richmond Rd, SW15   8780 1811   10–1A NEW
136-138 Minories, EC3   7680 1111   9–3D
1-7 Gt Thomas Apostle, EC4   7329 0001   9–3B NEW
*Now including the "great site with good views" that was until
recently Putney Bridge (RIP), this oriental chain continues to grow
and grow; its branches are "lavish", but the cooking can be "dull".
/ www.thaisq.co.uk; 10 pm; EC3 & EC4 closed Sat & Sun, WC2 closed Sun;
no smoking area.*

**Thailand SE14** £26 ❶❷④
15 Lewisham Way   8691 4040   1–3D
*"Outstanding" Thai/Laotian cooking has long been acclaimed
at this "unassuming" Lewisham "gem", run by a "pleasant"
husband (Scottish) and wife (Laotian) team; it also boasts
"an excellent selection of malt whiskies". / 11.30 pm; no Amex;
no smoking.*

**The Thatched House W6** £31 ❸❸❷
115 Dalling Rd   8748 6174   7–1B
*There's some "surprisingly good", if simple, food to be had –
and in "huge portions" – at this lesser-known Hammersmith
gastropub, which boasts a "bubbly" atmosphere and a brilliant
garden. / www.thatchedhouse.com; 10 pm; no Amex; no smoking area.*

**3G W1** NEW
6 Little Portland St   7631 0700   3–1C
*From the backers of Trois Garçons (who also own the successful
Loungelover bar), this late-2005 newcomer may bring new
standards of camp to the West End dining experience; the aim
is a 'loungey' environment, half way between a bar and
a restaurant.*

### 3 Monkeys SE24                    £34        ❸❸❸
136-140 Herne Hill   7738 5500   1–4C
A "brightly-lit" nouvelle Indian in Herne Hill, with a wide south
east London following; ratings have slipped since it changed hands
last year, though, and it is increasingly found "pricey for where
it is". / www.3monkeysrestaurant.com; 11 pm; D only; smoking in bar only.

### Throgmorton EC2  NEW              £32        ④❸❸
27a Throgmorton St   7588 5165   9–2C
For a simple, bloke-ish City lunch, you might try the dining room
of this recently-relaunched venue – an extraordinary, late-
Victorian labyrinth; despite the involvement of Charles Fontaine
(of Quality Chop House fame), however, it's yet to pique much
interest amongst reporters. / www.throgmortons.com; 3 pm; L only, closed
Sat & Sun; no smoking area.

### Tiger Lil's                       £30        ④④④
270 Upper St, N1   7226 1118   8–2D
15a Clapham Common S'side, SW4   7720 5433   10–2D
"You choose, they cook it for you", at these DIY-wok joints; it can
make for a "cheap and entertaining" evening, especially in a
group, but "you can have an atrocious meal as easily as a good
one". / www.tigerlils.com; N1 11 pm, SW4 Fri & Sat midnight; Mon-Thu
closed L.

### Tiger Tiger SW1                   £37        ⑤⑤④
29 Haymarket   7930 1885   4–4A
Unless you want to be picked up, it's hard to see why you'd seek
out this West End multi-bar/restaurant complex; even a reporter
who tips it for a "good-value" lunch says: "avoid it in the evenings
at all cost!" / www.tigertiger.co.uk; 11 pm.

### Timo W8                           £44
343 Kensington High St   7603 3888   7–1D
This "neighbourhood" modern Italian in Kensington has
traditionally served "upscale" cooking in a rather "bring-your-own-
atmosphere" environment; a régime-change half way through the
survey led to very erratic feedback, however, so we've left
it unrated. / 11 pm; no smoking; booking: max 8.

### Toast NW3                         £38        ④❷❷
50 Hampstead High St   7431 2244   8–1A
Airy Hampstead hang-out – curiously located above the tube
station – whose "excellent bar" and generally "competent" food
make it a handy High Street haven; daytime set menus,
in particular, are "a steal". / www.toastnw3.com; midnight.

### Tobia NW3  NEW                    £26        ❷❸④
1st Floor, 2a Lithos Rd   7431 4213   1–1B
"Tucked-away above a community centre", this small newcomer
offers "a slice of Ethiopia, off the Finchley Road", with "friendly"
service and spicy, authentic scoff; (note that Wed and Fri are
mainly vegan, and that Sat night is traditional dancing night).
/ www.tobiarestaurant.co.uk; 11.30 pm.

### Toff's N10 £27 ❷❶④

38 Muswell Hill Broadway 8883 8656 1–1B
A "very crowded" and "wonderfully friendly" Muswell Hill
institution, where many north Londoners insist you get
"the capital's best fish 'n' chips". / 10 pm; closed Sun; no smoking area;
no booking, Sat.

### Tokyo City EC2 £30 ❷④④

46 Gresham St 7726 0308 9–2B
"Useful" and "always quick" – this City oriental not only has
a "convenient" location, near the Bank of England, but also
serves "great sushi" and other Japanese fare; its Thai dishes are
less of an attraction. / www.tokyocity.co.uk; 9.45 pm; closed Sat & Sun.

### Tokyo Diner WC2 £17 ❸❸④

2 Newport Pl 7287 8777 4–3B
"Exactly what it says" – this "cramped", "no-fuss" Chinatown
veteran serves "basic Japanese food at cheap prices".
/ www.tokyodiner.com; midnight; no Amex; no smoking area; no booking,
Fri & Sat.

### TOM AIKENS SW3 £77 ❸❷❸

43 Elystan St 7584 2003 5–2C
Most reporters are "blown away" by the cooking at Tom Aikens's
much-fêted Chelsea two-year-old, lauding "exquisite
combinations" that look "worthy of an art gallery"; there are
increasing concerns, though, about "too much 'going on' on the
plate" – "I couldn't find my food for foams, jellies and mousses!"
/ www.tomaikens.co.uk; 11 pm; closed Sat & Sun; no smoking; booking: max 6;
set weekday L £42 (FP).

### Tom's W11 £26 ❸❸❸

226 Westbourne Grove 7221 8818 6–1B
"If you're willing to wait in line, you get the best brunch in town",
say fans of Tom Conran's "cramped" and "pricey" deli/café
favourite, in the heart of Notting Hill. / L only; no Amex; no smoking;
no booking.

### Tomato W1 £34 ❸❷④

54 Frith St 7437 0666 4–2A
A "consistently good" Soho stand-by, of note for its "lovely" pizza
and "quick" service; it can, however, be rather "noisy".
/ www.tomatogroup.com; 11.30 pm; closed Sun; set weekday L £21 (FP).

### Tootsies £30 ④④④

35 James St, W1 7486 1611 3–1A
177 New King's Rd, SW6 7736 4023 10–1B
107 Old Brompton Rd, SW7 7581 8942 5–2B
120 Holland Park Ave, W11 7229 8567 6–2A
148 Chiswick High Rd, W4 8747 1869 7–2A
196-198 Haverstock Hill, NW3 7431 3812 8–2A
1 Battersea Rise, SW11 7924 4935 10–2C
Putney Wharf, 30 Brewhouse St, SW15 8788 8488 10–2B
48 High St, SW19 8946 4135 10–2B
36-38 Abbeville Rd, SW4 8772 6646 10–2D
"Delicious" breakfasts, "consistently great" burgers and "nice"
milkshakes are cornerstones of the appeal of this "family-
friendly" chain. / www.tootsiesrestaurants.co.uk; 11 pm; no smoking area;
some booking restrictions apply.

**Toto's SW1** £60 ❷❷❶

Lennox Gardens Mews 7589 0075 5–2C

*A "dreamy" Knightsbridge mews setting and "excellent" staff help make this glamorous Italian a firm "favourite" for some reporters (and one that's "perfect for a date", probably of a more mature sort); prices can seem "stupendous", but the food is usually hailed as "delicious". / 11 pm; set weekday L £35 (FP).*

**Trader Vics**
**Hilton Hotel W1** £64 ⑤④❷

22 Park Ln 7208 4113 3–4A

*"Amazing drinks and décor" are what this kitsch, old Mayfair tiki-basement is all about – the (expensive) food is utterly beside the point. / www.tradervics.com; 12.30 am; closed Sat L & Sun L; no smoking area; set weekday L £37 (FP).*

**The Trafalgar Tavern SE10** £33 ④④❷

Park Row 8858 2909 1–3D

*"Full of tourists, but a fabulous location for a riverside Sunday lunch" – this "historic" Greenwich tavern offers a "traditional" package, which includes acceptable pub grub. / www.trafalgartavern.co.uk; 10 pm; closed Sun D; no Amex; no booking, Sun L.*

**Tree House SW13** £30 ④④❸

73 White Hart Ln 8392 1617 10–1A

*On the fringe of Barnes, this "lovely local" bar has "a great vibe for a relaxed bite"; it can seem "slightly expensive" for what it is, though, and "might do better to keep the food simpler".*

**Troika NW1** £25 ④④❸

101 Regent's Park Rd 7483 3765 8–2B

*An "authentic Russian feeling" permeates this ever-popular Primrose Hill café, where "pretty good" food comes "reasonably-priced". / www.trojka.co.uk; 10.30 pm; no smoking area.*

**Les Trois Garçons E1** £63 ④❸❶

1 Club Row 7613 1924 1–2D

*An "amazing camp interior" (complete with "stuffed animals wearing jewellery") pulls in punters by the limo-load to this "eccentric" but "seductive" East End pub-conversion; its "totally overpriced" Gallic cuisine is rather beside the point. / www.lestroisgarcons.com; 10.30 pm; D only, closed Sun; set D £46 (FP).*

**LA TROMPETTE W4** £48 ❶❶❷

5-7 Devonshire Rd 8747 1836 7–2A

*"Lucky Chiswick residents" have "west London's best restaurant" in one of their backstreets – it mixes "memorable" modern French cuisine, with "intelligent" service, "stylish" décor and an "extensive" wine list; the chef recently moved on to the Dorchester – let's hope for a smooth succession! / www.latrompette.co.uk; 11 pm; no smoking; booking: max 6.*

**Troubadour SW5** £30 ⑤④❶

265 Old Brompton Rd 7370 1434 5–3A

*A "chilled" Bohemian coffee house, which has been a "quirky" Earl's Court fixture since the '60s; it does "a decent breakfast" and "good nibbles", but the food's isn't really the point. / www.troubadour.co.uk; 11 pm; no Amex.*

### La Trouvaille W1     £43    ❸❶❷
12a Newburgh St   7287 8488   3–2C
*"Like being whisked to Paris for the evening"; "passionate" service
contributes much to the "intimate" and "quirky" charms of this
candlelit Soho bistro, where "unfussy" cooking comes
at "reasonable" prices.* / www.trouvaille.co.uk; 11 pm; closed Sun.

### Truc Vert W1     £44    ❸⑤④
42 North Audley St   7491 9988   3–2A
*A "charming" Mayfair "deli/bistro", where, say fans, the provincial
Gallic fare "never disappoints"; it's "crowded", though,
and service is "hit-and-miss".* / 9.30 pm; closed Sun D; no smoking.

### Tsunami SW4     £35    ❶❷❸
5-7 Voltaire Rd   7978 1610   10–1D
*"The location's odd, but who's complaining" given the
"sensational" ("especially for the money"), "Nobu-esque" cooking
at this "startling" Clapham oriental; "...and not a pretentious
wannabe in sight".* / www.tsunamirestaurant.co.uk; 11 pm, Sat 11.30 pm;
D only, closed Sun; no smoking area.

### Tugga SW3  [NEW]    £39    ❸❸❷
312-314 King's Rd   7351 0101   5–3C
*London's only trendy Portuguese – this new Chelsea
bar/restaurant boasts a lot of style (from the man who did Paris's
Buddha Bar); we thought the food pleasant rather than
spectacular on our May 2005 visit, but service tries hard.* / Rated
on Editors' visit; www.tugga.com; 10.30 pm.

### Tuttons WC2     £37    ④④❸
11-12 Russell St   7836 4141   4–3D
*A "lively" brasserie, on a picturesque corner, opposite Covent
Garden; fans says it's "surprisingly good, considering its touristy
location".* / 11.30 pm; smoking in bar only; set pre-theatre £24 (FP).

### Two Brothers N3     £25    ❷❷④
297-303 Regent's Park Rd   8346 0469   1–1B
*"It IS worth the queue", for this "deserving North London
stalwart", whose "wonderful fresh fish and chips" are hailed
by many as "the best in town".* / www.twobrothers.co.uk; 10.15 pm;
closed Mon & Sun; no smoking at D; no booking at D.

### 202 W11     £30    ④❷❶
202 Westbourne Grove   7727 2722   6–1B
*"Notting Hill or NYC?" – Nicole Farhi's "fun" hang-out strikes
Manhattan-savvy reporters as "so SoHo"; it's become
"THE place for a trendy brunch", even if "the beautiful people
outshine the food"; "the queue can be a pain".* / www.nicolefarhi.com;
L & afternoon tea only; no smoking; no booking.

### Ubon E14     £80    ❷④④
34 Westferry Circus   7719 7800   11–1B
*You don't just get "Nobu food minus the waiting list", at its less
hip Canary Wharf sibling – the room itself (with its "cracking
Thames-views") is "more attractive than the Park Lane original";
prices are equally "outrageous".* / www.noburestaurants.com; 10.15 pm;
closed Sat L & Sun; no smoking.

**Uli W11**  £29  ❷❶❷

16 All Saints Rd  7727 7511  6–1B
*"The friendliest host in London" adds an extra dimension to this
"perfect" Notting Hill local, which serves an "excellent mixed bag
of oriental dishes". / www.uli-oriental.co.uk; 11 pm; D only, closed Sun;
no Amex.*

**Umu W1**  £100  ④④④

14-16 Bruton Pl  7499 8881  3–2C
*A few cognoscenti eulogise the "authentic Kyoto cooking"
("with truly the best ingredients") at this "luxurious" Mayfair
newcomer; even they concede prices are "steep", though,
and most reporters find that the "extortionate" bill –
and "suffocating" service – mar the whole experience.
/ www.umurestaurant.com; 11 pm; closed Sun; no smoking; booking: max 14;
set weekday L £53 (FP).*

**The Union Café W1**  £37  ④④④

96 Marylebone Ln  7486 4860  3–1A
*"The food is nothing special", but the wine is "astonishing" –
not least because it comes "at retail prices" – at John Brinkley's
"rather canteeny" Marylebone venue. / www.brinkleys.com; 10.30 pm;
closed Sun D; no smoking area.*

**Uno SW1**  £38  ④④④

1 Denbigh St  7834 1001  2–4B
*In the Pimlico void, this "pricey" corner pizzeria has its uses; it's a
noisy place, though, and we suspect its popularity largely reflects
the lack of local competition. / 11.30 pm.*

**Le Vacherin W4**  £38  ❷❸④

76 South Pde  8742 2121  7–1A
*"Terrific French country cuisine", served in a very "authentic"
style, has already won a more-than-local fan club for this
"excellent neighbourhood spot" – "a great find in a grim bit
of Chiswick". / www.levacherin.co.uk; 10.30 pm; closed Mon L; no Amex;
no smoking.*

**The Vale W9**  £34  ❷❶❸

99 Chippenham Rd  7266 0990  1–2B
*"What every good local should be like" – this Maida Hill stalwart
offers a "simple, but interesting" menu that's "very good value-
for-money"; the service is "always friendly", too. / 11 pm; closed
Mon L, Sat L & Sun D; no Amex; no smoking area.*

**Vama SW10**  £40  ❶❷❸

438 King's Rd  7351 4118  5–3B
*"Tantalising", "light" dishes make this very popular Chelsea
"jewel" one of "the most 'authentic' of the contemporary curry
houses". / www.vama.co.uk; 11 pm.*

**Vasco & Piero's Pavilion W1**  £42  ❷❶❸

15 Poland St  7437 8774  3–1D
*"Friendly staff with a personal touch" add much to the slightly
"eccentric" appeal of this Soho "stalwart", which "feels like
someone's living room" ("in a good way"); its "honest" Italian
cooking is "good value", too. / www.vascosfood.com; 11 pm; closed
Sat L & Sun.*

**Veeraswamy W1** £45

Victory Hs, 99 Regent St   7734 1401   3–3D

*London's longest-established Indian restaurant (1927),
near Piccadilly Circus, is to relaunch in late-2005 with a 'new',
more heritage-conscious look; this has been a "good all-rounder"
in recent times — let's hope they don't ruin it!*
/ www.realindianfood.com; 10.30 pm; no smoking area; booking: max 12;
set weekday L, Sun L & pre-theatre £29 (FP).

**El Vergel SE1** £16 ❶❶❷

8 Lant St   7357 0057   9–4B

*"Unsurpassed" Latin American fare — with "terrific flavours and
freshness", and at "knockdown" prices — makes this hidden
Borough gem an "absolutely wonderful" light lunch venue;
"it's just a crying shame they aren't open evenings or weekends".*
/ www.elvergel.co.uk; breakfast & L only, closed Sat & Sun; no credit cards;
no smoking.

**Vertigo
Tower 42 EC2** £46 ④❸❶

20-25 Old Broad St   7877 7842   9–2C

*"What a place! — shame about the food"; "fantastic views"
of "the sun setting over St Paul's" help make the 42nd floor
of the former NatWest tower "an excellent spot to strike a deal"
— be it of a business or romantic nature.* / www.vertigo42.co.uk;
9.15 pm; closed Sat & Sun; booking essential.

**Vesbar W12** £27 ④❸❸

15-19 Goldhawk Rd   8762 0215   7–1C

*On a grotty bit of road near Shepherd's Bush, this Fullers bar
provides a welcoming refuge; its scoff is not at all bad, especially
for brunch.* / 11 pm.

**Vic Naylors EC1** £38 ④❸❷

38 & 42 St John St   7608 2181   9–1B

*A "friendly" atmosphere ensures ongoing popularity — including
as an informal business venue — for this Smithfield bar/restaurant;
the food is rather beside the point.* / www.vicnaylor.com; 1 am; closed
Sat L & Sun.

**Il Vicolo SW1** £40 ❸❸④

3-4 Crown Passage   7839 3960   3–4D

*This "haven of good-value Italian food" is all the more worth
knowing about in the heart of St James's; it's no surprise that its
"cramped" premises are "always crowded and busy".*
/ www.ilvicoloonline.com; 10 pm; closed Sat & Sun.

**The Victoria SW14** £40 ❸④❷

10 West Temple   8876 4238   10–2A

*"Improved food, this year" complements the "light and airy
ambience" (especially in the "great conservatory") of this "rather
smart" gastropub, in a Sheen "backwater"; particularly after
"a long walk in Richmond Park", it makes a "perfect family
destination".* / www.thevictoria.net; 10 pm; smoking in bar only.

**Viet Hoa E2** £20 ❸④④
70-72 Kingsland Rd 7729 8293 1–2D
*"Zippy" dishes at "good prices" have earned a big reputation for*
*this "crowded" and "friendly", Formica-tables Shoreditch café;*
*the occasional reporter, though, "had heard great things, but felt*
*sorely let down". / 11.30 pm; no smoking area.*

**Viet-Anh NW1** £16 ❸❶⑤
41 Parkway 7284 4082 8–3B
*"Cheap", "freshly-cooked" chow and "charming" service win*
*praise for this "canteen-style" Vietnamese, in Camden Town.*
*/ 11 pm; no Amex; no smoking area.*

**Vijay NW6** £28 ❶❶❸
49 Willesden Ln 7328 1087 1–1B
*"Brilliant south Indian food" (at "very low prices") and "really*
*friendly" service combine to make this "low-key" Kilburn curry*
*house an "unbeatable-value" destination. / 10.45 pm, Fri & Sat*
*11.45 pm.*

**Villa Bianca NW3** £44 ④❸❷
1 Perrins Ct 7435 3131 8–2A
*"Resting on its laurels" (as ever) – this long-established*
*Hampstead Italian gets away with its "overpriced" food thanks*
*to its "delightful" and "romantic" setting, in a cute cobbled lane.*
*/ www.villabianca.co.uk; 11.30 pm.*

**Villandry W1** £41 ④④④
170 Gt Portland St 7631 3131 2–1B
*A grand Marylebone deli, whose "cold and echoey" restaurant*
*serves up food that's "nothing special" (and "expensive");*
*(the shop itself, however, is "great"). / www.villandry.com; 10.30 pm;*
*closed Sun D; smoking in bar only; booking: max 12.*

**The Vine NW5** £31 ④⑤❸
86 Highgate Rd 7209 0038 8–1B
*It has much "potential", but this "lovely" Kentish Town gastropub*
*– which has a great garden – has been "so up-and-down" of late.*
*/ www.thevinelondon.co.uk; 10.15 pm.*

**Vingt-Quatre SW10** £33 ④❸④
325 Fulham Rd 7376 7224 5–3B
*"A godsend very early, or very late in the day" – this "invaluable"*
*diner on Chelsea's 'Beach' offers decent burgers, breakfasts,*
*and so on, 24/7. / www.longshotplc.com; open 24 hours; no booking.*

**Vivat Bacchus EC4** £43 ❸❶❸
47 Farringdon St 7353 2648 9–2A
*"A treat for oenophiles" – this City-fringe basement offers*
*a distinctive, business-friendly formula which mixes "phenomenal"*
*wine ("with a South African bent") with "not-stunning-but-good"*
*food and "superb" cheese (chosen in an "impressive, walk-in*
*room"); notably "warm and attentive" service enlivens the plain*
*setting. / www.vivatbacchus.co.uk; 9.30 pm; closed Sat & Sun; set weekday L*
*£28 (FP).*

### Vrisaki N22 £29 ❷❷❸
73 Myddleton Rd   8889 8760   1–1C
The "mega-mezze" – "a huge variety of dishes, in leisurely
procession" – is the culinary star turn at this "charmingly tacky"
Bounds Green taverna; "don't even try to eat most of the cold
starters, or you'll run out of steam long before the end". / midnight;
closed Sun.

### W'sens SW1 NEW £52 ④④④
12 Waterloo Pl   7484 1355   2–3C
This "self-consciously kooky" West End débutant –
from Montpellier's famous Pourcel brothers – has inspired very
mixed reports; the doubters tend to be particularly emphatic
("possibly London's worst value-for-money"), but supporters insist
that this is an "elegant" place, with "exemplary" "experimental"
cuisine. / www.wsens.co.uk; 11 pm; closed Sat L & Sun D.

### Wagamama £23 ❸❸④
8 Norris St, SW1   7321 2755   4–4A
Harvey Nichols, Knightsbridge, SW1   7201 8000   5–1D
101a Wigmore St, W1   7409 0111   3–1A
10a Lexington St, W1   7292 0990   3–2D
4a Streatham St, WC1   7323 9223   2–1C
1 Tavistock St, WC2   7836 3330   4–3D
14a Irving St, WC2   7839 2323   4–4B
26a Kensington High St, W8   7376 1717   5–1A
The N1 Centre, Parkfield St, N1   7226 2664   8–3D   NEW
11 Jamestown Rd, NW1   7428 0800   8–3B
Royal Festival Hall, SE1   7021 0877   2–3D   NEW
50-54 Putney High St, SW15   8785 3636   10–2B   NEW
Jubilee Place, 45 Bank St, E14   7516 9009   11–1C
1a Ropemaker St, EC2   7588 2688   9–1C
22 Old Broad St, EC2   7256 9992   9–2C
Tower Pl, EC3   7283 5897   9–3D
109 Fleet St, EC4   7583 7889   9–2A
30 Queen St, EC4   7248 5766   9–3B
"Consistent", "satisfying" and "healthy" noodle dishes, "quickly"
served in a "fuss-free" modern environment – that's still the
"winning formula" at these "useful" (and kid-friendly) canteens;
you mustn't mind queues, though, or "snuggling up to your fellow
diners". / www.wagamama.com; 10 pm-10.45 pm; EC4 & EC2 closed
Sat & Sun; no smoking; no booking.

### Wakaba NW3 £45 ❷❸⑤
122a Finchley Rd   7586 7960   8–2A
It has "no atmosphere whatsoever" – why else employ a famous
architect? – but Mr Wakaba's ultra-"minimalistic" Japanese
veteran, opposite Finchley Road tube, still serves up some
"excellent sushi and sashimi". / 11 pm; closed Sun; set weekday L
£19 (FP).

### The Walmer Castle W11 £28 ❸④❷
58 Ledbury Rd   7229 4620   6–1B
"Chilled" Notting Hill pub favourite, liked for the
"very affordable" Thai fodder on offer in its first-floor dining
room. / 10.30 pm; closed weekday L.

**Walnut NW6** £32 ❸❸④
280 West End Ln   7794 7772   1–1B
The simple cuisine at this West Hampstead venture is "better than most locally", but it's still "a place to pop in to, rather than to spend the evening". / www.walnutwalnut.com; 10.30 pm; closed Mon, Tue-Sun D only; no Amex; no smoking area.

**Wapping Food E1** £46 ❸❸❷
Wapping Power Station, Wapping Wall   7680 2080   11–1A
A "bizarre", "über-cool" setting – in a former hydraulic power station – makes this "amazing" Wapping spot quite a "destination"; a wine list that "challenges pre-conceptions about Australia" is a further plus, and it's complemented by food "which varies from average to excellent". / 10.30 pm; closed Sun D.

**The Waterloo Fire Station SE1** £33 ⑤⑤④
150 Waterloo Rd   7620 2226   9–4A
At its best, this "informal, lively and hectic" South Bank bar/restaurant can still be a useful stand-by; its catering operation, however, is "overpriced" and "disappointing" nowadays. / 10.45 pm.

**The Waterway W9** £37 ❸⑤❸
54 Formosa St   7266 3557   8–4A
"When the weather is good, join the hoards by the canal", at this "buzzy" (and "smoky") waterside hang-out, near Little Venice; its gastropub fare is "reliable", but service can be "ridiculously slow". / www.thewaterway.co.uk; 10.45 pm; booking: max 12.

**The Well EC1** £36 ❸❸❸
180 St John St   7251 9363   9–1A
"A favourite Clerkenwell gastropub", offering cooking that's "wholesome" and "reasonably-priced". / www.downthewell.com; 10.30 pm.

**The Wells NW3** £41 ❸④❸
30 Well Walk   7794 3785   8–1A
A "lovely" dining room, overlooking the Heath, helps underpin the high popularity of this "stylish" Hampstead gastropub (which is "more a restaurant", really); the food, however – which started off here so well – "slipped" further this year.
/ www.thewellshampstead.co.uk; 10.15 pm; booking: max 8; set weekday L £29 (FP).

**Weng Wah House NW3** £30 ❸❷❸
240 Haverstock Hill   7794 5123   8–2A
Belsize Park's long-established "local-favourite" Chinese is "particularly popular for weekend dim sum"; it's "a bit variable", but performance is generally good across the board. / www.wengwahgroup.com; 11.30 pm.

**The Westbourne W2** £33 ❸⑤❷
101 Westbourne Park Villas   7221 1332   6–1B
It may be "packed with horrific poseurs" – especially the terrace on sunny days – but that's part of the enduring appeal of this "vibrant" Notting Hill gastropub, which serves "decent" fare, inefficiently. / www.westbourne.com; 10 pm; closed Mon L; need 4+ to book.

**The Wharf TW11**   £41   ④❸❷

22 Manor Rd   8977 6333   1–4A

*"You could be on holiday", when you're sitting on the terrace of this "stunningly-located" Thames-side bar/restaurant, near Teddington Lock; its brasserie fare is somewhere between "well-executed" and "mediocre". / www.walk-on-water.co.uk; 10 pm; no smoking area; set weekday L £27 (FP).*

**Wheeler's of St James's SW1**   £66   ❸❸④

12a Duke of York St   7930 2460   3–3D

*It's a good thing the "expensive" fish and seafood at this ancient St James's institution can be "very good", because its "funny", "cramped" corner premises create (surprisingly) "little atmosphere". / 11 pm; closed Sun.*

**White Cross TW9**   £23   ④④❸

Water Ln   8940 6844   1–4A

*"A pleasant location to eat near the Thames", this "crowded" Young's hostelry (downstream of Richmond Bridge) has a characterful interior and a nice, small beer garden; the staple fare is fine, but not really the point. / www.youngs.co.uk; L only; no Amex; no booking.*

**White Horse SW6**   £33   ❸❸❸

1 Parsons Grn   7736 2115   10–1B

*Parson's Green's leafily-located 'Sloaney Pony' remains a hit, particularly with a "noisy twenty- and thirtysomething crowd"; it does a "fantastic" summer BBQ, "never fails for Sunday lunch", and boasts a superior list of wines and real ales. / www.whitehorsesw6.com; 10.30 pm; no smoking in dining room.*

**The White Swan EC4**   £39   ❷❸❸

108 Fetter Ln   7242 9696   9–2A

*This second-floor dining room on the fringe of the City is "classy" (for somewhere over a pub), and serves "surprisingly good" food; now in its second year, it's "proving very popular". / www.thewhiteswanlondon.com; 10 pm; closed Sat & Sun.*

**Whits W8**   £42   ❸❷④

21 Abingdon Rd   7938 1122   5–1A

*"Charming" service and "inventive" cooking are helping establish this Kensington yearling as a "neighbourhood place, if not a destination". / www.whits.co.uk; 10.30 pm; closed Mon & Sun.*

**Whole Hog Canteen W6**  NEW   £28   ❸❷❸

99 Fulham Palace Rd   8748 2511   7–2C

*A boon for staff at Hammersmith's Charing Cross Hospital, this "great little diner" serves "simple" but hearty dishes at "knock-down" prices. / 9.45 pm; closed Mon D, Sat L & Sun; no smoking.*

**William IV NW10**   £27   ❸❸❸

786 Harrow Rd   8969 5944   1–2B

*It may be "in the middle of nowhere", but that does nothing to stop this Kensal Green boozer – which has a pleasant internal garden – from getting very "busy"; the food (recently changed to a tapas formula) is hailed by early reporters as "surprisingly good and authentic". / www.william-iv.co.uk; 10.30 pm, Fri & Sat 11 pm.*

### Willie Gunn SW18 £36 ④④❸
422 Garratt Ln  8946 7773  10–2B
This "relaxed" Earlsfield bar/restaurant used to enjoy 'local hero'
status; some still say it's "great to have in SW18", but a number
of former fans say "it's gone very downhill". / 11 pm.

### Wiltons SW1 £74 ❸❸❸
55 Jermyn St  7629 9955  3–3C
Nowhere are the "traditional" values of "real old English dining"
enshrined more faithfully than at this "impeccably consistent" and
"rather stiff" clubland legend; Jerome Ponchelle's fish dishes
(in particular) may be "simple", but they're "perfect"… as long
as you don't mind them being "vastly overpriced".
/ www.wiltons.co.uk; 10.30 pm; closed Sat & Sun; jacket required.

### Windows on the World
### Park Lane Hilton Hotel W1 £80 ⑤④❷
22 Park Ln  7208 4021  3–4A
Thanks to the "brilliant" views ("ask for a window table"),
"you feel on top of the world" at this 28th-floor Mayfair eyrie –
a favourite for "romance" and for brunch; unfortunately, prices
for the "average" food are pretty "stunning", too. / 10.30 pm, Fri &
Sat 11.30 pm; closed Sat L & Sun D; jacket required; set weekday L £40 (FP).

### The Windsor Castle W8 £26 ❸④❶
114 Campden Hill Rd  7243 9551  6–2B
This "unique" (in west London anyhow) coaching inn,
near Notting Hill Gate, has a charming and ancient interior,
and a large walled garden that's "ideal when the sun shines";
the simple fare it offers is "consistently well-cooked".
/ www.windsor-castle-pub.co.uk; 10 pm; no smoking area at L; no booking.

### Wine Factory W11 £30 ④❷❸
294 Westbourne Grove  7229 1877  6–1B
"The food is pretty bad" (well, actually, the pizza's OK), but the
wine is "great" ("basically it's sold at off-licence prices"), at this
"buzzing" Notting Hill spot; no surprises, then, that it's a John
Brinkley production. / www.brinkleys.com; 11 pm.

### Wine Gallery SW10 £27 ④❸❷
49 Hollywood Rd  7352 7572  5–3B
A "top-value wine list" ("especially for Chelsea") is the star turn
at John Brinkley's long-established hang-out (which has a "great"
rear garden); the "cheap and easy" food plays rather
a supporting rôle. / www.brinkleys.com; 11 pm; no Amex.

### The Wine Library EC3 £22 ⑤❷❶
43 Trinity Sq  7481 0415  9–3D
"Forget the food" ("a basic buffet") – "the wine's the thing",
at this "Dickensian" City cellar, where a huge range of bottles
come at retail prices (plus modest corkage); book. / 8 pm; L & early
evening only, closed Sat & Sun.

### Winkles E2 £38 ❶❷⑤
238 Roman Rd  8880 7450  1–2D
"Lovely fish", "superb seafood", "shame about the ambience" –
that's the whole story on this "brave" modern café, in Bethnal
Green. / www.winklesseafood.com; 10.30 pm; closed Mon L; no smoking area.

### Wizzy SW6 NEW £31 ❷④❸
616 Fulham Rd   7736 9171   10–1B

*Wizzy is a charming hostess, and her small, tastefully-decorated Fulham newcomer provides a high-quality introduction to Korean cooking; portions can be stingy, though, and service on our July 2005 visit – when the restaurant had been open for some time – verged on bungling. / Rated on Editors' visit; 11.30 pm.*

### Wódka W8 £44 ❸❷❷
12 St Alban's Grove   7937 6513   5–1B

*"Forget the food, just go for the amazing vodkas" – that's long been the standard advice on this "quietly-situated", "fun" and rather "romantic" Kensington Pole; its "hearty" cooking, however, was more often deemed "delicious" this year. / www.wodka.co.uk; 11.15 pm; closed Sat L & Sun L; set always available £28 (FP).*

### Wolfe's WC2 £32 ❸④❸
30 Gt Queen St   7831 4442   4–1D

*"Wonderful Kobe beefburgers" star in a number of reports on this long-established, genuinely American-feeling fixture, on the fringe of Covent Garden. / www.wolfes-grill.net; 11.45 pm, Sun 8.45 pm; no smoking area.*

### THE WOLSELEY W1 £50 ❸❸❷
160 Piccadilly   7499 6996   3–3C

*Messrs Corbin & King's star-studded Continental-style café, by the Ritz, is a "dramatic" location for any occasion (including "the ultimate breakfast" or "a perfect tea"); its "comfort" dishes – from the long main menu – "can border on average", though, and a few reporters find the place plain "over-hyped"; (n.b. it lost its head chef and head pastry chef post-survey). / www.thewolseley.com; midnight; no smoking area.*

### Wong Kei W1 £17 ④⑤⑤
41-43 Wardour St   7437 8408   4–3A

*"An absolute classic for quick, cheap Chinese food in Chinatown"; disappointingly to some reporters, service can be "quite friendly nowadays" – "a few years ago, they practically threw it at you!" / 11.30 pm; no credit cards; no booking.*

### Woodlands £28 ❷❷④
37 Panton St, SW1   7839 7258   4–4A
77 Marylebone Ln, W1   7486 3862   2–1A
12-14 Chiswick High Rd, W4   8994 9333   7–2B

*"Great south Indian food" wins many fans for these "reliable" and "good-value" veggies; their ambience is somewhere between "serene" and "depressing". / www.woodlandsrestaurant.co.uk; 10.45 pm.*

### Yas W14 £30 ❸❸④
7 Hammersmith Rd   7603 9148   7–1D

*"No-frills", "classic" Persian dishes – served well into the wee hours – make it worth remembering this "basic" café, opposite Olympia. / www.yasrestaurant.com; 5 am.*

**Yas on the Park W2**                    £27        ❸❸④
31-33 Sussex Pl   7706 2633   6–2D
*This Bayswater sibling to Olympia's Yas offers "surprisingly good"
(if "standard") Iranian dishes, with a "fair price/quality ratio" –
"it's a mystery why, given it's in an ill-served part of town, it isn't
more popular". / www.yasrestaurant.com; 11.15 pm; no smoking area.*

**Yatra W1**                             £42        ❸❷❸
34 Dover St   7493 0200   3–3C
*"It's lost some of its initial wow-factor, but the food and service
are still excellent", at this funky Mayfair Indian, which never quite
seems to get the following it deserves. / www.yatra.co.uk; 11 pm; closed
Sat L & Sun; set weekday L £22 (FP).*

**YAUATCHA W1**                          £38        ❶❸❷
Broadwick Hs, 15-17 Broadwick St   7494 8888   3–2D
*"Exquisite" dim sum and "hip" décor make Alan Yau's Soho
yearling a sort of "Hakkasan at half the price"; sometimes
"under-whelming" service (including assiduous table-turning) can
grate, though, and some reporters "prefer the ground-floor tea
room" (with its "stunning pastries") to the "cramped" main
dining area in the basement. / 11.30 pm; no smoking.*

**Yelo**                                 £24        ❸❷❷
136a Lancaster Rd, W11   7243 2220   6–1A   NEW
8-9 Hoxton Sq, N1   7729 4626   9–1D
*"Hip" but "reliable", this Thai diner has some great alfresco
tables on Hoxton Square; there are no reports yet on its new
sibling, near Ladbroke Grove tube. / www.yelothai.com; 11 pm;
no booking.*

**Yi-Ban**                               £29        ❷❸❷
Imperial Wharf, Imperial Rd, SW6   7731 6606   5–4B   NEW
Regatta Centre, Dockside Rd, E16   7473 6699   11–1D
*The original branch of this Chinese duo (near Royal Albert DLR)
boasts Thames and City Airport views, and is especially worth
seeking out for its "top dim sum"; it's early days for its
(more expensive) offshoot, in a development near Chelsea
Harbour. / www.yi-ban.co.uk; 11 pm; closed Sun; SW6 no smoking area.*

**Yming W1**                             £30        ❶❶❸
35-36 Greek St   7734 2721   4–2A
*"Unusual" Chinese dishes – "better than any in Chinatown" –
lead many reporters to seek out this "unassuming" Soho fixture
(whose "exterior gives no hint of the quality within"); the staff are
"so helpful and polite" – "let them tell you what to order".
/ www.yminglondon.com; 11.45 pm; closed Sun; no smoking area.*

**Yo! Sushi** £27 ④④④
St Albans Hs, 57 Haymarket, SW1   7930 7557   4–4A  **NEW**
Harvey Nichols, Knightsbridge, SW1   7201 8641   5–1D
15 Woodstock St, W1   7629 0051   3–1B  **NEW**
Trocadero, 17 Rupert St, W1   7434 2724   3–3D
Selfridges, 400 Oxford St, W1   7318 3944   3–1A
52 Poland St, W1   7287 0443   3–1D
myhotel, 11-13 Bayley St, WC1   7636 0076   2–1C
Fulham Broadway Centre, SW6   7385 6077   5–4A
Unit 7 Paddington Station, W2   7706 9550   6–1C
Whiteley's, 151 Queensway, W2   7727 9392   6–1C
N1 Centre, 37 Parkfield St, N1   7359 3502   8–3D
02 Centre, 255 Finchley Rd, NW3   7431 4499   8–2A
Unit 3b Belvedere Rd, SE1   7928 8871   2–3D
95 Farringdon Rd, EC1   7841 0785   9–1A
For "a quick snack", or as "a great place for kids", these
gimmicky conveyor-sushi joints have their fans; their dishes are
still too often "stodgy and lacking flavour and finesse", though –
curiously, in-store branches, such as at Selfridges, seem the best
bets. / www.yosushi.co.uk; 10 pm-11 pm; no smoking; no booking.

**Yoshino W1** £38 ❷❷④
3 Piccadilly Pl   7287 6622   3–3D
This "pure Japanese" – a tiny, "minimalist" "bolt hole", a "stone's
throw from Piccadilly Circus" – often has a majority of oriental
diners; "helpful" staff serve "excellent-quality sushi at reasonable
prices". / www.yoshino.net; 10 pm; closed Sun.

**Young Bin EC2** £28 ❸❸⑤
3 St Alphage Highwalk   7638 9151   9–2C
Distinctively dated Korean, on the fringe of the Barbican, where
the "famous" (in nearby offices, anyway) buffet is a highlight.
/ 9.30 pm; closed Sat & Sun; no smoking area.

**Yum Yum N16** £23
183-187 Stoke Newington High St   7254 6751   1–1D
We noted an impending move of this "very busy" Stoke
Newington Thai in last year's guide; as this edition goes to press,
we're told that the restaurant will – finally! – decamp to the
address above in late-2005. / 11 pm, Sat & Sun 11.30 pm;
no smoking area.

**Yuzu NW6** £36 ❶❷④
102 Fortune Green Rd   7431 6602   1–1B
"A great 'neighbourhood' contemporary Japanese" –
this "cramped" West Hampstead oriental is hailed for its
"excellent" food (including "always-fresh" sushi), and "stylish"
presentation. / www.yuzu-restaurants.com; 10.30 pm; closed Mon,
Tue-Fri D only, Sat & Sun open L & D; no smoking.

**ZAFFERANO SW1** £51 ❶❷❷
15 Lowndes St   7235 5800   5–1D
"Still the best Italian in town", for many reporters, this "hype-
free" Belgravian offers "perfectly-flavoured" food and "great
(unobtrusive) service"; the only real gripe is that the tables "are a
bit too close". / www.atozrestaurants.com; 11 pm.

**Zaika W8** £48 ❷❸❸

1 Kensington High St   7795 6533   5–1A

Still *"towards the top of the premier league of London's nouvelle Indians"* – new chef Sanjay Dwivedi has more than ably picked up where Vineet Bhatia left off, at this *"smart"* former banking hall, opposite Kensington Gardens. / www.zaika-restaurant.co.uk; 10.45 pm; closed Sat L; set weekday L & pre-theatre £32 (FP).

**Zamoyski NW3** £27 ④❸❷

85 Fleet Rd   7794 4792   8–2A

*"A long list of vodkas"*, *"plentiful"* portions of hearty nosh, and a *"cosy"* setting make this South Hampstead Pole a classic, *"cheap and cheerful"* destination. / 10.50 pm; D only; no Amex; no smoking area.

**Zamzama NW1** £23 ❸❸❸

161-163 Drummond St   7387 6699   8–4C

An *"interesting"*, high-tech Little India subcontinental, where *"the Bollywood on the TV screens"* is a *"distraction"* from the *"reliable"* cooking. / 11.15 pm; closed Sat L & Sun; no smoking area.

**Zen Central W1** £44 ❷❸④

20-22 Queen St   7629 8089   3–3B

A *"much more interesting menu than most Chinese restaurants"* is still a feature of this once-eminent Mayfair destination; its 'period-piece' 80s-minimalist décor, however, is now *"due for a make-over"*. / www.zencentralrestaurant.com; 11.15 pm.

**ZeNW3 NW3** £37 ❷❸❸

83 Hampstead High St   7794 7863   8–2A

*"Perhaps not the best in London, but as a local it can't be faulted"* – this glazed-fronted venue, in the heart of Hampstead serves *"reliable, upper-end"* Chinese cooking, in a *"dated"*, '80s-minimalist setting. / www.zenw3.com; 11 pm; no Amex.

**Zero Degrees SE3** £25 ❸❷❷

29-31 Montpelier Vale   8852 5619   1–4D

*"Very decent"* brews help fuel the *"very lively buzz"* at this stylish (if slightly *"echoey"*) Blackheath microbrewery; the *"simple"* food – especially *"large pizzas, with interesting toppings"* – gives *"little cause for complaint"*. / www.zerodegrees.co.uk; 11 pm; no smoking area.

**The Zetter EC1** £40 ❸❸❸

86-88 Clerkenwell Rd   7324 4455   9–1A

This *"casual, bright and buzzy"* yearling, attached to a Clerkenwell design-hotel, serves *"good food of the something-for-everyone type"*; *"after all the launch-hype"*, though, it can seem *"a bit of a let-down"*. / www.thezetter.com; 11 pm.

**Ziani SW3** £39 ❸❷❷

45-47 Radnor Walk   7352 2698   5–3C

*"You play sardines"*, at this *"hectic"* Chelsea Italian, but – with the help of its *"amusing"* staff – it *"always lifts the spirits"*. / 11 pm; set Sun L £24 (FP).

### Zilli Fish W1  £48  ❸❸❸
36-40 Brewer St   7734 8649   3–2D
*Aldo Zilli's "bustling" Soho corner site offers "great fish, simply cooked", served by "chirpy-yet-charming" Italian staff; "it's a little pricey", though, and sometimes gets too "noisy". / www.zillialdo.com; 11.15 pm; closed Sun D.*

### Zimzun SW6  £26  ❸❷❸
Fulham Broadway Centre   7385 4555   5–4A
*"Surprisingly good for somewhere in a shopping mall" – this handy Fulham pit stop offers consistent oriental fare at "excellent" prices. / www.zimzun.co.uk; 10.30 pm.*

### Zinc  £41  ⑤⑤⑤
21 Heddon St, W1   7255 8899   3–2C
11 Jerdan Pl, SW6   7386 2250   5–4A
*If you like "noisy, pub-type experience", you may see the point of this Conran brasserie chain – if you don't, its "shoddy" cuisine, "abysmal" service and "poor" atmosphere can sometimes make a visit "a disaster". / www.conran.com; 11 pm, W1 Thu-Sat 11.30 pm; W1 closed Sun; W1 smoking in bar only.*

### Zizzi  £28  ④④❸
110-116 Wigmore St, W1   7935 2336   3–1A
33-41 Charlotte St, W1   7436 9440   2–1C
35-38 Paddington St, W1   7224 1450   2–1A
20 Bow St, WC2   7836 6101   4–2D
73-75 Strand, WC2   7240 1717   4–4D
214 Fulham Rd, SW10   7351 5160   5–3B
194-196 Earl's Court Rd, SW5   7373 0126   5–2A
231 Chiswick High Rd, W4   8747 9400   7–2A
202-208 Regent's Park Rd, N3   8371 6777   1–1B
1-3 Hampstead Ln, N6   8374 0090   8–1B
87 Allitsen Rd, NW8   7722 7296   8–3A
35-37 Battersea Rise, SW11   7924 7311   10–2C
4-5 King St, TW9   8332 2809   1–4A
33 Westferry Circus, E14   7512 9257   11–1B
*"Cheerful" branches, "upmarket" toppings and a "child-friendly" attitude are among the plus-points of this modern pizza-and-pasta chain; overall, however, ratings lag those of PizzaExpress (which is now under the same ownership). / www.askcentral.co.uk; 11 pm; no smoking area; some booking restrictions apply.*

### Zucca W11  £38  ④❸④
188 Westbourne Grove   7727 0060   6–1B
*It's curious that this Notting Hill Italian perennially "lacks buzz", as it's consistently praised as a "good neighbourhood stand-by", which specialises in "above-average pizza". / 11 pm; no Amex; no booking, Sat L.*

### Zuccato  £32  ④❸④
02 Centre, 255 Finchley Rd, NW3   7431 1799   8–2A
41 Bow Ln, EC4   7329 6364   9–2C
*Critics accuse this funny Italian duo – one member in a Finchley shopping mall, the other in the City – of offering "average" food in a "boring" (rather "'80s") setting; they are pretty "inoffensive", though, and do some "good" pizza. / NW3 11.30 pm, EC4 10.30 pm; EC4 closed Sat & Sun; no smoking area.*

**ZUMA SW7**                              £60     **❶❸❶**

5 Raphael St   7584 1010   5–1C

*"You can see the Chelsea football team, Penelope Cruz and Robin Williams…all in one night!", at this "painfully hip" Knightsbridge Japanese, whose "fantastic" food "rivals Nobu", and whose "always-buzzing" setting makes for "a better all-round experience".* / www.zumarestaurant.com; 11 pm; no smoking; booking: max 8.

# INDEXES & CUISINES

## BREAKFAST
*(with opening times)*

### Central

Amato *(8)*
Apostrophe: *all branches (7)*
Asia de Cuba *(7)*
Atrium *(8)*
Automat *(Sat & Sun 11)*
Baker & Spice: *all branches (7)*
Balans: *all branches (8)*
Bank Aldwych *(Mon-Fri 7, Sat 8, Sun 11.30)*
Bar Italia *(7)*
Berkeley Square Café *(9.30)*
Bistro 1: *W1 (Sun 11)*
Brasserie Roux *(6.30, Sat & Sun 7)*
Café Bagatelle *(10)*
Café Bohème *(8 )*
Café des Amis du Vin *(Sun brunch 11.30)*
Carluccio's Caffè: *all branches (10)*
Cecconi's *(8)*
Chez Gérard: *Chancery Ln WC2 (8)*
Christopher's *(Sat & Sun 11.30)*
The Cinnamon Club *(Mon-Fri 7.30)*
Connaught (Angela Hartnett) *(7)*
Cork & Bottle *(11)*
Crivelli's Garden *(10)*
Dorchester Grill *(7)*
Eagle Bar Diner *(Sun 11)*
Eat & Two Veg *(8)*
Exotika *(7.30)*
The Fifth Floor (Café) *(10, Sun 11)*
5 Cavendish Square *(8)*
Food for Thought *(9.30)*
Fortnum's, The Fountain *(8.30)*
43 South Molton *(Mon-Sat 11.30)*
La Fromagerie Café *(8)*
Fuzzy's Grub: *SW1 (7)*
La Galette *(10)*
Giraffe: *all branches (7.45, Sat & Sun 9)*
Goring Hotel *(7)*
Grocer on Warwick Café *(8.30)*
Ha! Ha!: *all branches (Sat & Sun 10)*
Homage *(Mon-Sat 9)*
Hush *(Mon-Fri 7.30)*
Indigo *(6.30)*
Inn the Park *(8)*
Jaan *(8)*
The Lanesborough *(7)*
Leon *(8)*
Loch Fyne: *all branches (9)*
Maison Bertaux *(8.30)*
Mash *(8, Sat 11.30)*
Mediterranean Kitchen: *WC2 (10)*
Mju *(7)*
Monmouth Coffee Company: *WC2 (8)*
Nicole's *(10)*
One-O-One *(7)*
Oriel *(8.30)*
Oscar *(7, Sat & Sun 8)*
Le Pain Quotidien *(7)*
Pasta Brown: *Bedford St WC2 (Mon-Sat 8)*
Pâtisserie Valerie: *all branches (7.30)*

Paul: *all branches (7.30)*
Pearl *(6.30)*
Pizza on the Park *(9)*
The Portrait *(10)*
The Providores *(9, Sat & Sun 10)*
Tapa Room (Providores) *(9, Sat & Sun 10)*
Refuel *(7)*
Rhodes W1 *(6.30, Sat & Sun 7)*
Rib Room *(7)*
RIBA Café *(8)*
Richoux: *all branches (8)*
The Ritz *(7, Sun 8)*
Royal Academy *(10)*
La Rueda: *all branches (7.30)*
Serafino *(7)*
Simpsons-in-the-Strand *(Mon-Fri 7.15)*
06 St Chad's Place *(8)*
Sketch (Parlour) *(Mon-Fri 8, Sat 10)*
Sotheby's Café *(9.30)*
Spoon at Sanderson *(7)*
Star Café *(7)*
Stock Pot: *SW1 (7)*
Tate Britain *(10)*
Tootsies: *W1 (11)*
Truc Vert *(7.30, Sun 9.30)*
Tuttons *(9.30)*
Villandry *(8.30)*
Windows on the World *(7)*
The Wolseley *(Sat & Sun 9)*
Yauatcha *(10)*

### West

Abbaye: *SW7 (9)*
Adams Café *(7.30, Sat 8.30)*
Annie's: *W4 (Tue-Sun 10)*
Aquasia *(7)*
Aubaine *(8, Sun 9)*
Babes 'n' Burgers *(10 am)*
Baker & Spice: *all branches (7)*
Balans West: *all branches (8)*
Beaufort House *(9.30)*
Bedlington Café *(8)*
Beirut Express *(7)*
Bibendum *(8)*
Bistrot 190 *(7)*
Blakes Hotel *(7.30)*
Blue Kangaroo *(9.30)*
Bluebird Café *(8)*
La Brasserie *(8, Sun 9)*
Brunello *(7)*
Bush Bar & Grill *(Sat & Sun 11.30)*
Café Crêperie de Hampstead: *SW7 (10)*
Café Laville *(10)*
Capital Hotel *(7, Sun 7.30)*
Carluccio's Caffè: *all branches (10)*
Chelsea Bun Diner *(7)*
Chelsea Kitchen *(7.30)*
Cheyne Walk Bras' *(Sat & Sun 10)*
The Cross Bar *(9)*
Ed's Easy Diner: *SW3 (Sat & Sun 9)*
Electric Brasserie *(8)*
Food@TheMuse *(11, Fri-Sun 10)*
Fresco *(8)*
Ghillies: *all branches (10)*
Giraffe: *all branches (7.45, Sat & Sun 9)*
Gravy *(Sat & Sun 10)*

Harlem: *W2 (10.30)*
I Thai *(7)*
Joe's Café *(9.30)*
Julie's *(9)*
Langan's Coq d'Or *(Sat & Sun 10.30)*
Lisboa Patisserie *(8)*
Loch Fyne: *all branches (9)*
Loco Locale: *SW6 (Sat & Sun 11)*
Lucky Seven *(8)*
Lundum's *(9)*
Maroush: *l) 21 Edgware Rd W2 (10)*
Le Metro *(7.30)*
Mona Lisa *(6.30)*
Pâtisserie Valerie: *all branches (7.30)*
Picasso *(8)*
Ranoush: *W2 (9)*
Raoul's Café *(8.30)*
Richoux: *all branches (8)*
Ruby Lounge & Sequoia Bar *(Sat & Sun 11)*
La Rueda: *all branches (7.30)*
S & M Café: *all branches (7.30)*
Sophie's Steakhouse *(Sat & Sun 11)*
Stock Pot: *SW3 (8)*
Tartine: *SW3 (11)*
Tom's *(8, Sun 9)*
Tootsies: *W4 (10); W11 (8, Sat & Sun 9); SW7 (Sat & Sun 10); SW6 (Sat & Sun 10.30)*
Troubadour *(9)*
202 *(8.30, Sun & Mon 10)*
Vesbar *(Sat & Sun 10)*
Vingt-Quatre *(open 24 hours)*
Zinc: *SW6 (Sat & Sun 10)*

### North
The Almeida *(9, summer only)*
The Arches *(11.30)*
Baker & Spice: *all branches (7)*
Banners *(9, Sat & Sun 10)*
Base: *NW3 (8)*
Café Mozart *(8, Sat & Sun 9)*
Carluccio's Caffè: *all branches (10)*
Chamomile *(7)*
The Elk in the Woods *(10)*
Fig *(7, Sat 8, Sun 9 )*
Florians *(Sat & Sun 11)*
Gallipoli: *Upper St N1 x2 (10.30)*
Giraffe: *all branches (7.45, Sat & Sun 9)*
The Green *(Sun 11.30 )*
Ha! Ha!: *all branches (Sat & Sun 10)*
Harry Morgan's *(11.30)*
Iznik *(10.30)*
Landmark (Winter Garden) *(7)*
Richoux: *all branches (8)*
S & M Café: *all branches (7.30)*
Shish: *NW2 (Sat & Sun 10)*
Toast *(11)*
Tootsies: *NW3 (10, Sat & Sun 9)*
Troika *(8.30)*
Zuccato: *NW3 (10.30)*

### South
Amano Café *(7)*
Annie's: *SW13 (Tue-Sun 10)*
Balham Kitchen & Bar *(8)*
Bar du Musee *(Sat & Sun 11)*
Bar Estrela *(9)*

Bermondsey Kitchen *(Sat & Sun 11.30)*
The Blue Pumpkin *(11.30, Sat & Sun 10.30)*
Bodean's: *SW4 (Sat & Sun 10)*
Boiled Egg *(9)*
Le Bouchon Bordelais *(10)*
Café Portugal *(8)*
Canyon *(Sat & Sun 11)*
Carluccio's Caffè: *all branches (10)*
Chapter Two *(8.30)*
The County Hall Rest' *(6.30, Sat & Sun 7)*
Dexter's Grill *(11, Sat & Sun 10)*
Ditto *(Sat & Sun 9.30)*
Eco Brixton: *SW9 (8.30)*
Ferrari's *(10)*
Gastro *(8)*
Ghillies: *all branches (10)*
Giraffe: *all branches (7.45, Sat & Sun 9)*
Hudson's *(10)*
Inside *(Sat 11)*
Loch Fyne: *all branches (9)*
Monmouth Coffee Company: *SE1 (7.30)*
Pomino *(Sat & Sun 10)*
Le Pont de la Tour Bar & Grill *(Sat & Sun 10)*
Rapscallion *(10.30)*
La Rueda: *all branches (7.30)*
Scoffers *(10.30)*
Tapas Brindisa *(Fri & Sat 9)*
Tartine: *TW9 (11, Sat 10.30)*
Tate Restaurant *(10)*
Tate Café *(10)*
Tootsies: *SW15 (11, Sat & Sun 10); SW19 (9); SW4 (Sat & Sun 10); SW11 (Sat 9.30, Sun 10.30)*
El Vergel *(8.30)*
The Victoria *(7)*

### East
Apostrophe: *all branches (7)*
Benugo: *St John St EC1 (7.30)*
Bonds *(7)*
Brick Lane Beigel Bake *(24 hrs)*
Carluccio's Caffè: *all branches (10)*
Chez Gérard: *EC2 (8)*
Club Mangia *(7)*
Coq d'Argent *(Mon-Fri 7.30)*
Epicurean Pizza Lounge *(Sat & Sun 11 )*
Flâneur *(Sat & Sun 9)*
Fox & Anchor *(7)*
The Gun *(Sat & Sun 10.30)*
Hadley House *(10)*
Hope & Sir Loin *(7)*
Lilly's *(Sat & Sun 11)*
Malmaison *(7, Sat & Sun 8)*
1 Lombard Street *(7.30)*
Pâtisserie Valerie: *all branches (7.30)*
E Pellicci *(6.15)*
Perc%nto *(6.45)*
The Place Below *(7.30)*
Quadrato *(7, Sat & Sun 8)*
The Royal Exchange *(8)*
S & M Café: *all branches (7.30)*
St John Bread & Wine *(9, Sat & Sun 10 )*

Smiths (Ground Floor) *(7)*
Story Deli *(9 am)*
Terminus *(7, Sat & Sun 7.30)*
Wapping Food *(10.30, Sat & Sun 11)*
The Well *(10.30)*
The Zetter *(7)*
Zuccato: *EC4 (8)*

## BRUNCH MENUS

### Central
Amato
Aurora
The Avenue
Balans: *all branches*
Bank Aldwych
Boisdale
Boxwood Café
Brasserie Roux
Le Caprice
Christopher's
Circus
The Fifth Floor (Café)
La Fromagerie Café
Fuzzy's Grub: *SW1*
La Galette
Giraffe: *all branches*
Hush
Indigo
Inn the Park
The Ivy
Joe Allen
The Lanesborough
Mash
Nicole's
Oriel
Pâtisserie Valerie: *Marylebone High St W1, Old Compton St W1*
La Perla: *WC2*
The Portrait
The Providores
Tapa Room (Providores)
Rainforest Café
RIBA Café
Serafino
Tootsies: *W1*
Villandry
Windows on the World
The Wolseley

### West
The Abingdon
Admiral Codrington
Aquasia
Aubaine
Balans West: *all branches*
Beach Blanket Babylon
Beaufort House
Bistrot 190
Blue Elephant
Bluebird
Bluebird Café
La Brasserie
Bush Bar & Grill
Cactus Blue
Café Laville
Chelsea Bun Diner
Cheyne Walk Bras'
Deli

Chutney Mary
Cross Keys
The Crown & Sceptre
Electric Brasserie
The Enterprise
L'Etranger
First Floor
Giraffe: *all branches*
Gravy
Henry J Beans
Joe's Brasserie
Joe's Café
Langan's Coq d'Or
Lucky Seven
Lundum's
Notting Hill Brasserie
The Oak
Ottolenghi: *all branches*
Picasso
PJ's
Raoul's Café
Ruby Lounge & Sequoia Bar
S & M Café: *all branches*
Sophie's Steakhouse
Stone Mason's Arms
Taqueria
Tom's
Tootsies: *SW6, SW7, W11*
Troubadour
202
The Vale
Vesbar
Vingt-Quatre
Zuma

### North
The Arches
Artigiano
Banners
La Brocca
Café Mozart
Camden Brasserie
Chamomile
Cottons
The Drapers Arms
The Engineer
Giraffe: *all branches*
Landmark (Winter Garden)
Ottolenghi: *all branches*
S & M Café: *all branches*
Toast
Tootsies: *NW3*
The Vine

### South
Alma
Balham Kitchen & Bar
Bermondsey Kitchen
The Blue Pumpkin
Boiled Egg
Butlers Wharf
  Chop-house
Canyon
Chez Lindsay
Cinnamon Cay
Gastro
Giraffe: *all branches*
Hudson's
Inside

Lamberts
Ost. Antica Bologna
Polygon Bar & Grill
Pomino
Le Pont de la Tour
   Bar & Grill
Prego
Ransome's Dock
Rapscallion
Scoffers
The Sequel
Tate Café
Tootsies: *SW15, SW19, SW4*
Willie Gunn

*East*
Aquarium
Armadillo
The Clerkenwell Dining Room
The Crown
1802
Flâneur
Frocks
Just The Bridge
Quadrato
S & M Café: *all branches*
Smiths (Ground Floor)
Wapping Food
Winkles

## BUSINESS

*Central*
Adam Street
Al Duca
Alloro
Amaya
Atrium
Automat
The Avenue
Axis
Bank Aldwych
Bank Westminster
Bellamy's
Bentley's
Boisdale
Brasserie Roux
Le Caprice
Cecconi's
Chez Gérard: *both W1, both WC2*
China Tang
Christopher's
The Cinnamon Club
Circus
Connaught (Angela Hartnett)
Diverso
Dorchester Grill
Drones
Eddalino
Elena's L'Etoile
L'Escargot
The Fifth Floor
Fiore
Foliage
Le Gavroche
Gordon Ramsay at Claridge's
Goring Hotel
Green's
The Greenhouse

The Guinea
Homage
Indigo
The Ivy
Jaan
Just St James
Ken Lo's Memories
The Lanesborough
Langan's Brasserie
Lindsay House
Locanda Locatelli
Mango Tree
Matsuri: *all branches*
Mirabelle
Miyama
Mon Plaisir
Mosaico
Neal Street
Nicole's
O'Conor Don
Odin's
115 at Hodgson's
One-O-One
L'Oranger
Orrery
Le Palais du Jardin
Patterson's
Pearl
Pengelley's
Pétrus
Pied à Terre
Quilon
Refuel
Rhodes W1
Rib Room
RIBA Café
Rowley's: *W1*
Rules
Santini
Savoy Grill
J Sheekey
Shepherd's
Simpsons-in-the-Strand
Six-13
Le Soufflé
The Square
Tamarind
Teca
Veeraswamy
Il Vicolo
Wiltons
Windows on the World
The Wolseley
Zafferano
Zen Central

*West*
Aubergine
Bibendum
Bluebird
Bluebird Club & Dining Rooms
Capital Hotel
Clarke's
1880
Gordon Ramsay
Launceston Place
The Ledbury

Poissonnerie
de l'Avenue
The Tenth

*North*
Frederick's
Odette's
Yuzu

*South*
Blueprint Café
Butlers Wharf
Chop-house
Chez Gérard: *SE1*
The County Hall Rest'
Delfina Studio Café
Oxo Tower (Bras')
Oxo Tower (Rest')
Le Pont de la Tour

*East*
Bar Bourse
Bevis Marks
Bleeding Heart
Boisdale of Bishopsgate
Bonds
Brasserie Rocque
Café du Marché
Caravaggio
The Chancery
Chez Gérard: *EC2, EC3*
City Miyama
Coq d'Argent
The Don
Eyre Brothers
Gow's
Imperial City
Just Gladwins
Lanes
Luc's Brasserie
Malmaison
Moro
Novelli in the City
1 Lombard Street
Pacific Oriental
Paternoster Chop House
Prism
Quadrato
Refettorio
Rhodes 24
Singapura: *EC3*
Sri Siam City
Sweetings
Tatsuso
Vertigo
Vivat Bacchus

**BYO**

*(Bring your own wine at minimal
corkage. Note for £5-£15 per
bottle, you can normally
negotiate to take your own wine
to many, if not most, places.)*

*Central*
Exotika
Food for Thought
Fryer's Delight
Golden Hind
Hazuki

India Club
Ragam

*West*
Adams Café
Alounak
Bedlington Café
Blah! Blah! Blah!
Café 209
Café Laville
Chelsea Bun Diner
El Gaucho: *SW3*
Hammersmith Café
Kandoo
Mawar
Mirto
Mohsen
Pappa Ciccia: *Munster Rd SW6*
Rôtisserie Jules: *SW7*
Tendido Cero

*North*
Ali Baba
Diwana B-P House
Geeta
Huong-Viet
Vijay
Zamoyski

*South*
Amaranth
Eco Brixton: *SW9*
Fat Boy's: *W4*
Fish Club
Hot Stuff
Mirch Masala: *SW16, SW17*
O'Zon
Thai Corner Café

*East*
Lahore Kebab House
The Light
Mangal
New Tayyabs
The Place Below
Tokyo City
The Wine Library

**CHILDREN**

*(h – high or special chairs
m – children's menu
p – children's portions
e – weekend entertainments
o – other facilities)*

*Central*
Abeno *(hp)*
About Thyme *(h)*
The Admiralty *(h)*
Al Duca *(m)*
Al Hamra *(h)*
Al Sultan *(hp)*
Alloro *(hp)*
Amato *(hp)*
Aperitivo *(h)*
Asia de Cuba *(h)*
Auberge: *all branches (m)*
Automat *(h)*
Axis *(hm)*
Back to Basics *(hp)*

Bank Aldwych *(hmo)*
Bank Westminster *(hm)*
Bar Italia *(hp)*
Beiteddine *(hp)*
Belgo Centraal: *all branches (hm)*
Benares *(h)*
Benihana: *W1 (h)*
Bentley's *(h)*
Beotys *(pm)*
Berkeley Square Café *(m)*
Bertorelli's: *Frith St W1 (hme); Charlotte St W1, WC2 (me)*
Blandford Street *(p)*
Bodean's: *all branches (hme)*
Boudin Blanc *(p)*
Boxwood Café *(mo)*
Brahms *(hp)*
Brasserie Roux *(h)*
Brian Turner *(hp)*
British Museum *(hp)*
Browns: *all central branches (hm)*
Café Bagatelle *(h)*
Café Bohème *(m)*
Café Fish *(hm)*
Café in the Crypt *(ho)*
Café Pacifico *(hm)*
Caffè Caldesi *(h)*
Caldesi *(hp)*
Camerino *(hp)*
Le Caprice *(hp)*
Carluccio's Caffè: *all branches (h)*
Cecconi's *(h)*
Chai Pani *(hp)*
Chez Gérard: *all central branches (me)*
Chimes *(p)*
The Chinese Experience *(h)*
Chisou *(h)*
Chor Bizarre *(hp)*
Chowki *(h)*
Christopher's *(hm)*
Chuen Cheng Ku *(h)*
Ciao Bella *(hp)*
Cigala *(hm)*
The Cinnamon Club *(h)*
Cipriani *(hp)*
Como Lario *(hp)*
Connaught (Angela Hartnett) *(hm)*
Cristini: *all branches (p)*
The Criterion Grill *(hp)*
Crivelli's Garden *(hm)*
Delfino *(h)*
Destino *(h)*
Deya *(hp)*
Diverso *(p)*
Dorchester Grill *(hm)*
Drones *(p)*
The Easton *(p)*
Eat & Two Veg *(h)*
ECapital *(h)*
Ed's Easy Diner: *Rupert St W1, WC2 (hm); Moor St W1 (m)*
Eddalino *(hp)*
Efes II: *all branches (h)*
L'Estaminet *(p)*
Fairuz: *W1 (h)*
Fakhreldine *(hp)*
The Fifth Floor *(hp)*

The Fifth Floor (Café) *(ho)*
Fine Burger Company: *all branches (hmeo)*
Fiore *(p)*
Foliage *(hm)*
La Fontana *(p)*
Footstool *(h)*
Fortnum's, The Fountain *(hpm)*
Fung Shing *(h)*
Fuzzy's Grub: *SW1 (h)*
Gaby's *(hp)*
La Galette *(h)*
Garbo's *(hp)*
Garlic & Shots *(p)*
Gaucho Grill: *all central branches (h)*
Gay Hussar *(hp)*
Getti: *all branches (hp)*
Gili Gulu *(m)*
Giraffe: *W1 (hme)*
Golden Dragon *(h)*
Gordon Ramsay at Claridge's *(h)*
Goring Hotel *(hm)*
Gourmet Pizza Co.: *all branches (h)*
Goya: *all branches (hp)*
Green's *(p)*
Greig's *(hp)*
Ha! Ha!: *all branches (m)*
Hamburger Union: *all branches (h)*
Harbour City *(h)*
Hard Rock Café *(hmo)*
Hardy's *(hp)*
Hare & Tortoise: *all branches (h)*
Harry Ramsden's *(hm)*
Homage *(hp)*
Hush *(hm)*
Imperial China *(h)*
Incognico *(h)*
L'Incontro *(h)*
Indigo *(hp)*
Inn the Park *(hp)*
Ishbilia *(h)*
Ishtar *(h)*
Italian Kitchen *(hm)*
Itsu: *Wardour St W1 (h)*
The Ivy *(hp)*
Jaan *(m)*
Jade Garden *(h)*
Joy King Lau *(h)*
Just Oriental *(h)*
Just St James *(hp)*
Kai Mayfair *(h)*
Kazan *(hp)*
Kettners *(h)*
Koba *(h)*
The Lanesborough *(hm)*
Langan's Bistro *(p)*
Langan's Brasserie *(p)*
Latium *(hp)*
Little Italy *(h)*
The Little Square *(hp)*
Livebait: *all branches (me)*
Locanda Locatelli *(hpo)*
Loch Fyne: *WC2 (hm)*
Malabar Junction *(m)*
Mango Tree *(h)*
Maroush: *all branches (h)*

Masala Zone: *all branches (hm)*
Mash *(hpo)*
Maxwell's: *WC2 (hm)*
maze *(h)*
Mediterranean
  Kitchen: *all branches (hm)*
Mekong *(h)*
Mela *(h)*
Michael Moore *(p)*
Mimmo d'Ischia *(hp)*
Mirabelle *(h)*
Mitsukoshi *(hpm)*
Mju *(h)*
Mon Plaisir *(p)*
Mongolian Barbecue: *all branches (h)*
Mosaico *(hp)*
Motcombs *(p)*
Mr Kong *(h)*
Nahm *(hm)*
Navarro's *(h)*
Neal Street *(h)*
New Mayflower *(hp)*
New World *(h)*
Nicole's *(hp)*
Nobu *(h)*
Noodle Noodle: *all branches (h)*
North Sea Fish *(hp)*
Noura: *Hobart Pl SW1,
  Jermyn St SW1 (hp)*
Odin's *(p)*
Olivo *(h)*
One-O-One *(hm)*
Oriel *(p)*
Original Tajines *(h)*
Orrery *(h)*
Orso *(ho)*
Oscar *(hp)*
Ozer *(hm)*
Papageno *(hm)*
Paradiso Olivelli: *WC1 (hp);
  Gt Titchfield St W1 (p)*
Passione *(p)*
Pasta Brown: *all branches (hp)*
Patterson's *(hp)*
Paul: *all branches (h)*
Pearl *(hp)*
Pengelley's *(h)*
Pétrus *(h)*
Pizza on the Park *(he)*
Planet Hollywood *(hm)*
Il Pomodorino *(hp)*
Poons *(h)*
La Porchetta
  Pizzeria: *all branches (hp)*
La Porte des Indes *(h)*
Porters English Restaurant *(hmo)*
The Portrait *(he)*
La Poule au Pot *(h)*
Princess Garden *(hp)*
The Providores *(hp)*
Tapa Room (Providores) *(h)*
Quaglino's *(hm)*
Quilon *(h)*
Quirinale *(p)*
Quo Vadis *(p)*
Quod *(hm)*
Rainforest Café *(hmeo)*
Ranoush: *all branches (hp)*

Rasa Maricham: *WC1 (h)*
Red Veg *(h)*
Refuel *(hp)*
Reubens *(hp)*
Rhodes W1 *(h)*
Rib Room *(hm)*
RIBA Café *(h)*
Richoux: *all central branches (hp)*
The Ritz *(hm)*
Rocket: *W1 (hp)*
Roka *(h)*
Rowley's: *SW1 (hp)*
Royal Academy *(h)*
Royal China: *all branches (h)*
La Rueda: *all branches (hp)*
Rules *(h)*
Rusticana *(hp)*
Sale e Pepe *(p)*
Santini *(p)*
Sapori *(hp)*
Sarastro *(hm)*
Sardo *(p)*
Sartoria *(hp)*
Satsuma *(h)*
Savoy Grill *(h)*
Savoy Hotel (Banquette) *(hp)*
Seafresh *(hp)*
Serafino *(p)*
Shampers *(p)*
J Sheekey *(hp)*
Shepherd's *(p)*
Signor Sassi *(hp)*
Six-13 *(hp)*
Smollensky's: *WC2 (hme)*
Sofra: *all branches (hp)*
Soho Spice *(h)*
Le Soufflé *(hp)*
Souk *(hm)*
La Spiga *(hp)*
Spoon at Sanderson *(h)*
Sri Thai Soho *(m)*
Stock Pot: *SW1 (p)*
Strada: *all central branches (h)*
Sumosan *(h)*
Tamarind *(h)*
Taro: *all branches (h)*
La Tasca: *WC2 (hm)*
Tate Britain *(hm)*
Texas Embassy Cantina *(hm)*
TGI Friday's: *W1 (hme)*
Thai Café *(hp)*
Tootsies: *W1 (hmo)*
Toto's *(hp)*
Trader Vics *(h)*
La Trouvaille *(hp)*
Truc Vert *(hp)*
Tuttons *(m)*
Umu *(h)*
The Union Café *(p)*
Uno *(h)*
Vasco & Piero's Pavilion *(p)*
Veeraswamy *(hm)*
Il Vicolo *(h)*
Villandry *(hm)*
Wagamama: *all central branches (hm)*
Windows on the World *(h)*
Wolfe's *(hm)*

The Wolseley (he)
Woodlands: all branches (h)
Yo! Sushi: Poland St W1, Rupert St W1, WC1 (h)
Zafferano (hp)
Zen Central (hp)
Zilli Fish (hp)
Zinc: all branches (h)
Zizzi: all branches (hp)

### West

Abbaye: all branches (h)
The Abingdon (hp)
Abu Zaad (h)
L'Accento Italiano (h)
Admiral Codrington (h)
Al-Waha (h)
Alounak (h)
Anarkali (h)
The Anglesea Arms (h)
The Anglesea Arms (hp)
Annie's: all branches (hm)
Aquasia (h)
The Ark (h)
Arturo (m)
As Greek As It Gets (h)
Assaggi (hp)
Aubaine (h)
Aubergine (p)
Aziz (hp)
Azou (h)
Babes 'n' Burgers (hm)
Babylon (hp)
Balans: W8 (h)
Base: all branches (h)
Belvedere (h)
Ben's Thai (p)
Benihana: SW3 (h)
Benugo: SW7 (h)
Bibendum (h)
Big Easy (hm)
Bistrot 190 (h)
Blakes Hotel (h)
El Blasõn (p)
Blue Elephant (he)
Blue Kangaroo (hpmeo)
Blue Lagoon: W14 (h)
Bluebird (hmo)
Bluebird Café (hm)
The Bollo House (h)
Bombay Brasserie (h)
Bombay Palace (hp)
The Brackenbury (h)
La Brasserie (o)
Brasserie de l'Auberge (hp)
Brasserie St Quentin (hp)
Brilliant (hp)
Brunello (o)
The Burlington (hm)
Bush Bar & Grill (hm)
Bush Garden Café (hpm)
Cactus Blue (hp)
Café 209 (p)
Café Crêperie de Hampstead: SW7 (h)
Café Lazeez: SW7 (hm)
Café Med: all branches (h)
Carluccio's Caffè: all branches (h)

Carpaccio's (hp)
Chelsea Bun Diner (hpm)
Cheyne Walk Bras' (hp)
Chez Kristof (hp)
Chutney Mary (h)
The Collection (h)
Le Colombier (hp)
Coopers Arms (p)
Costa's Grill (p)
Cotto (h)
The Cow (p)
Cristini: all branches (p)
The Cross Bar (p)
Cross Keys (hp)
The Crown & Sceptre (h)
Crussh: W8 (h)
Da Mario (hpm)
Dan's (p)
Daphne's (hp)
De Cecco (hp)
Deep (hp)
La Delizia (hm)
Devonshire House (pm)
E&O (heo)
Ealing Park Tavern (ho)
Ed's Easy Diner: SW3 (hm)
Edera (p)
Electric Brasserie (hp)
Elistano (p)
Esenza (hp)
Est Est Est: all branches (me)
L'Etranger (h)
La Famiglia (hp)
Fat Boy's: W5 (hp)
First Floor (hpm)
Fish Hoek (p)
Fishworks: W4 (hpm)
Formosa Dining Room (hp)
1492 (h)
Foxtrot Oscar (hp)
Frankie's (hpm)
Frantoio (hp)
Fresco (h)
Friends (hp)
Galicia (p)
The Gate (h)
Gaucho Grill: SW3 (h)
Geale's (hp)
Giraffe: all west branches (hme)
Glaisters (hp)
Gourmet Burger Kitchen: all branches (hp)
Gravy (h)
The Green Olive (hm)
The Grove (hm)
Haandi (h)
Halepi: all branches (hp)
Hare & Tortoise: all branches (h)
Harlem: all branches (hm)
The Havelock Tavern (hp)
Henry J Beans (hm)
I Thai (h)
Island (hm)
Itsu: SW3 (h)
Jim Thompson's: all branches (hm)
Joe's Café (p)
Julie's (ho)

Julie's Wine Bar (hmo)
Kandoo (h)
kare kare (hp)
Kensington Place (hm)
Khan's (hpm)
Khan's of Kensington (p)
Langan's Coq d'Or (hm)
Latymers (h)
Loch Fyne: SW6 (hme)
Loco Locale: SW6 (he)
Lou Pescadou (hm)
Lowiczanka (hp)
Lucio (hp)
Lucky Seven (h)
Luna Rossa (p)
Lundum's (hp)
Made in Italy (hp)
Madhu's (h)
Maggie Jones's (h)
Malabar (h)
The Mall Tavern (hp)
Mandalay (hp)
Mandarin Kitchen (h)
Manicomio (hp)
Marechiaro (hp)
Maroush: all branches (h)
Masala Zone: all branches (hm)
Mawar (hp)
Mediterranean
  Kitchen: all branches (hm)
Mediterraneo (hp)
Memories of India (hp)
Le Metro (p)
Meza (h)
Miraggio (h)
Mirto (hp)
Mohsen (h)
Mona Lisa (hp)
Montpeliano (hp)
Monza (p)
Moroccan Tagine (hp)
Nathalie (hp)
Noor Jahan: all branches (p)
Notting Grill (hp)
Notting Hill Brasserie (h)
Nuovi Sapori (hp)
Nyonya (h)
The Oak (p)
The Oratory (p)
Osteria Basilico (hp)
Osteria dell'Arancio (h)
Il Pagliaccio (hmo)
The Painted Heron: SW10 (hp)
The Papaya Tree (p)
Pappa Ciccia: all branches (hme)
Paradise by Way of
  Kensal Green (hm)
Patio (p)
Pellicano (h)
La Perla: SW6 (hm)
The Phoenix (p)
Picasso (hp)
The Pig's Ear (hp)
The Pilot (h)
Pissarro's (hp)
PJ's (hp)

Poissonnerie
  de l'Avenue (p)
Ognisko Polskie (hp)
Il Portico (p)
Pucci Pizza (hp)
Queen's Head (hm)
Racine (h)
Randall & Aubin: SW10 (h)
Ranoush: all branches (hp)
Raoul's Café (h)
Rasoi Vineet Bhatia (p)
The Red Pepper (p)
Relais de Paris (hp)
Riccardo's (hmo)
Richoux: SW3 (hp)
The River Café (hpo)
The Rocket (hp)
Rodizio Rico: W2 (h)
Rôtisserie Jules: all branches (hme)
Royal China: all branches (h)
La Rueda: all branches (hp)
S & M Café: all branches (pm)
Sabai Sabai (hp)
Sagar (h)
The Salisbury Tavern (hm)
San Frediano (hp)
San Lorenzo (hp)
Santa Lucia (hp)
Scalini (hp)
Seven Stars (hp)
Shikara (p)
Shish: all branches (hme)
Silks & Spice: W4 (h)
606 Club (p)
Smollensky's: W6 (hm)
Snows on the Green (hp)
Sophie's Steakhouse (hmo)
Spago (h)
Sticky Fingers (hme)
Stock Pot: SW3 (hm)
Strada: SW5 (h); SW6 (hm)
La Tasca: all west branches (hm)
The Tea Palace (h)
Tendido Cero (p)
The Tenth (h)
Texas Lone Star (hme)
TGI Friday's: all west branches (hme)
The Thai (h)
The Thatched House (hp)
Timo (p)
Tom's (h)
Tootsies: SW6, SW7, W11 (hmo)
La Trompette (h)
Troubadour (h)
202 (o)
Le Vacherin (hp)
The Vale (hp)
Vama (hp)
Wagamama: W8 (hm)
The Walmer Castle (h)
The Waterway (p)
White Horse (hp)
William IV (h)
Wine Gallery (p)
Wódka (h)
Woodlands: all branches (h)
Yas (hp)

Yas on the Park (h)
Yi-Ban: all branches (hp)
Yo! Sushi: all west branches (h)
Zaika (h)
Ziani (p)
Zinc: all branches (h)
Zizzi: all branches (hp)
Zucca (h)
Zuma (he)

**North**
Afghan Kitchen (h)
Ali Baba (h)
The Almeida (h)
Anglo Asian Tandoori (p)
Artigiano (p)
L'Artista (h)
L'Aventure (hp)
Banners (hm)
Bar Mezé: all branches (h)
The Barnsbury (hp)
Base: all branches (h)
Bastille (hmp)
Belgo Noord: all branches (hm)
Benihana: NW3 (hme)
Bistro Aix (hp)
La Brocca (hp)
Browns: N1 (hm)
Bu San (h)
The Bull (h)
Café de Maya (h)
Café Med: all branches (hm)
Café Mozart (hpe)
La Cage Imaginaire (p)
Camden Brasserie (h)
Cantina Italia (p)
Carluccio's Caffè: all branches (h)
Casale Franco (p)
Chamomile (hp)
Chez Liline (hp)
Cottons (ph)
Crown & Goose (h)
Cru (h)
Cuba Libre (p)
Cube & Star (h)
Daphne (hp)
dim T café: NW3 (hm)
Don Pepe (hp)
The Drapers Arms (hpm)
The Duke of Cambridge (hp)
Ed's Easy Diner: NW3 (hm)
The Engineer (hm)
Est Est Est: all branches (me)
Fifteen (ho)
Fig (ho)
Fine Burger Company: all branches (hmeo)
Florians (hp)
The Fox Reformed (hp)
Fratelli la Bufala (hp)
Frederick's (hm)
Freemasons Arms (hp)
Gallipoli: Upper St N1, Upper St N1 (h)
The Garden Café (hm)
Gaucho Grill: NW3 (h)
Geeta (hp)
Giraffe: all north branches (hme)
Globe Restaurant (m)

Good Earth: NW7 (h)
Gourmet Burger Kitchen: all branches (hp)
Great Nepalese (p)
The Green (p)
The Greyhound (hp)
Ha! Ha!: all branches (m)
Haché (hp)
Halepi: all branches (hp)
The Haven (hp)
The Highgate (hp)
The House (hpm)
Hoxton Apprentice (h)
Huong-Viet (h)
Istanbul Iskembecisi (hp)
Jashan: all branches (h)
Jim Thompson's: all branches (hm)
The Junction Tavern (p)
Landmark (Winter Garden) (hmo)
Lansdowne (h)
Lemonia (p)
The Little Bay: NW6 (h)
Lola's (hpo)
Mango Room (hp)
Manna (h)
Marine Ices (hp)
Masala Zone: all branches (hm)
Mediterranean Kitchen: all branches (hm)
Mesclun (h)
Mestizo (hm)
Metrogusto (hpm)
Morgan M (p)
Mosaica (hp)
Nautilus (hp)
No 77 Wine Bar (p)
Ottolenghi: N1 (h)
The Parsee (p)
Pasha (p)
Pescador Too (hp)
Petit Auberge (p)
Le Petit Prince (p)
Philpotts Mezzaluna (hp)
Phoenix Palace (h)
La Piragua (p)
Pizzeria Oregano (hm)
La Porchetta Pizzeria: all branches (hp)
The Pumphouse (hoep)
Rani (hm)
Rasa Travancore: N16 (h)
Rasa (h)
The Real Greek (hp)
Richoux: NW8 (hpm)
Rosmarino (hp)
Royal China: all branches (h)
S & M Café: all branches (pm)
Sabor (hp)
Sabras (po)
Le Sacré-Coeur (hp)
St Johns (hp)
Sakonis (h)
The Salusbury (hp)
San Carlo (p)
San Daniele (hm)
Sardo Canale (h)

Sargasso Sea *(hm)*
Sarracino *(hp)*
Seashell *(hp)*
Sedir *(h)*
Shish: *all branches (hme)*
Silks & Spice: *NW1 (h)*
Singapore Garden *(h)*
Sofra: *all branches (hp)*
Solly's Exclusive *(hp)*
Strada: *N1, NW1 (h); N6 (hm)*
La Superba *(hp)*
Tiger Lil's: *all branches (hpme)*
Toast *(hm)*
Tobia *(m)*
Toff's *(hm)*
Tootsies: *NW3 (hmo)*
Troika *(hp)*
Two Brothers *(hm)*
Vijay *(p)*
The Vine *(hp)*
Wagamama: *all north branches (hm)*
Walnut *(hp)*
The Wells *(p)*
Weng Wah House *(hp)*
Yo! Sushi: *all north branches (h)*
Yum Yum *(h)*
Yuzu *(hm)*
Zamoyski *(p)*
Zamzama *(h)*
ZeNW3 *(h)*
Zizzi: *all branches (hp)*
Zuccato: *NW3 (hm)*

### South

A Cena *(hp)*
The Abbeville *(hp)*
Al Forno *(hp)*
Alma *(hp)*
Amano Café *(p)*
Annie's: *all branches (hm)*
Antipasto & Pasta *(h)*
Antipasto e Pasta *(h)*
Arancia *(hp)*
Auberge: *all branches (m)*
The Aviary *(hp)*
Babur Brasserie *(hp)*
Balham Kitchen & Bar *(hp)*
Baltic *(hm)*
The Banana Leaf Canteen *(hm)*
Bankside: *SE1 (h)*
Bar du Musee *(h)*
Bar Estrela *(hp)*
Bar Mezé: *all branches (h)*
Barcelona Tapas: *SE22 (hp)*
Beauberry House *(hm)*
Bengal Clipper *(h)*
Bermondsey Kitchen *(hpm)*
The Blue Pumpkin *(hm)*
Blueprint Café *(hp)*
Bodean's: *all branches (hme)*
Boiled Egg *(hme)*
Le Bouchon Bordelais *(hmo)*
Bread & Roses *(hp)*
The Bridge *(hm)*
Browns: *TW9 (hm)*
Buchan's *(hp)*
Buona Sera: *SW11 (h)*
Burnt Chair *(p)*

Butlers Wharf
   Chop-house *(h)*
Café Portugal *(hp)*
Cantina del Ponte *(hm)*
Cantina Vinopolis *(h)*
Il Cantuccio di Pulcinella *(h)*
Canyon *(hmo)*
Carluccio's Caffè: *all branches (h)*
Chakalaka *(hpo)*
Champor-Champor *(h)*
Chapter Two *(hp)*
Chez Bruce *(h)*
Chez Gérard: *SE1 (me)*
Chez Lindsay *(h)*
Cinnamon Cay *(h)*
The County Hall Rest' *(hm)*
Dalchini *(h)*
Del Buongustaio *(hp)*
The Depot *(hm)*
Dexter's Grill *(hme)*
Dish Dash *(p)*
Ditto *(hpm)*
don Fernando's *(hp)*
Earl Spencer *(hp)*
Eco: *SW4 (hp)*
El Rincón Latino *(hp)*
Enoteca Turi *(h)*
Est Est Est: *all branches (me)*
EV *(h)*
Evo *(hp)*
Fat Boy's: *all south branches (h)*
The Fentiman Arms *(p)*
Ferrari's *(hp)*
Fina Estampa *(hp)*
La Finca *(h)*
Fine Burger Company: *all branches (hmeo)*
The Fire Stables *(hp)*
Fish Club *(hme)*
Fish in a Tie *(h)*
fish! *(hm)*
The Food Room *(hp)*
Four Regions: *SE1 (h)*
Franklins *(hp)*
The Freemasons *(hp)*
Fujiyama *(h)*
Gastro *(p)*
Ghillies: *SW18 (hp)*
Giraffe: *SW11 (hme); SE1 (hpme)*
Glas *(h)*
The Glasshouse *(hpm)*
Gourmet Burger
   Kitchen: *all branches (hp)*
Gourmet Pizza Co.: *all branches (hp)*
The Greyhound *(h)*
Hampton's Restaurant *(hm)*
Hare & Tortoise: *all branches (h)*
Harlem: *all branches (h)*
The Hartley *(h)*
Hudson's *(p)*
Indian Ocean *(hp)*
Inshoku *(h)*
Inside *(p)*
Kastoori *(p)*
Kew Grill *(m)*
Kwan Thai *(h)*
Lamberts *(hpm)*
La Lanterna *(h)*

Laughing Gravy (hp)
The Lavender: SW11, SW9 (p)
The Light House (hm)
Livebait: all branches (me)
Lobster Pot (hp)
Loch Fyne: TW2 (hp)
Loco Locale: SE3 (he); SE1 (hme)
Ma Cuisine: TW9 (hp); TW1 (p)
Ma Goa (hm)
La Mancha (h)
The Mason's Arms (po)
Matilda's (p)
Meson don Felipe (p)
Mezzanine (hp)
Mirch Masala: all branches (h)
Mongolian Barbecue: all branches (h)
Morel (hp)
Murano (hpm)
MVH (hp)
Naked Turtle (hmeo)
Newton's (hpo)
Niksons (hp)
Nosh (hm)
O'Zon (hm)
Olley's (hm)
Ost. Antica Bologna (p)
Oxo Tower (Bras') (hm)
Oxo Tower (Rest') (hm)
The Painted Heron: SE11 (p)
The Palmerston (hp)
Panzella (hp)
Pappa Ciccia: all branches (hme)
Paradiso Olivelli: SE1 (hp)
The People's Palace (hpm)
The Pepper Tree (h)
Petersham Nurseries (h)
Le Petit Max (hp)
Phoenix (hm)
Pizza Metro (hp)
Pizzeria Castello (hp)
Polygon Bar & Grill (hp)
Pomino (mhe)
Le Pont de la Tour (h)
Le Pont de la Tour
   Bar & Grill (h)
Prego (hm)
Putney Station (p)
Ransome's Dock (hp)
Real Burger World (hm)
Real Greek Souvlaki &
   Bar: all branches (hm)
Redmond's (m)
Rick's Café (hp)
Riva (hp)
Riviera (hp)
Rocket Riverside: SW15 (hpe)
RSJ (p)
La Rueda: all branches (hp)
San Lorenzo Fuoriporta (hmo)
Sarkhel's: SW18 (hm)
Scoffers (hm)
The Sea Cow: SE22 (pm)
Settle Inn (hp)
Shakespeare's Globe (hm)
The Ship (p)
Silka (p)
Smollensky's: TW1 (hme)

Sonny's (hpe)
Spread Eagle (hp)
Sree Krishna (h)
Strada: SW4 (h); SW11, SW13 (hm)
The Sun & Doves (hp)
Tandoori Nights (h)
Tas: all branches (h)
Tas Pide: all branches (h)
Tate Restaurant (hmo)
Tate Café (hpm)
Tentazioni (p)
Thai Elephant (h)
3 Monkeys (hmo)
Tiger Lil's: all branches (hpme)
Tootsies: all south branches (hmo)
The Trafalgar Tavern (hp)
Tsunami (h)
El Vergel (o)
The Victoria (hmo)
Wagamama: SW15 (h)
The Waterloo
   Fire Station (hpm)
The Wharf (hm)
Willie Gunn (h)
Yo! Sushi: SE1 (hm)
Zero Degrees (hp)
Zizzi: all branches (hp)

***East***
Abbaye: all branches (h)
Alba (hp)
Apium (h)
Aquarium (ho)
Auberge: all branches (m)
Aurora (h)
The Bar & Grill (hm)
Bar Bourse (p)
Barcelona Tapas: E1, Beaufort Hs,
   St Botolph St EC3, EC4 (em)
Bertorelli's: all east branches (me)
Il Bordello (h)
Browns: all east branches (hm)
Café Med: all branches (hm)
Café Spice Namaste (hp)
Cantaloupe (p)
Carluccio's Caffè: all branches (h)
Carnevale (p)
Cat & Mutton (hp)
Cây Tre (hm)
The Chancery (hpm)
Chez Gérard: EC4 (hme); EC2,
   EC3 (me)
(Ciro's) Pizza Pomodoro: EC2 (h)
Club Gascon (p)
Club Mangia (h)
Coach & Horses (hp)
Coco (h)
Coq d'Argent (h)
The Crown (hp)
Crussh: Unit 21 Jubilee Pl E14 (h)
The Eagle (p)
1802 (h)
Epicurean Pizza Lounge (p)
Exmouth Grill (hp)
Eyre Brothers (m)
Faulkner's (hm)
La Figa (hp)
Fish Shop (p)
Fishmarket (h)

The Fox (p)
Frocks (p)
Gaucho Grill: E14 (h); EC3 (hp)
Gourmet Pizza Co.: all branches (h)
The Gun (h)
The Gunmakers (p)
Hadley House (hp)
Haz (h)
Itsu: E14 (h)
Lahore Kebab House (p)
The Light (p)
Lilly's (hp)
Malmaison (h)
Meson los Barilles (h)
Missouri Grill (hm)
Miyabi (h)
Moro (h)
Mustards Brasserie (p)
New Tayyabs (h)
Novelli in the City (p)
The Peasant (p)
Plateau (hp)
La Porchetta
   Pizzeria: all branches (hp)
Portal (h)
Quadrato (hme)
The Quality Chop House (p)
The Real Greek Souvlaki: all
   branches (hm)
Refettorio (h)
The Rivington Grill (p)
Royal China: all branches (h)
The Royal Exchange (p)
S & M Café: all branches (pm)
St John (h)
St John Bread & Wine (h)
Santa Maria de Buen Ayre (hp)
Scuzi: all branches (hm)
Shanghai (hp)
Shish: all branches (hme)
Smiths (Top Floor) (h)
Smiths (Dining Rm) (hp)
Smiths (Ground Floor) (hp)
Smollensky's: all east branches (hm)
Sofra: all branches (hp)
Sông Quê (hp)
Strada: EC1 (h)
Taberna Etrusca (p)
Tas Pide: all branches (h)
La Tasca: E14 (hm)
Terminus (h)
Ubon (hp)
Viet Hoa (h)
Wagamama: all east branches (hm)
Wapping Food (h)
The Well (hpm)
Winkles (hp)
Yi-Ban: all branches (hp)
Yo! Sushi: EC1 (h)
The Zetter (hp)
Zizzi: all branches (hp)

# ENTERTAINMENT
*(Check times before you go)*

## Central
Atlantic Bar & Grill
   *(DJ, Fri & Sat)*
Axis
   *(jazz, Tue & Wed)*
Bank Aldwych
   *(jazz, Sun)*
Bank Westminster
   *(DJ, Fri & Sat)*
Bohème Kitchen
   *(DJ, Sun)*
Boisdale
   *(jazz, Mon-Sat)*
Café Bohème
   *(jazz, Thu & Sun)*
Café du Jardin
   *(jazz pianist, Wed-Sat)*
Café Fish
   *(pianist, Mon-Wed & Sun)*
Camerino
   *(jazz, Mon)*
Le Caprice
   *(pianist, nightly)*
Circus
   *(DJ, Thu-Sat)*
Connaught (Angela Hartnett)
   *(pianist, nightly)*
Destino
   *(DJ, nightly)*
Dover Street
   *(live music, nightly)*
Eagle Bar Diner
   *(DJ, Wed-Sat)*
The Easton
   *(DJ, Fri )*
Efes II: Gt Portland St W1
   *(belly dancer, nightly)*
Floridita
   *(live cuban music, nightly)*
Foliage
   *(jazz, Mon-Sat)*
Goring Hotel
   *(pianist, nightly)*
Hakkasan
   *(DJ, nightly)*
Imperial China
   *(pianist, Thu-Sat)*
Indigo
   *(film brunches, Sun)*
Ishbilia
   *(live music, Thu-Sat)*
Jaan
   *(live music, nightly)*
Joe Allen
   *(pianist, Mon-Sat; jazz, Sun)*
Just St James
   *(pianist, Fri & Sat)*
Kai Mayfair
   *(harpist, Sat)*
Kettners
   *(pianist, nightly)*
The Lanesborough
   *(dinner dance, Fri & Sat; jazz, Sun brunch)*
Langan's Brasserie
   *(jazz, nightly)*
Levant
   *(belly dancer, nightly)*
Little Italy
   *(DJ, Fri & Sat)*
Mamounia
   *(belly dancer, nightly)*
Maroush: V) 3-4 Vere St W1
   *(music & dancing, nightly)*

Mash
(DJ, Thu-Sat)
Mirabelle
(pianist, Tue-Sat & Sun L)
Momo
(live world music, Mon-Wed)
Noble Rot
(DJ, Fri & Sat)
Noura Central: Jermyn St SW1
(DJ, Thu-Sat)
O'Conor Don
(DJ, Thu)
Opium
(DJ, Tue-Sat)
Oscar
(film club, Sun)
Pengelley's
(DJ in bar, Thu-Sat)
Pizza on the Park
(jazz, nightly)
Planet Hollywood
(DJ, nightly)
La Porte des Indes
(jazz, Sun brunch)
Quaglino's
(jazz, nightly; pianist, Sat & Sun brunch)
Quod
(pianist, Sun)
Rainforest Café
(nightclub, Thu-Sat)
Red Fort
(DJ, Thu-Sat)
Rib Room
(pianist, Mon-Sat)
The Ritz
(band, Fri & Sat )
Royal Academy
(jazz, Fri)
Sarastro
(opera, Sun & Mon)
Sartoria
(pianist, Fri & Sat)
Simpsons-in-the-Strand
(pianist, nightly)
Smollensky's: WC2
(pianist, Mon-Sat; DJ, Fri & Sat, jazz band; Sun )
Soho Spice
(DJ, Fri & Sat)
Le Soufflé
(pianist, Tue-Sat)
Souk
(belly dancer, live music & DJ, Thu-Sat )
Taman gang
(DJ, nightly)
Thai Square: SW1
(DJ, Fri & Sat)
Trader Vics
(guitarist, nightly)
Windows on the World
(dinner dance, Fri & Sat; jazz, Sun brunch)

*West*

Aquasia
(singer & pianist, Mon-Sat; jazz, Sun)
Aziz
(belly dancer, Fri & Sat; Persian music, Sun)
Babes 'n' Burgers
(children's film night Fri)
Belvedere
(pianist, nightly)
Benugo: SW7
(jazz, Wed)
Big Easy
(band, nightly)
Bluebird
(DJ , Fri & Sat)

Bombay Brasserie
(pianist & singer, nightly)
Cactus Blue
(DJ, Thu-Sat)
Café Lazeez: SW7
(classical music or jazz, Fri & Sat)
Café Med: W6
(jazz, Sun)
Chutney Mary
(jazz, Sun)
(Ciro's) Pizza Pomodoro: SW3
(live music, nightly)
The Collection
(DJ, nightly)
Cristini:
(jazz, Wed)
Da Mario
(disco, Wed-Sat; magician, Wed)
FireHouse
(DJ, Thu-Sat)
Levantine
(belly dancer, nightly)
Lomo
(guitarist, Mon-Thu)
Lonsdale
(DJ, Sat & Sun)
Lowiczanka
(live music, Fri-Sun)
Maroush: I) 21 Edgware Rd W2
(music & dancing, nightly)
Mr Wing
(jazz, Fri & Sat)
Nikita's
(Russian music, Fri & Sat)
Notting Hill Brasserie
(jazz, nightly)
The Prince Bonaparte
(DJ, Sun)
Ruby Lounge & Sequoia Bar
(DJ, Thu-Sat)
Seven Stars
(jazz, Sun)
606 Club
(jazz, Latin, R&B, nightly)
Spago
(live music, Thu-Sat)
Sugar Hut
(DJ, Fri & Sat)
Texas Lone Star
(country music, thrice weekly; magician, Sun (winter only))
Tugga
(DJ, Tue-Sun)
Vama
(jazz, Sun)
William IV
(DJ, Fri & Sat)
Zinc: SW6
(jazz, Sun D)

*North*

La Brocca
(jazz, Thu)
Cottons
(band, Sun; DJ, Thu- Sat)
Don Pepe
(singer & organist, Thu-Sat)
Florians
(jazz, Sun)
The Garden Café
(live jazz, Wed & Thu; DJ, Fri & Sun)
The Greyhound
(DJ, Sun)
Landmark (Winter Garden)
(pianist & musicians, daily)
Lola's
(pianist, Thu-Sat)

The Pumphouse
*(DJ, Fri & Sat)*
Shish: *NW2*
*(DJ, Fri)*
Thai Square: *N1*
*(DJ, Thu-Sat)*
Toast
*(DJ, Mon)*
Troika
*(Russian music, Fri & Sat)*
Villa Bianca
*(guitarist, twice weekly; pianist, weekends)*
Weng Wah House
*(karaoke, nightly)*
Zamoyski
*(Russian music, Sat)*

**South**
Archduke Wine Bar
*(jazz, nightly)*
Balham Kitchen & Bar
*(DJ, Fri & Sat)*
Baltic
*(jazz, Sun)*
Bengal Clipper
*(pianist, nightly)*
Cantina del Ponte
*(live music, Thu)*
Chakalaka
*(face painting, Sat & Sun)*
The County Hall Rest'
*(guitarist, Thu & Fri)*
La Finca
*(DJ, Thu-Sat)*
Fujiyama
*(DJ, Mon-Thu)*
Ghillies: *SW18*
*(jazz, Sun L)*
Harlem: *SW9*
*(DJ, Mon-Sat)*
The Hartley
*(live music, Tue)*
La Lanterna
*(live music, Fri)*
Laughing Gravy
*(jazz, Thu)*
La Mancha
*(live music, nightly)*
Meson don Felipe
*(guitarist, nightly)*
Naked Turtle
*(live jazz, nightly)*
Oxo Tower (Bras')
*(Jazz, nightly)*
Le Pont de la Tour
  Bar & Grill
*(jazz pianist, nightly)*
Prego
*(live music, Sun brunch & Fri)*
Putney Station
*(live music, Wed)*
Rocket Riverside: *SW15*
*(live music, Sun, Sept-June only)*
La Rueda: *SW4*
*(Spanish music & dancing, Fri & Sat)*
Tas: *Borough High St SE1*
*(guitarist, nightly); The Cut SE1*
*(live music, nightly)*
Tas Pide: *SE1*
*(guitarist, nightly)*
Thai Square: *SW15*
*(DJ, Fri & Sat)*

**East**
Aquarium
*(jazz, Sun)*
Aurora
*(pianist, nightly)*

Barcelona Tapas: *EC4*
*(disco, Thu & Fri)*
Bistrothèque
*(transvestite show Wed)*
Café du Marché
*(pianist & bass, nightly)*
Cantaloupe
*(DJ, Fri & Sat)*
(Ciro's) Pizza Pomodoro: *EC2*
*(live music, Mon-Fri; DJ Sat)*
Coco
*(jazz, Sun; DJ, Fri-Sun)*
Coq d'Argent
*(pianist, Sat; jazz, Fri & Sun L)*
1802
*(DJ, Wed-Fri)*
Elephant Royale
*(live music, Wed-Sat)*
Epicurean Pizza Lounge
*(DJ, Fri & sat)*
Frocks
*(singer, Thu-Fri)*
The Green
*(DJ, Fri)*
Home
*(DJ, Thu-Sat)*
The Light
*(DJ, Thu-Sat)*
Lightship
*(jazz, Mon & Wed)*
LMNT
*(opera, Sun)*
Medcalf
*(DJ, Fri )*
1 Lombard Street
*(pianist, Mon & Fri)*
Pacific Oriental
*(disco, Thu & Fri)*
Le Rendezvous du Café
*(jazz, nightly)*
Le Saint Julien
*(live jazz, Thu)*
Scuzi: *E14*
*(live music, Wed-Sat)*
Shish: *EC1*
*(DJ, Thu & Fri)*
Silks & Spice: *EC4*
*(DJ, Thu & Fri)*
Smiths (Dining Rm)
*(DJ, Fri & Sat)*
Smiths (Ground Floor)
*(DJ, Thu-Sat)*
Smollensky's: *E1*
*(pianist, Thu & Sat)*
Thai Square City: *EC3*
*(DJ, Fri)*
Tokyo City
*(karaoke)*
The Well
*(DJ, Fri)*
Yi-Ban: *E16*
*(band, Fri & Sat)*

**LATE**
*(open till midnight or later as
shown; may be earlier Sunday)*

**Central**
Asia de Cuba *(midnight, Sat 1 am)*
Atlantic Bar & Grill
Automat *(1 am)*
The Avenue *(midnight, Fri & Sat
12.30 am)*
Balans: *Old Compton St W1 (24 hours);
Old Compton St W1 (5 am, Sun 1 am)*
Bar Italia *(open 24 hours, Sun 3 am)*

Beiteddine
Boulevard
Browns: *WC2*
Café Bohème *(2.45 am)*
Café du Jardin
Café Lazeez: *W1 (Fri & Sat 1.30 am)*
Le Caprice
Circus
Le Deuxième
Dover Street *(2 am)*
Eagle Bar Diner *(midnight, ex Mon & Sun)*
Ed's Easy Diner: *both W1 (midnight, Fri & Sat 1 am)*
Fakhreldine
Floridita *(2 am)*
Garlic & Shots *(Thu - Sat 12.15 am)*
Gaucho Grill: *W1*
Goya: *Lupus St SW1 (for tapas midnight)*
Hakkasan *(midnight, ex Mon & Sun)*
Hard Rock Café *(1 am)*
Ishtar
Itsu: *all central branches (Fri & Sat midnight)*
The Ivy
Joe Allen *(12.45 am)*
Kettners
Little Italy *(4 am)*
Maroush: *V) 3-4 Vere St W1 (12.30 am)*
Maxwell's: *all branches*
Melati *(Fri & Sat midnight)*
Mr Chow
Mr Kong *(2.45 am)*
New Mayflower *(3.45 am)*
Noura: *William St SW1 ; Hobart Pl SW1, Jermyn St SW1, W1 (12.30am, Thu-Sat 1am)*
Orso
Ozer
Paradiso Olivelli: *all branches*
The Penthouse *(1 am)*
Ping Pong
Pizza on the Park
Planet Hollywood *(1 am)*
Quaglino's *(midnight, Fri & Sat 1 am)*
Ranoush: *SW1*
La Rueda: *all branches (Sat & Sun midnight)*
Satsuma *(Fri & Sat midnight)*
Savoy Hotel (Banquette)
J Sheekey
Smollensky's: *WC2 (Thu-Sat midnight 12.15 am)*
Sofra: *all branches*
Soho Spice *(Mon-Tue midnight, Wed-Sat 2 am)*
Souk
La Spiga *(Wed-Sat midnight)*
Stock Pot: *W1*
TGI Friday's: *all branches (Fri & Sat midnight)*
Tokyo Diner
Trader Vics *(12.30 am)*
The Wolseley
Yo! Sushi: *Poland St W1*

### West
Balans: *W4, W8 ; SW5 (2 am)*
Beach
  Blanket Babylon
Beirut Express *(1 am)*
Big Easy *(Fri & Sat 12.20 am)*
Bistrot 190
Blue Elephant
Buona Sera: *all branches*
Café Lazeez: *SW7 (12.30 am)*
Cheyne Walk Bras'
(Ciro's) Pizza
  Pomodoro: *SW3 (1 am)*
Ed's Easy Diner: *SW3 (Fri & Sat 1 am)*
Fairuz: *W2*
Harlem: *all branches (2 am)*
Khan's of Kensington *(Fri & Sat midnight)*
Lomo
Lou Pescadou
Maroush: *I) 21 Edgware Rd W2 (1.45 am); IV) 68 Edgware Rd W2 (12.30 am); SW3 (3.30 am)*
Meza *(1.30 am)*
Il Pagliaccio
Paradiso Olivelli: *all branches*
Pucci Pizza
Ranoush: *SW3 ; W8 (1.30 am); W2 (2.30 am)*
La Rueda: *all branches (Sat & Sun midnight)*
606 Club *(12.30 am-1.30 am)*
TGI Friday's: *all branches (Fri & Sat midnight)*
Vingt-Quatre *(24 hours)*
Yas *(5 am)*

### North
Cuba Libre *(Fri & Sat midnight)*
Ed's Easy Diner: *NW3 (Fri & Sat 1 am)*
Gallipoli: *all branches (Fri & Sat midnight)*
Gaucho Grill: *NW3*
Istanbul Iskembecisi *(5 am)*
Kovalam *(Fri & Sat midnight)*
Maxwell's: *all branches*
Le Mercury *(1 am)*
Mestizo
Pasha *(Fri & Sat midnight)*
La Porchetta Pizzeria: *all north branches*
Rodizio Rico: *N1*
Sofra: *all branches*
Toast
Vrisaki

### South
Buona Sera: *all branches*
Fujiyama *(12.45 am, Sat & Sun midnight)*
Gastro
Harlem: *all branches (2 am)*
Matilda's
Mirch Masala: *all branches*
Paradiso Olivelli: *all branches*
La Rueda: *all branches (Sat & Sun midnight)*
Sree Krishna *(Fri & Sat midnight)*
Tiger Lil's: *SW4 (Fri & Sat midnight)*

### East
Barcelona Tapas: *EC4 (2.30 am)*
Brick Lane Beigel Bake *(24 hours)*
Cellar Gascon
(Ciro's) Pizza Pomodoro: *EC2*
The Green *(Thu-Sat midnight)*
Mangal

La Porchetta Pizzeria: EC1
Scuzi: all branches
Sofra: all branches
Vic Naylors (1 am)

## NO-SMOKING AREAS
### (* completely no smoking)

### Central
Abeno Too*
About Thyme
The Admiralty
Apostrophe: all branches*
Archipelago
Asia de Cuba
Atrium*
Baker & Spice: all branches*
Balans: all branches
Benares*
Beotys
Bertorelli's: all branches
Bistro 1: WC2
Black & Blue: W1
Blandford Street
Blue Lagoon: all branches
Bodean's: W1*
Boulevard
Boxwood Café*
Brahms
Brasserie Roux
Brian Turner
British Museum*
Broadway Bar & Grill
Browns: all branches
Busaba Eathai: Wardour St W1, WC1*
Café Bagatelle*
Café Bohème
Café Fish
Café in the Crypt
Café Lazeez: all branches
Caldesi
Carluccio's Caffè: all central branches
Le Cercle*
Chada: all branches
Chai Pani
Chez Gérard: all branches
Chor Bizarre
Chowki
Chuen Cheng Ku
The Cinnamon Club
Cocoon*
Como Lario
Connaught (Angela Hartnett)*
Cork & Bottle
Cristini: all branches
Crivelli's Garden*
Crussh: SW1*
Curryleaf: all branches
dim T: W1
Eat & Two Veg
Ebury Street Wine Bar
Ed's Easy Diner: all central branches*
Eddalino
Efes II: all branches
Exotika*
Feng Sushi: SW1*
The Fifth Floor (Café)
Fine Burger Company: W1*

Fishworks: all branches*
Food for Thought*
Footstool
Fortnum's, The Fountain
La Fromagerie Café*
Gaby's
La Galette*
Getti: all branches
Giardinetto
Gili Gulu*
Giraffe: all branches*
Golden Hind
Gordon Ramsay at Claridge's*
Goring Hotel
Gourmet Pizza Co.: all branches
Goya: Ecclestone Pl SW1
Greig's
Grocer on Warwick Café*
Hamburger Union: all branches*
Hard Rock Café*
Hardy's
Hare & Tortoise: WC1*
Harry Ramsden's
Homage
Hunan
Ikkyu
Indigo*
Inn the Park*
Ishtar*
Itsu: Wardour St W1*
Joe Allen
Kazan
Kettners
Konditor & Cook: all branches*
Kulu Kulu: WC2*; W1
Leon*
Lindsay House
Livebait: all branches
Loch Fyne: all branches
Maggiore's*
Maison Bertaux
Malabar Junction
Masala Zone: all branches*
Maxwell's: WC2
Mediterranean
   Kitchen: all branches
Mela
Melati
Michael Moore*
Michiaki*
Mildred's*
Mitsukoshi
Mju
Monmouth Coffee
   Company: all branches*
Nahm*
Neal Street
New Culture
   Revolution: all branches
New World
Nicole's*
Nobu
Noodle Noodle: all branches*
Occo
Odin's
115 at Hodgson's
One-O-One

L'Oranger
Oriel
Orrery
Orso
Oscar
Page in Pimlico*
Le Pain Quotidien*
Pan-Asian Canteen
Pasta Brown: *all branches*
Patara: *all branches*
Pâtisserie Valerie: *all branches*
Patterson's
Paul: *all branches*
Pearl
Pétrus*
Pied à Terre
Ping Pong*
Pizza on the Park
Planet Hollywood
Il Pomodorino
Poons
Porters English Restaurant
The Portrait*
The Providores*
Tapa Room (Providores)*
Quilon
Quo Vadis
Quod
Rainforest Café*
Rasa Maricham: *WC1\*; both W1*
Red Veg*
Reubens*
RIBA Café*
Richoux: *all branches*
The Ritz*
Roka*
Roussillon
Royal Academy*
Royal Court Bar
Rules*
Rusticana
Salt Yard*
Sardo
Satsuma*
Savoy Grill*
Savoy Hotel (Banquette)*
Shepherd's
Sketch (Lecture Rm)
Sketch (Parlour)*
Smollensky's: *WC2*
Soho Spice
Sotheby's Café*
Le Soufflé
Souk
La Spighetta
Spoon at Sanderson
Sri Thai Soho
Star Café
Stock Pot: *all branches*
Strada: *all branches*
Sumosan
Taro: *all branches\**
Tate Britain*
TGI Friday's: *W1*
Thai Café
Thai Pot
Thai Square: *all branches*

Tokyo Diner
Tomato*
Trader Vics
Truc Vert*
Tuttons*
Umu*
The Union Café
Veeraswamy
Villandry*
Wagamama: *all central branches\**
Wolfe's
The Wolseley
Yauatcha*
Yming
Yo! Sushi: *both SW1, Poland St W1,*
  *Oxford St W1, Rupert St W1, WC1\**
Zizzi: *all branches*

**West**
Abbaye: *all branches*
The Abingdon
Abu Zaad
Al San Vincenzo*
Anarkali
The Anglesea Arms
Aquasia
Arturo
As Greek As It Gets
Aubaine*
Babes 'n' Burgers*
Babylon*
Baker & Spice: *all branches\**
Balans West: *all branches*
Basilico: *SW6\**
Beaufort House*
Bedlington Café*
Ben's Thai
Big Easy
Bistrot 190
Black & Blue: *all west branches*
El Blasõn
Blue Kangaroo*
Blue Lagoon: *all branches*
Bombay Brasserie
Bombay Palace
The Brackenbury*
Brasserie de l'Auberge
Brilliant
The Builder's Arms
The Burlington
Bush Garden Café*
Cactus Blue
Café Crêperie de
  Hampstead: *SW7\**
Café Laville
Café Lazeez: *all branches*
Capital Hotel*
Carluccio's Caffè: *all west branches*
Chelsea Kitchen
Chez Marcelle
Choys
Churchill Arms
Chutney Mary
Clarke's*
Costa's Grill
Cristini: *all branches*
The Crown & Sceptre
Crussh: *all west branches\**

Daquise
Ealing Park Tavern*
Ed's Easy Diner: SW3
1880*
Est Est Est: W4
La Famiglia
Fat Boy's: all branches
Feng Sushi: all west branches*
Fish Hoek
Fishworks: all branches*
Formosa Dining Room*
1492
Frantoio
Fresco
The Frontline Club
Geale's
Ginger
Giraffe: all branches*
Glaisters
Gordon Ramsay*
Gourmet Burger
    Kitchen: all branches*
The Green Olive
The Grove
Haandi
Hare & Tortoise: W5
Hole in the Wall
Inaho*
Island
Itsu: SW3*
Jim Thompson's: all branches
kare kare
Khan's
Khan's of Kensington
Khyber Pass
Kulu Kulu: SW7
Latymers*
The Ledbury*
Loch Fyne: all branches
Loco Locale: all branches
Lots Road
Lowiczanka
Lucio
Luna Rossa
Mandalay*
Manicomio
Mao Tai: all branches
Masala Zone: all branches*
Matriciano
Mawar
Mediterranean
    Kitchen: all branches
Mediterraneo
Mona Lisa
Moroccan Tagine
New Culture Rev'n: all branches
Nikita's
Noor Jahan: W2
Notting Grill
Notting Hill Brasserie
Nyonya*
Old Parr's Head
The Oratory*
Osteria Basilico*
Osteria dell'Arancio
The Papaya Tree
Patara: all branches

Patio
Pâtisserie Valerie: all branches
The Phoenix
Pissarro's
Queen's Head
Racine
Raoul's Café*
Rasoi Vineet Bhatia*
Richoux: all branches
The River Café*
Sabai Sabai
Sagar
San Frediano
Santa Lucia
The Scarsdale
Seven Stars
Shikara
Shish: all branches*
Silks & Spice: all branches
Standard Tandoori
Stock Pot: all branches
Strada: all branches
Tartine: SW3
The Tea Palace*
The Tenth
TGI Friday's: all west branches
The Thai
Thai Bistro*
Thai Square: all branches
The Thatched House
Timo*
Tom Aikens*
Tom's*
La Trompette*
202*
Le Vacherin*
The Vale
Wagamama: W8*
White Horse*
Whole Hog Canteen*
The Windsor Castle
Yas on the Park
Yo! Sushi: all west branches*
Zizzi: all branches
Zuma*

**North**
The Almeida
Anglo Asian Tandoori
L'Artista
Les Associés
Baker & Spice: all branches*
Bar Mezé: all branches
The Barnsbury
Base: all north branches
Bistro Aix
Black & Blue: NW3
Browns: all branches
The Bull*
Café de Maya
Café Japan*
Café Mozart*
La Cage Imaginaire
Cantina Italia
Carluccio's Caffè: N1, NW3
Casale Franco
Chamomile
Chez Liline

Chutneys*
Cottons
Cube & Star*
Diwana B-P House*
The Drapers Arms*
The Duke of Cambridge
Ed's Easy Diner: NW3
Est Est Est: N1
Fifteen*
Fig*
Fine Burger Company: all north branches*
Fishworks: all branches*
Florians
The Fox Reformed
Fratelli la Bufala
Frederick's
Freemasons Arms*
Furnace
The Garden Café*
Giraffe: all branches*
Globe Restaurant
Gourmet Burger Kitchen: all branches*
Great Nepalese
The Greyhound
Haché*
Halepi: NW3
The Haven*
The Highgate
The House
Hoxton Square Bar & Kitchen
Isarn*
Jashan: HA0*
Jim Thompson's: all branches
Kaifeng*
Kovalam
Landmark (Winter Garden)
The Little Bay: NW6
Little Earth Cafe*
Mango Room
Manna*
Marine Ices*
Masala Zone: all branches*
Mediterranean Kitchen: all branches
Mestizo
Metrogusto
Morgan M*
Mosaica
New Culture Rev'n: all branches
Odette's*
The Parsee
Phoenix Palace
Pizzeria Oregano
La Porchetta Pizzeria: all north branches
Queen's Head & Artichoke
Rani*
Rasa Travancore: N16*
Rasa*
Richoux: all branches
Rodizio Rico: N1
Rosmarino
Sabras
Sakonis*
San Carlo
San Daniele

Sardo Canale
Sarracino
Seashell
Shish: all branches*
Silks & Spice: all branches
Solly's Exclusive*
Strada: all branches
Sushi-Say*
Thai Square: all branches
Tiger Lil's: all branches
Toff's
Troika
Two Brothers*
Viet-Anh
Wagamama: all north branches*
Walnut
Yo! Sushi: all north branches*
Yum Yum
Yuzu*
Zamoyski
Zamzama
Zizzi: all branches
Zuccato: all branches

## South

Amano Café*
Amaranth
The Anchor & Hope*
Archduke Wine Bar
Auberge: all south branches
The Aviary*
Babur Brasserie
Balham Kitchen & Bar
The Banana Leaf Canteen
Bankside: all branches
Bar Estrela
Bar Mezé: all branches
Basilico: SW14*
Bermondsey Kitchen
The Blue Pumpkin*
Le Bouchon Bordelais
Bread & Roses
The Bridge*
Browns: all branches
Burnt Chair*
La Buvette*
Café Portugal
Cantina Vinopolis*
Canyon
Carluccio's Caffè: SW15
Chada: all branches
Chakalaka
Chapter Two*
Chez Bruce*
Chez Gérard: all branches
The County Hall Rest'*
Dalchini*
The Depot
Dexter's Grill
Ditto
don Fernando's
Eco: SW4
Emile's
Enoteca Turi
Est Est Est: SW19
EV*
Evo
Fat Boy's: all branches

The Fentiman Arms
Ferrari's
La Finca
Fine Burger Company: SW12*
The Fire Stables
Fish Club*
Fish in a Tie
fish!
The Food Room
The Freemasons*
Fujiyama
Gastro*
Giraffe: all branches*
Glas*
The Glasshouse*
Gourmet Burger
   Kitchen: all branches*
Gourmet Pizza Co.: all branches
Hampton's Restaurant*
The Hartley
Indian Ocean
Inshoku
Inside
Just India
Kew Grill*
Konditor & Cook: all branches*
Kwan Thai
Lamberts
La Lanterna
The Light House
Livebait: all branches
Lobster Pot
Loch Fyne: all branches
Loco Mensa: all branches
Louvaine
Ma Cuisine: all branches*
Ma Goa*
McClements*
Mezzanine*
Mirch Masala: SW17*
Monmouth Coffee
   Company: all branches*
Morel*
Murano*
MVH
Naked Turtle
Newton's
Niksons
The Painted Heron: SE11
The Palmerston
Panzella
The People's Palace*
The Pepper Tree
Le Petit Max*
Phoenix
Pizza Metro
Prego
Putney Station
Ransome's Dock
Real Burger World*
Redmond's*
Rick's Café
Riviera
Rocket Riverside: SW15
Sarkhel's: SW18
The Sea Cow: SE22*
Shakespeare's Globe*

Silka*
Sonny's
Spread Eagle
Sree Krishna
Strada: all branches
The Sun & Doves
Talad Thai*
Tandoori Nights
Tas: Borough High St SE1
Tate Restaurant*
Tate Café*
Thai Elephant
Thai Square: all branches
Thailand*
3 Monkeys*
Tiger Lil's: all branches
Tootsies: SW11, SW15
Tsunami
El Vergel*
Wagamama: SW15*
The Wharf
Yo! Sushi: SE1*
Zero Degrees
Zizzi: all branches

*East*
Abbaye: all branches
Apium*
Apostrophe: all branches*
Aquarium
Arkansas Café
Bankside: all branches
Bertorelli's: all branches
Bevis Marks*
Brick Lane Beigel Bake*
Browns: all branches
Carluccio's Caffè: all east branches
Chamberlain's
Chez Gérard: all branches
Cicada
Club Mangia
Coco
The Crown*
Crussh: all east branches*
Curryleaf: all branches
1802
Ekachai
Elephant Royale
Eyre Brothers
Faulkner's
La Figa
Fish Shop
Flâneur*
Gourmet Pizza Co.: all branches
Gow's
The Grapes*
Itsu: E14*
Just Gladwins
K10*
Kasturi
Kurumaya*
Malmaison
Mehek
Moshi Moshi: all branches*
New Tayyabs
Ye Olde
   Cheshire Cheese
Pacific Oriental

Pâtisserie Valerie: *all branches*
Pham Sushie
The Place Below*
La Porchetta Pizzeria: *EC1*
Potemkin*
Quadrato
Rudland Stubbs
St John
Santa Maria de Buen Ayre*
Savarona
Scuzi: *all branches*
Searcy's Brasserie
Shish: *all branches*
Silks & Spice: *all branches*
Singapura: *all branches*
Sông Quê
South
Sri Siam City
Story Deli*
Strada: *all branches*
Tatsuso
Terminus
Thai Square City: *all branches*
Throgmorton
Ubon
Viet Hoa
Wagamama: *all east branches*
Winkles
Yo! Sushi: *EC1*
Young Bin
Zizzi: *all branches*
Zuccato: *all branches*

**OUTSIDE TABLES**
**(* particularly recommended)**
*Central*
About Thyme
Al Hamra*
Al Sultan
Apostrophe: *Barrett St W1, WC2*
Archipelago
L'Artiste Musclé*
Auberge: *W1*
Aurora*
Back to Basics
Baker & Spice: *SW1*
Bank Westminster
Bar Italia
Benugo: *all branches*
Bertorelli's: *both W1*
Bistro 1: *all branches*
Black & Blue: *W1*
Blandford Street
Boisdale
Boudin Blanc*
Boulevard
Brahms*
Brian Turner
Busaba Eathai: *WC1*
Café Bohème
Café des Amis du Vin*
Café du Jardin
Caffè Caldesi
Camerino
Caraffini
Carluccio's Caffè: *Market Pl W1*
Chada: *W1*

Chez Gérard: *Dover St W1, East Ter, Covent Garden WC2*; SW1, Charlotte St W1, Chancery Ln WC2*
Ciao Bella
Cigala
The Contented Vine
Il Convivio
Cristini: *all branches*
Delfino
The Easton
Ed's Easy Diner: *Moor St W1*
Efes Restaurant: *Gt Titchfield St W1*
Embassy
The Endurance
Fairuz: *W1*
The Fifth Floor (Café)
Fine Burger Company: *W1*
43 South Molton
Gabrielles*
La Galette
Garlic & Shots
Getti: *all branches*
Giraffe: *all branches*
Gordon's Wine Bar*
Goya: *all branches*
The Greenhouse
Greig's
Ha! Ha!: *all central branches*
Hardy's
Hush*
Imperial China
Inn the Park*
Ishbilia
Ishtar
Italian Kitchen
Jaan*
Jenny Lo's
Langan's Bistro
Leon
Little Italy
The Little Square
Mamounia
Mash
Mediterranean Kitchen: *all branches*
Mekong
Mela
Michael Moore
Mirabelle*
Momo
Mongolian Barbecue: *WC2*
Motcombs
Noble Rot
Nobu
Occo
L'Oranger
Oriel*
Original Tajines
Orrery
Oscar
Ozer
Page in Pimlico
Papageno
Paradiso Olivelli: *WC1*
Pasta Brown: *all branches*
Pâtisserie Valerie: *Motcomb St SW1, Piccadilly W1, Marylebone High St W1*
The Perseverance

El Pirata
Porters English Restaurant
La Poule au Pot*
Tapa Room (Providores)
Reubens
RIBA Café*
Richoux: *South Audley St W1*
The Ritz*
Roka
La Rueda: *all branches*
Running Horse
Salt Yard
Santini
Sapori
Sardo
Satsuma
Seafresh
Serafino
Signor Zilli
06 St Chad's Place
Sofra: *St Christopher's Pl W1*;
     *Shepherd St W1*
Spoon at Sanderson*
Stock Pot: *W1*
Strada: *Market Pl W1*;
     *New Burlington St W1*
Texas Embassy Cantina
Tomato
Tootsies: *W1*
Toto's*
La Trouvaille
Truc Vert
Tuttons
Uno
Villandry
Wolfe's
Yo! Sushi: *Woodstock St W1*
Zilli Fish
Zinc: *W1*
Zizzi: *Paddington St W1, Bow St WC2*

**West**
Abbaye: *SW7*
The Abingdon*
Admiral Codrington*
Al-Waha
The Anglesea Arms
The Anglesea Arms
Annie's: *all branches*
Aquasia*
The Ark
Arturo
The Atlas*
Babylon*
Balans: *W4*
Base: *all branches*
Beach
   Blanket Babylon
Beaufort House
Bedlington Café
Belvedere*
Benugo: *all branches*
Bibendum Oyster Bar
Big Easy
Black & Blue: *all west branches*
Bluebird Café*
The Bollo House
Bombay Brasserie
Bombay Palace

The Brackenbury*
La Brasserie
Brinkley's*
The Builder's Arms
The Burlington
Bush Bar & Grill*
Bush Garden Café
Cactus Blue
Café Crêperie de
   Hampstead: *SW7*
Café Laville*
Café Lazeez: *SW7*
Café Med: *W6*
Chelsea Kitchen
Chez Kristof*
Deli
Le Colombier*
Costa's Grill
Cotto
Cristini: *all branches*
The Crown & Sceptre*
Crussh: *W12*
Dan's*
Daphne's*
De Cecco*
Deep*
La Delizia
Devonshire House
Dove
E&O
Ealing Park Tavern
Edera
Electric Brasserie
Elistano
Il Falconiere
La Famiglia*
The Farm
Fat Boy's: *W5*
FireHouse
First Floor
Fishworks: *W4*
Friends
The Gate*
El Gaucho: *SW3*
Geale's
Giraffe: *all branches*
Glaisters*
Gourmet Burger Kitchen: *W4*
Gravy
The Green Olive
The Grove
Haandi
The Havelock Tavern
Henry J Beans*
Hole in the Wall*
I Thai
Jim Thompson's: *SW6*
Joe's Brasserie
Julie's
Julie's Wine Bar*
Kandoo
kare kare
The Ladbroke Arms*
Latymers
The Ledbury
Levantine
Lisboa Patisserie

Loco Locale: SW6
Lou Pescadou
Luna Rossa
Lundum's
Made in Italy
The Mall Tavern
Manicomio*
Mao Tai: SW3
Matriciano
Mediterranean
   Kitchen: all branches
Mediterraneo
Mohsen
Mona Lisa
Montpeliano
Monza*
Moroccan Tagine
Noor Jahan: W2
Notting Grill
The Oak
Old Parr's Head*
The Oratory
Osteria dell'Arancio
Il Pagliaccio
The Painted Heron: all branches
Pappa Ciccia: all branches
Paradise by Way of
   Kensal Green*
Pâtisserie Valerie: all west branches
Pellicano
The Pen
Père Michel
The Phoenix
Picasso
The Pilot*
Poissonnerie
   de l'Avenue
Ognisko Polskie*
Il Portico
Pucci Pizza
Queen's Head*
Randall & Aubin: SW10
Raoul's Café*
The Red Pepper
Relais de Paris
Riccardo's
The River Café*
The Rocket
Rôtisserie Jules: SW7
La Rueda: all branches
Santa Lucia
The Scarsdale*
Seven Stars
Smollensky's: W6
Sporting Page
Stone Mason's Arms
Stratford's
The Swan*
La Tasca: W5
Tendido Cero
Thai Noodle Bar
The Thatched House*
Tom's*
Tootsies: SW6, SW7, W11
La Trompette
Troubadour
Tugga

202
Uli*
Le Vacherin
Vama
Vingt-Quatre
The Waterway*
The Westbourne*
White Horse*
William IV*
The Windsor Castle*
Wine Factory
Wine Gallery*
Yas on the Park
Yi-Ban: all branches
Zinc: SW6
Zizzi: W4
Zucca

**North**
The Arches
Artigiano*
L'Artista
Les Associés
L'Aventure*
Baker & Spice: NW6
The Barnsbury
Base: all branches
Bastille
The Belsize
Black & Blue: NW3
La Brocca
The Bull
Café Med: NW8
Café Mozart*
La Cage Imaginaire
Casale Franco*
Chamomile
The Chapel*
Crown & Goose
Cuba Libre
Daphne*
dim T café: NW3
The Drapers Arms
The Duke of Cambridge
The Elk in the Woods
The Engineer*
Fig
Florians
The Fox Reformed*
Fratelli la Bufala
Frederick's*
Freemasons Arms*
Gallipoli: all branches
The Garden Café*
Gaucho Grill: NW3
Giraffe: all branches
Gourmet Burger
   Kitchen: all north branches
The Green
The Greyhound
Haché
Harry Morgan's
The Highgate
The Hill
The House
Hoxton Apprentice*
Hoxton Square Bar & Kitchen
Isarn

Jashan: HA0
The Junction Tavern
Lansdowne
Lemonia
The Little Bay: NW6
The Lord Palmerston
Masala Zone: N1
Maxwell's: NW3
Mediterranean
   Kitchen: all branches
Metrogusto
Mosaica
No 77 Wine Bar
The Northgate
Ottolenghi: N1
Pasha
Petit Auberge
Philpotts Mezzaluna
La Porchetta Pizzeria: NW1
The Pumphouse*
Queen's Head & Artichoke
Queen's Pub & Dining Rm
Rasa
The Real Greek
Richoux: NW8
Rosmarino*
S & M Café: N1
Le Sacré-Coeur
St Johns
The Salusbury
San Carlo*
Sardo Canale
Sargasso Sea
Sedir
Silks & Spice: NW1
Singapore Garden
Sofra: NW8
Solly's Exclusive
Strada: N1
La Superba*
Tootsies: NW3
Troika
Villa Bianca
The Vine*
Walnut
The Wells*
Yelo: N1
Yuzu
Zuccato: NW3

**South**
The Abbeville
Al Forno
Amano Café*
The Anchor & Hope
Annie's: all branches
Antipasto & Pasta
Antipasto e Pasta
Arancia
Archduke Wine Bar
Auberge: all south branches
The Aviary
Balham Kitchen & Bar
Baltic
Bar du Musee*
Bar Estrela*
Bar Mezé: SW11
Barcelona Tapas: SE22

Beauberry House*
The Blue Pumpkin
Bodean's: SW4
Boiled Egg*
Le Bouchon Bordelais
Bread & Roses*
The Bridge*
Browns: all south branches
Brula
Buchan's
Buona Sera: SW11
Butlers Wharf
   Chop-house*
La Buvette
Café Portugal
Cantina del Ponte*
Il Cantuccio di Pulcinella
Canyon*
The Castle*
Chez Gérard: SE1
Cinnamon Cay
The Depot*
Dexter's Grill
don Fernando's
Duke of Cambridge
Earl Spencer
Eco: all branches
EV
Evo
Fat Boy's: W4*; TW1
Feng Sushi: SE1
The Fentiman Arms
Ferrari's
Fine Burger Company: SW12
Firezza
Fish Club
fish!*
The Fox & Hounds
Franklins
The Freemasons
Gastro
Ghillies: SW18
Giraffe: all branches
Gourmet Burger Kitchen: SW11
Gourmet Pizza Co.: SE1*
The Greyhound
Hot Stuff
Hudson's
Kwan Thai*
La Lanterna
The Lavender: all branches
The Light House
Little Bay: SW11
Loch Fyne: TW2
Loco Mensa: SE1
Louvaine
Ma Cuisine: all branches
The Mason's Arms
Matilda's
Murano
MVH
Naked Turtle
Nancy Lam's Enak Enak
Newton's
Niksons
Nosh
Numero Uno

Ost. Antica Bologna
Oxo Tower (Bras')*
Oxo Tower (Rest')
The Painted Heron: *all branches*
The Palmerston
Panzella
Pappa Ciccia: *all branches*
Paradiso Olivelli: *SE1*
The Pepper Tree
Petersham Nurseries*
Le Petit Max
Phoenix
Pizza Metro
Pomino
Le Pont de la Tour*
Le Pont de la Tour
   Bar & Grill*
Popeseye: *SW15*
Prego
Ransome's Dock*
Rapscallion
Real Greek Souvlaki &
   Bar: *all branches*
Riva
Riviera*
Rocket Riverside: *SW15*
La Rueda: *all branches*
San Lorenzo Fuoriporta
Scoffers
The Sequel
Settle Inn*
The Ship*
Spread Eagle
Strada: *SW11*
The Sun & Doves*
Tandoori Nights
Tas: *The Cut SE1*
Tas Pide: *SE1*
Thai on the River*
Thai Square: *SW15*
Tootsies: *all south branches*
El Vergel
The Victoria
The Waterloo
   Fire Station
White Cross*
Zizzi: *SW11*

### East
Apostrophe: *EC2*
Aquarium*
Arkansas Café
Armadillo
Bar Capitale: *all branches*
Benugo: *all branches*
Bevis Marks*
Bleeding Heart*
Brasserie Rocque*
Browns: *E14*
Café Spice Namaste*
Carluccio's Caffè: *all east branches*
Carnevale*
Cat & Mutton
Chamberlain's
Cicada
(Ciro's) Pizza Pomodoro: *EC2*
Club Mangia
Coach & Horses

Coco
Coq d'Argent*
The Crown
The Eagle
1802*
Elephant Royale*
Epicurean Pizza Lounge
The Evangelist
Exmouth Grill
La Figa
First Edition
Fish Shop
The Fox
Frocks*
Gaucho Grill: *E14*
Gourmet Pizza Co.: *E14*
The Green
The Gun
The Gunmakers
Hadley House
Just The Bridge
The Light
Lightship*
Lilly's
The Little Bay: *EC1*
LMNT
Medcalf
The Morgan Arms
Moro
New Tayyabs
Paternoster Chop House*
Pâtisserie Valerie: *E1*
The Peasant
Perc%nto
The Place Below*
Plateau*
La Porchetta Pizzeria: *EC1*
Quadrato*
The Real Greek
   Souvlaki: *all branches*
Royal China: *E14*
The Royal Exchange
S & M Café: *E1*
Santa Maria de Buen Ayre
Scuzi: *E14*
Shish: *EC1*
Singapura: *EC4*
Smiths (Top Floor)*
Smiths (Ground Floor)
Smollensky's: *E14*
Sofra: *EC1*
Story Deli*
Taberna Etrusca*
La Tasca: *E14*
Terminus
Wapping Food
The Well
Winkles
Yi-Ban: *all branches*

## PRIVATE ROOMS

**(for the most comprehensive
listing of venues for functions –
from palaces to pubs – see
*Harden's London Party &
Corporate Event Guide*, available
in all good bookshops)
* particularly recommended**

### Central

About Thyme (45)
Adam Street (60,40,15)*
The Admiralty (30,60)
Alastair Little (25)
Albannach (20)
Alloro (16)
Amaya (14)
Aperitivo (30)
Archipelago (35)
L'Artiste Musclé (25)
Asia de Cuba (40)
Atlantic Bar & Grill (70)*
Atrium (14)
Auberge: W1 (100)
Aurora (20)
Axis (48)*
Bam-Bou (12,14,20)
Bank Aldwych
Bank Westminster (22,22)*
Belgo Centraal: WC2 (25,30)
Benares (12,18,22)
Benihana: W1 (10)
Bentley's (14)*
Beotys (6,60)
Berkeley Square Café (14)
Bertorelli's: Charlotte St W1 (20,45);
    Frith St W1 (80)
Bistro 1: W1 (20)
Blandford Street (18)
Boisdale (22)*
Boudin Blanc (14)
Boulevard (90)
Boxwood Café (16)
Brasserie Roux (12)
Brian Turner (60)
British Museum (16,16)
Broadway Bar & Grill (30)
Browns: WC2 (120,80,50);
    W1 (16,8,8,4)
Busaba Eathai: WC1 (15)
Café Bagatelle (80)
Café des Amis du Vin (75)
Café du Jardin (60)
Café Fish (70)
Café in the Crypt (70)
Café Lazeez: W1 (10)
Caldesi (20)
Chada: W1 (35)
Chez Gérard: Charlotte St W1 (12);
    Dover St W1 (15); Chancery Ln WC2 (40)
Chiang Mai (30)
Chimes (30)
Chisou (6,6)
Chor Bizarre (30)
Christopher's (40)
Chuen Cheng Ku (40,100)
Cigala (40)
The Cinnamon Club (50,25)

Circus (16)
Cocoon (14)*
Como Lario (30)
Connaught (Angela
    Hartnett) (12,24,50)
The Contented Vine (20,45)
Il Convivio (14)
Cristini: all branches (12)
CVO Firevault (8,8)
Defune (8)
Destino (14)
Dover Street (65,120)
Drones (45)
The Ebury (35)
ECapital (40)
Eddalino (30)
Efes Restaurant: Gt Titchfield St
    W1 (45)
Elena's L'Etoile (10,14,16,34)
L'Escargot (24,60)*
L'Estaminet (14)
Fairuz: W1 (30)
5 Cavendish Square (24)
Floridita (4,56)
Fortnum's, The Fountain (56)
43 South Molton (15)
Fung Shing (20,50)
Gabrielles (30)
Garbo's (40)
Garlic & Shots (25)
Gay Hussar (12,24)*
Getti: SW1 (50); W1 (80)
Giardinetto (15)
Golden Dragon (40)
Golden Hind (25)
Gonbei (16)
Gordon Ramsay at
    Claridge's (30,10,12,60)
Goring Hotel (15,10,50)*
Goya: Ecclestone Pl SW1 (45); Lupus St
    SW1 (60)
Green's (36)
The Greenhouse (10)*
Greig's (8,16,40)
Grumbles (10)
The Guinea (22)
Hakkasan (80)
Harbour City (80,60,50)
Hardy's (12,16,32)
Hazuki (20)
Homage (35)
Hush (15,60)
Ikeda (12)
Ikkyu (12)
Imperial China (180)
L'Incontro (32)
Indigo (30,50)
Ishbilia (5)
Ishtar (6)
The Ivy (60)*
Joy King Lau (60)
Just St James (140)
Kai Mayfair (6,12)
Kazan (20,30)
Ken Lo's Memories (12,14)
Kettners (4,90)*
Koba (12)
The Lanesborough (120)

Levant *(10,12)*
Lindsay House *(8,12,24,32)**
The Little Square *(14)*
Loch Fyne: *WC2 (50)*
Luigi's *(14,20,35)*
Maggiore's *(32)*
Malabar Junction *(40)*
Mamounia *(35)*
— Manzi's *(45)*
Maroush: *V) 3-4 Vere St W1 (90)*
Mash *(10,20,30,60,100)*
Matsuri: *WC1 (10); SW1 (18)*
maze *(8)*
Mediterranean Kitchen: *WC2 (30)*
Mela *(40)*
Melati *(32)*
Messanges *(50)*
Michael Moore *(16)*
Michiaki *(18)*
Mildred's *(24)*
Mimmo d'Ischia *(20,28)*
Mint Leaf *(60)*
— Mirabelle *(36,48)*
Mitsukoshi *(12,22)*
Momo *(100)*
Mon Plaisir *(28)*
Mosaico *(24)*
Motcombs *(18,32)*
Mr Chow *(10,60,75)*
Nahm *(30)*
Neal Street *(24)*
New World *(200)*
Noble Rot *(50)*
Nobu *(130)*
North Sea Fish *(40)*
O'Conor Don *(60)*
Occo *(20)*
115 at Hodgson's *(15,20,20)*
L'Oranger *(24)**
Oriel *(40)*
Oscar *(70)*
Page in Pimlico *(35)*
Pan-Asian Canteen *(100)*
Papageno *(120)*
Pappagallo *(20)*
Paradiso Olivelli: *WC1 (50)*
Passione *(18)*
Pasta Brown: *Bow St WC2 (50)*
Patara: *Greek St W1 (30)*
Patterson's *(32)*
Pearl *(12)*
The Penthouse *(32)*
The Perseverance *(25)*
Pétrus *(16)**
Pied à Terre *(12)*
Pizza on the Park *(80)*
Planet Hollywood *(100)*
Pomegranates *(12,12)*
Il Pomodorino *(12,15)*
La Porte des Indes *(12-80)*
Porters English Restaurant *(36)*
La Poule au Pot *(14)*
Princess Garden *(50,50,50)*
Quaglino's *(44)*
Quo Vadis *(12,14,30,80)*
Quod *(10,50,60,70)*
Rainforest Café *(20,100,360)*

Rasa Samudra: *Charlotte St W1 (10,50); Dering St W1 (60)*
Red Fort *(150)*
Refuel *(12)*
Rib Room *(18)*
RIBA Café *(20)*
Richoux: *South Audley St W1 (6)*
The Ritz *(20,50)**
Rocket: *W1 (35)*
Roussillon *(26)*
Royal China: *W1 (12,12,12)*
Royal Court Bar *(20)*
Rules *(12,16,18,24)**
Rusticana *(12)*
Santini *(30)*
Sarastro *(4-28)*
Sartoria *(20,40)*
Savoy Grill *(50)**
Serafino *(28)*
— Shampers *(45)*
Shepherd's *(32)**
Signor Sassi *(30)*
Signor Zilli *(70)*
→ Simpsons-in-the-
Strand *(50,120,140)*
Six-13 *(24)*
Sketch (Gallery) *(74)**
Sketch (Lecture Rm) *(24,130)*
Sketch (Parlour) *(24)*
Sofra: *Shepherd St W1 (16); WC2 (19)*
Soho Spice *(30)*
Souk *(7,10,20,30,15)*
Spoon at Sanderson *(50)*
The Square *(18)**
Sri Thai Soho *(26,32)*
Star Café *(35)*
Sugar Reef *(20)*
Sumosan *(70)*
Taman gang *(10)**
Tamarind *(100)*
Texas Embassy Cantina *(200)*
Thai Café *(22)*
Thai Square: *SW1 (8)*
Toto's *(20)**
Trader Vics *(50)*
La Trouvaille *(8-15)*
Tuttons *(50)*
Umu *(12,12)*
Vasco & Piero's Pavilion *(36)*
Veeraswamy *(40)*
Il Vicolo *(45)*
Villandry *(12)*
W'sens *(30)*
Wheeler's of St James's *(4,20)*
Wiltons *(18)**
Windows on the World *(150)*
Wolfe's *(25)*
Yatra *(100)*
Yming *(12,18)*
Zen Central *(20)**
Zinc: *W1 (40)*
**West**
Abbaye: *SW7 (40)*
L'Accento Italiano *(25)*
Adams Café *(24)*
Anarkali *(40)*
Annie's: *W4 (30)*

Aquasia *(14-180)*
Arturo *(15)*
The Atlas *(40)*
Aziz *(50)*
Babes 'n' Burgers *(Family Room)*
Babylon *(12)**
Beach
  Blanket Babylon *(30)**
Belvedere *(20)*
Ben's Thai *(20)*
Benihana: *SW3 (12)*
Bistrot 190 *(16,70)*
Blah! Blah! Blah! *(35)*
Blakes Hotel *(36)*
El Blasón *(20)*
Blue Lagoon: *W14 (30)*
Bluebird *(30,42)*
Bluebird Club & Dining
  Rooms *(24)*
Bombay Palace *(25)*
The Brackenbury *(30)*
Brasserie St Quentin *(20)**
Brilliant *(120)*
Brinkley's *(20,20,45)*
Brunello *(8)*
Busabong *(15)*
Bush Bar & Grill *(50)*
Cactus Blue *(35,75)*
Café Lazeez: *SW7 (55)*
Cambio de Tercio *(22)*
Capital Hotel *(12,24)**
Carpaccio's *(45)*
Charlotte's Place *(16)*
Chelsea Bun Diner *(50)*
Cheyne Walk Bras': *(80)**
Chez Kristof *(50)*
Chez Marcelle *(40)*
Chutney Mary *(24)**
Cibo *(12,16)*
Clarke's *(40)*
The Collection *(50)*
Le Colombier *(30)*
Coopers Arms *(25)*
Costa's Grill *(20)*
Cotto *(35)*
Crazy Homies *(30)*
Cristini: *all branches (12)*
Cross Keys *(40,120)*
Da Mario *(100)*
Dan's *(12,30)**
Daphne's *(40)*
Daquise *(25,50)*
De Cecco *(20)*
Demera *(25)*
E&O *(18)**
Edera *(16)*
Eight Over Eight *(14)**
1880 *(50)*
Il Falconiere *(20,35)*
First Floor *(29,40)**
1492 *(30)*
Foxtrot Oscar *(30)*
The Frontline Club *(100)*
El Gaucho: *SW3 (50)*
Geale's *(25)*
Ginger *(30)*
Glaisters *(40)*

Gravy *(10)*
The Green Olive *(20)*
The Grove *(30)*
Haandi *(12)*
I Thai *(16)*
The Ifield *(24)*
Joe's Brasserie *(25)*
Julie's *(12,16,24,32,45)*
Julie's Wine Bar *(12,45,60)*
kare kare *(20)*
Kensington Place *(45)**
Khan's *(200)*
Langan's Coq d'Or *(20)*
Launceston Place *(12)*
Locanda Ottoemezzo *(20,20)*
Lomo *(20)*
Lonsdale *(25)*
Lou Pescadou *(50)*
Lowiczanka *(40)*
Lucio *(18)*
Luna Rossa *(50)*
Lundum's *(18)*
Made in Italy *(20)*
Madhu's *(35)*
Malabar *(25)*
The Mall Tavern *(20)*
Manicomio *(30)*
Mao Tai: *SW6 (30)**
Masala Zone: *SW5 (20)*
Matriciano *(40)*
Mediterranean Kitchen: *both W8 (40); SW7 (50)*
Memories of India *(30)*
Meza *(44)*
Mirto *(30)*
Mr Wing *(5,5)*
Nam Long *(12,16)*
Napulé *(25)*
Nathalie *(22)*
Nikita's *(6,6,15,15)**
Noor Jahan: *W2 (16)*
Notting Grill *(20)*
Notting Hill Brasserie *(4-44)**
Nuovi Sapori *(30)*
The Oak *(40)*
Osteria dell'Arancio *(25)*
Il Pagliaccio *(60)*
Paradise by Way of
  Kensal Green *(22,110)*
Pasha *(20)*
Patara: *Fulham Rd SW3 (16)*
Pellicano *(25)*
Père Michel *(20)*
The Pilot *(40)*
PJ's *(60)*
Poissonnerie
  de l'Avenue *(20)*
Ognisko Polskie *(150)*
Pucci Pizza *(50)*
Racine *(16)*
Raoul's Café *(18)*
Rasoi Vineet Bhatia *(8,12)**
Riccardo's *(8)*
Richoux: *SW3 (30)*
Rodizio Rico: *W2 (60)*
Royal China: *W2 (15,20)*
La Rueda: *SW6 (50)*
San Frediano *(10)*

San Lorenzo *(30)*
Santa Lucia *(40)*
Snows on the Green *(10,15)*
Standard Tandoori *(55)*
Star of India *(12,12)*
Stone Mason's Arms *(30)*
Stratford's *(30)*
Le Suquet *(16,25)*
Tandoori Lane *(16)*
Tawana *(50)*
The Tenth *(110)*
The Thai *(40)*
Thai Noodle Bar *(25)*
The Thatched House *(50)*
Timo *(15,20)*
Troubadour *(120,34)*
Tugga *(12)*
Le Vacherin *(30)*
The Vale *(20,20,70)*
Vama *(30)*
Vesbar *(80)*
White Horse *(45)*
Whits *(30)*
William IV *(35)*
Wine Factory *(45)*
Wine Gallery *(20,20,45)*
Wizzy *(30)*
Wódka *(30)*
Woodlands: *W4 (100)*
Yas *(34)*
Yas on the Park *(35)*
Zucca *(40)*
Zuma *(12,14)*

**North**

Afghan Kitchen *(25)*
The Almeida *(20)*
Anglo Asian Tandoori *(30)*
The Arches *(25)*
The Belsize *(16)*
Bradley's *(65)*
The Bull *(14,150)*
Café Med: *NW8 (12,30)*
Cantina Italia *(30)*
The Chapel *(30)*
Chutneys *(60,35)*
Crown & Goose *(20)*
Cru *(20)*
Cube & Star *(16)*
Daphne *(50)*
dim T café: *NW3 (40)*
Diwana B-P House *(35)*
The Engineer *(18,32)*
Fine Burger Company: *N1 (30)*
Florians *(15,50)*
Fratelli la Bufala *(25)*
Frederick's *(18,32)*
Furnace *(40)*
Geeta *(45)*
Good Earth: *NW7 (30)*
The Green *(12)*
Gung-Ho *(24)*
Halepi: *NW3 (60)*
The Haven *(50)*
The Highgate *(70)*
The Hill *(20)*
Hoxton Apprentice *(25)*
Huong-Viet *(28)*

Jim Thompson's: *N21 (40,30)*
Lemonia *(40)*
The Lord Palmerston *(30)*
Mango Room *(30)*
Masala Zone: *N1 (20)*
Mediterranean Kitchen: *N1 (30)*
Le Mercury *(50)*
Mestizo *(80)*
Metrogusto *(30)*
Morgan M *(14)*
Odette's *(8)*\*
OQO Bar *(20)*
The Parsee *(18)*
Petit Auberge *(35)*
Phoenix Palace *(10,20)*
Queen's Pub & Dining Rm *(40)*
Rasa Travancore: *N16 (25)*
The Real Greek *(6,20)*
Rosmarino *(10)*
Royal China: *NW8 (15,20)*
Sardo Canale *(30)*
Seashell *(25)*
Sedir *(50)*
Silks & Spice: *NW1 (80)*
Singapore Garden *(7)*
Solly's Exclusive *(100)*
La Superba *(20)*
Sushi-Say *(6)*
Tiger Lil's: *N1 (40)*
Villa Bianca *(40)*
The Vine *(30,15)*
Vrisaki *(14)*
The Wells *(35)*
Weng Wah House *(80)*
Yum Yum *(60)*
Zamoyski *(40)*
Zamzama *(40)*
ZeNW3 *(24)*

**South**

Alma *(70)*
Amaranth *(30)*
Annie's: *SW13 (35)*
Antipasto & Pasta *(30)*
Arancia *(8)*
Archduke Wine Bar *(25,40)*
Auberge: *Sandell St SE1 (150); Tooley St SE1 (200)*
Balham Kitchen & Bar *(25,50)*
Baltic *(35)*
Bar du Musee *(14)*
Barcelona Tapas: *SE22 (15)*
Beauberry House *(15,60)*
Bombay Bicycle Club: *SW12 (20)*
Le Bouchon Bordelais *(50)*
Bread & Roses *(80)*
Brula *(10,20)*
Buchan's *(25,50)*
The Castle *(30)*
Chakalaka *(30)*
Champor-Champor *(8)*
Chez Bruce *(22)*
Chez Gérard: *SE1 (60)*
Chez Lindsay *(30)*
The County Hall Rest' *(50)*
Del Buongustaio *(50)*
Delfina Studio Café *(25,40)*
Dexter's Grill *(40)*

Dish Dash *(30)*
Ditto *(23)*
don Fernando's *(100)*
Duke of Cambridge *(20)*
Earl Spencer *(100)*
Emile's *(45,35)*
Enoteca Turi *(30)*
The Fentiman Arms *(45)*
Fina Estampa *(40)*
La Finca *(100)*
Fish in a Tie *(40,20,60)*
Four Regions: *SE1 (160)*
Franklins *(25)*
Fujiyama *(40,25)*
Garrison *(25)*
The Greyhound *(25)*
Hare & Tortoise: *SW15 (30)*
Inc Bar &
    Restaurant *(20,40,40,100)*
La Lanterna *(85,50)*
Little Bay: *SW11 (80)*
Lobster Pot *(14)*
Louvaine *(22)*
Ma Cuisine: *TW1 (30)*
Ma Goa *(35)*
La Mancha *(60)*
Matilda's *(50,60)*
McClements *(8)*
Murano *(50)*
MVH *(15,25)*
Naked Turtle *(80,100)*
Nancy Lam's Enak Enak *(20)*
Nosh *(20)*
Panzella *(16)*
Pizzeria Castello *(20,30)*
Pomino *(30)*
Le Pont de la Tour *(20)*
Le Pont de la Tour
    Bar & Grill *(20)*
Prego *(40)*
Putney Station *(30,40)*
Rocket Riverside: *SW15 (28)*
RSJ *(24,30)*
San Lorenzo Fuoriporta *(20,30)*
Scoffers *(14)*
Shakespeare's Globe *(30,50,200)*
The Ship *(16)*
Sonny's *(30)*
Spread Eagle *(35)*
Sree Krishna *(50,60)*
Talad Thai *(40)*
Tentazioni *(25)*
Thailand *(28)*
The Trafalgar Tavern *(200)\**
The Waterloo
    Fire Station *(80)*
The Wharf *(50)*
White Cross *(40)*

### East

Abbaye: *EC1 (100)*
Alba *(30)*
Aquarium *(70)*
Armadillo *(25)*
Bar Bourse *(100)*
Barcelona Tapas: *EC4 (30); Beaufort
    Hs, St Botolph St EC3 (75)*
Bistrothèque *(36)*

Bleeding Heart *(50)*
Boisdale of Bishopsgate *(40)*
Bonds *(8,8,16)*
Browns: *EC2 (120); E14 (14)*
Café du Marché *(30,60)\**
Café Spice Namaste *(40)*
Cat & Mutton *(60)*
Cây Tre *(40)*
Chez Gérard: *EC2 (12); EC3 (45)*
Cicada *(70)*
City Miyama *(4,4,8,10)*
The Clerkenwell Dining
    Room *(40)*
Club Mangia *(100)*
Coco *(150)*
The Crown *(32)*
Curryleaf: *EC1 (30)*
$ *(12)*
The Don *(24)\**
Drunken Monkey *(10,30)*
The Evangelist *(100)*
Fox & Anchor *(24)*
Frocks *(30)*
George & Vulture *(14,16,24)*
Gt Eastern Dining Rm *(200)*
The Green *(50)*
The Gun *(12 & 20)*
The Gunmakers *(12)*
Home *(16)*
Hope & Sir Loin *(25)*
Imperial City *(16,80)\**
Lanes *(28)*
Leadenhall Tapas Bar *(30,60)*
The Light *(200)*
Lightship *(35)*
Malmaison *(12)*
Missouri Grill *(14)*
Miyabi *(28)*
Moro *(14)*
New Tayyabs *(40)*
Novelli in the
    City *(4,16,10,25,16,70)*
Ye Olde
    Cheshire Cheese *(40,54)*
1 Blossom Street *(6,12,26)*
1 Lombard Street *(50)*
Pacific Oriental *(40)*
The Peasant *(20)*
Perc%nto *(16,26,40,64)*
Plateau *(24)*
Portal *(10)*
Prism *(20,40,75)\**
Rajasthan *(40)*
The Real Greek
    Souvlaki: *EC1 (40)*
Refettorio *(30)*
Le Rendezvous du Café *(30,60)*
The Rivington Grill *(25)*
Royal China: *E14 (15,20)*
Rudland Stubbs *(12)*
S & M Café: *E1 (45)*
St John *(18)*
Satu Bar & Kitchen *(50)*
Shanghai *(45,50)*
Shish: *EC1 (60)*
Silks & Spice: *EC4 (20)*
Singapura: *EC3 (12,80); EC2 (20,70);
    EC4 (30,100)*

Smiths (Top Floor) (26)
Smiths (Dining Rm) (26)
Smiths (Ground Floor) (26)
Smollensky's: E1 (20,60)
Taberna Etrusca (40)
Tas Pide: EC1 (40)
Tatsuso (6,8)
Throgmorton (150,100,84)*
Les Trois Garçons (8,10)*
The Well (70)
Yi-Ban: E16 (30)
Young Bin (30)
The Zetter (10,50)

## ROMANTIC

### Central

Andrew Edmunds
Archipelago
Asia de Cuba
Aurora
Bam-Bou
Bohème Kitchen
Boudin Blanc
Café Bohème
Le Caprice
Chor Bizarre
Il Convivio
Crazy Bear
The Criterion Grill
CVO Firevault
Destino
Diverso
Dorchester Grill
Elena's L'Etoile
L'Escargot
French House
Le Gavroche
Gay Hussar
Gordon's Wine Bar
The Greenhouse
Hakkasan
Hush
The Ivy
Kettners
The Lanesborough
Langan's Bistro
Langan's Brasserie
Levant
Lindsay House
The Little Square
Locanda Locatelli
Maggiore's
Mimmo d'Ischia
Mirabelle
Momo
Mon Plaisir
Noble Rot
Nobu
Odin's
Opium
L'Oranger
Orrery
Pomegranates
La Porte des Indes
La Poule au Pot
The Ritz
Roussillon

Rules
St Moritz
Sarastro
J Sheekey
Souk
Taman gang
Toto's
La Trouvaille
Windows on the World
Zafferano

### West

Assaggi
Babylon
Beach
  Blanket Babylon
Belvedere
Bibendum
Blakes Hotel
Blue Elephant
La Bouchée
The Brackenbury
Brinkley's
Café Laville
Cambio de Tercio
Chez Kristof
Clarke's
Le Colombier
Dan's
Daphne's
E&O
Eight Over Eight
La Famiglia
Gordon Ramsay
I Thai
Iniga
Julie's
Julie's Wine Bar
Launceston Place
The Ledbury
Lundum's
Maggie Jones's
Manicomio
Mediterraneo
Mr Wing
Nam Long
Nikita's
Notting Hill Brasserie
Osteria Basilico
Paradise by Way of
  Kensal Green
Pasha
Patio
Pissarro's
Ognisko Polskie
The River Café
San Lorenzo
Star of India
Sugar Hut
Le Suquet
La Trompette
Tugga
Wódka
Zuma

### North

Anglo Asian Tandoori
L'Aventure
La Cage Imaginaire

Casale Franco
The Engineer
Frederick's
Iznik
Lola's
Le Mercury
Odette's
OQO Bar
Oslo Court
San Carlo
Villa Bianca
Zamoyski

**South**
Arancia
Bar du Musee
Beauberry House
Brula
Champor-Champor
Chez Bruce
Cinnamon Cay
The Depot
Ditto
The Glasshouse
Louvaine
MVH
Oxo Tower (Bras')
Petersham Nurseries
Le Pont de la Tour
Ransome's Dock
Scoffers
Spread Eagle
Tree House

**East**
Bleeding Heart
Café du Marché
Club Gascon
Elephant Royale
The Fox
Frocks
Lightship
LMNT
Moro
Potemkin
Les Trois Garçons
Vertigo

Cantina del Ponte
Carluccio's Caffè: SW15
The County Hall Rest'
The Depot
Four Regions: SE1
Gourmet Pizza Co.: SE1
Kwan Thai
Oxo Tower (Bras')
Oxo Tower (Rest')
The People's Palace
Le Pont de la Tour
    Bar & Grill
Riviera
Rocket Riverside: SW15
Shakespeare's Globe
Tate Restaurant
The Trafalgar Tavern

**East**
Aquarium
Coq d'Argent
1802
Elephant Royale
The Grapes
Just The Bridge
Plateau
Rhodes 24
Smiths (Top Floor)
Ubon
Vertigo
Yi-Ban: E16

## ROOMS WITH A VIEW

**Central**
Crivelli's Garden
Fakhreldine
Foliage
Inn the Park
Orrery
The Portrait
Windows on the World

**West**
Aquasia
Babylon
Belvedere
Café Laville
Pissarro's
The Tenth

**South**
Blueprint Café
Butlers Wharf
    Chop-house

## NOTABLE WINE LISTS

**Central**
Adam Street
Andrew Edmunds
Boisdale
Café des Amis du Vin
Camerino
Le Cercle
Cigala
Connaught (Angela Hartnett)
The Contented Vine
Cork & Bottle
The Ebury
L'Escargot
The Fifth Floor
Fino
Foliage
Fortnum's, The Fountain
La Fromagerie Café
Le Gavroche
Gordon Ramsay at Claridge's
Gordon's Wine Bar
The Greenhouse
Hardy's
The Ivy
Kai Mayfair
Locanda Locatelli
Maggiore's
Mirabelle
Noble Rot
Olivo
Orrery
Pétrus
Pied à Terre
The Providores
Quo Vadis

Roussillon
St Moritz
Savoy Grill
Shampers
Sotheby's Café
Le Soufflé
The Square
Tate Britain
Teca
The Union Café
Zafferano

**West**
Bibendum
Brinkley's
Brunello
Clarke's
Le Colombier
The Cross Bar
L'Etranger
Gordon Ramsay
Le Metro
The Oratory
Osteria dell'Arancio
Racine
The River Café
Tom Aikens
La Trompette
White Horse
Wine Factory
Wine Gallery

**North**
Cru

Lola's
Metrogusto
Odette's
The Real Greek

**South**
Burnt Chair
Cantina Vinopolis
Chez Bruce
Enoteca Turi
The Glasshouse
The Greyhound
McClements
Le Pont de la Tour
Putney Station
Ransome's Dock
Redmond's
Riva
RSJ
Tentazioni

**East**
Alba
Bleeding Heart
Cellar Gascon
Club Gascon
Coq d'Argent
The Don
Moro
Vivat Bacchus
Wapping Food
The Wine Library

An asterisk (*) after an entry indicates exceptional or very good cooking

## AMERICAN

### Central
Automat (W1)
Bodean's (W1)
Broadway Bar & Grill (SW1)
Christopher's (WC2)
Joe Allen (WC2)
Maxwell's (WC2)
Planet Hollywood (W1)
Rainforest Café (W1)
Smollensky's (WC2)
TGI Friday's (W1, WC2)

### West
Babes 'n' Burgers (W11)
Big Easy (SW3)
Harlem (W2)
Lucky Seven (W2)
PJ's (SW3)
Smollensky's (W6)
Sticky Fingers (W8)
Texas Lone Star (SW7)
TGI Friday's (SW6, W2)

### North
Maxwell's (NW3)

### South
Bodean's (SW4)
Harlem (SW9)
Smollensky's (TW1)

### East
Arkansas Café (E1)
Christopher's In The City (EC3)
Missouri Grill (EC3)*
Smollensky's (E1, E14)

## AUSTRALIAN

### Central
The Easton (WC1)

### South
Cinnamon Cay (SW11)*

### East
The Princess (EC2)

## BELGIAN

### Central
Belgo Centraal (WC2)

### West
Abbaye (SW7)

### North
Belgo Noord (NW1)

### East
Abbaye (EC1)

## BRITISH, MODERN

### Central
About Thyme (SW1)
Adam Street (WC2)
Alastair Little (W1)
Andrew Edmunds (W1)*
Atlantic Bar & Grill (W1)
Atrium (SW1)
Aurora (W1)
The Avenue (SW1)
Axis (WC2)
Bank Aldwych (WC2)
Bank Westminster (SW1)
Bellamy's (W1)
Berkeley Square Café (W1)
Blandford Street (W1)
Brian Turner (W1)
Café du Jardin (WC2)
Le Caprice (SW1)*
Circus (W1)
The Contented Vine (SW1)
Cork & Bottle (WC2)
CVO Firevault (W1)
Le Deuxième (WC2)
Ebury Street Wine Bar (SW1)
Embassy (W1)
The Fifth Floor (SW1)
Footstool (SW1)
43 South Molton (W1)
French House (W1)
Galvin (W1)
Ha! Ha! (W1, WC2)
Homage (WC2)
Hush (W1)
Indigo (WC2)
Inn the Park (SW1)
The Ivy (WC2)
Just St James (SW1)
The Lanesborough (SW1)
Langan's Brasserie (W1)
Lindsay House (W1)
The Little Square (W1)
Mash (W1)
Messanges (SW1)
Nicole's (W1)
Noble Rot (W1)
115 at Hodgson's (WC2)
Oscar (W1)
Patterson's (W1)*
The Perseverance (WC1)
The Portrait (WC2)
Quaglino's (SW1)
Refuel (W1)
Rhodes W1 (W1)
RIBA Café (W1)
Silk (W1)
Simpsons-in-the-Strand (WC2)
Six-13 (W1)
Smithy's (WC1)
Sotheby's Café (W1)*
Le Soufflé (W1)*
Tate Britain (SW1)
British Museum (WC1)

Tuttons *(WC2)*
The Union Café *(W1)*
Villandry *(W1)*
The Wolseley *(W1)*
Zinc *(W1)*

### West

The Abingdon *(W8)*
Abingdon Road *(W8)*
Admiral Codrington *(SW3)*
The Anglesea Arms *(W6)\**
The Anglesea Arms *(SW7)*
Babylon *(W8)*
Beach Blanket Babylon *(W11)*
Belvedere *(W8)*
Bistrot 190 *(SW7)*
Bluebird *(SW3)*
The Bollo House *(W4)*
The Brackenbury *(W6)\**
Brinkley's *(SW10)*
The Builder's Arms *(SW3)*
The Burlington *(W4)*
Bush Bar & Grill *(W12)*
Café Med *(W6)*
Clarke's *(W8)\**
The Collection *(SW3)*
Coopers Arms *(SW3)*
Cotto *(W14)\**
The Crown & Sceptre *(W12)*
Dan's *(SW3)*
Devonshire House *(W4)*
Dove *(W6)*
Ealing Park Tavern *(W5)*
1880 *(SW7)\**
The Farm *(SW6)*
First Floor *(W11)*
Formosa Dining Room *(W9)*
The Frontline Club *(W2)*
Gravy *(W4)*
Harwood Arms *(SW6)*
The Havelock Tavern *(W14)\**
Hole in the Wall *(W4)*
The Ifield *(SW10)*
Island *(W2)*
Joe's Brasserie *(SW6)*
Joe's Café *(SW3)*
Julie's *(W11)*
Julie's Wine Bar *(W11)*
Kensington Place *(W8)*
The Ladbroke Arms *(W11)\**
Launceston Place *(W8)*
Lots Road *(SW10)*
The Mall Tavern *(W8)*
Le Metro *(SW3)*
Notting Hill Brasserie *(W11)\**
The Oratory *(SW3)*
Paradise by Way of
   Kensal Green *(W10)*
The Pen *(SW6)*
The Phoenix *(SW3)*
The Pig's Ear *(SW3)*
The Pilot *(W4)*
Pissarro's *(W4)*
The Prince Bonaparte *(W2)\**
Raoul's Café *(W9)*

The Rocket *(W3)*
Ruby Lounge & Sequoia
   Bar *(W11)*
The Salisbury Tavern *(SW6)*
Sam's Brasserie *(W4)*
Seven Stars *(W4)*
Snows on the Green *(W6)*
Sophie's Steakhouse *(SW10)*
Stone Mason's Arms *(W6)*
The Tea Palace *(W11)*
The Tenth *(W8)*
The Thatched House *(W6)*
The Vale *(W9)\**
Vingt-Quatre *(SW10)*
The Waterway *(W9)*
The Westbourne *(W2)*
White Horse *(SW6)*
Whits *(W8)*
Whole Hog Canteen *(W6)*

### North

The Barnsbury *(N1)*
Bastille *(N1)*
The Belsize *(NW3)*
Bradley's *(NW3)*
The Bull *(N6)*
Café Med *(NW8)*
The Chapel *(NW1)*
Crown & Goose *(NW1)*
The Drapers Arms *(N1)*
The Duke of Cambridge *(N1)\**
The Elk in the Woods *(N1)*
The Engineer *(NW1)*
Fig *(N1)*
Frederick's *(N1)*
Freemasons Arms *(NW3)*
The Garden Café *(NW1)*
Globe Restaurant *(NW3)*
The Green *(NW2)*
The Greyhound *(NW10)*
Ha! Ha! *(N10)*
The Haven *(N20)*
The Highgate *(NW5)*
The Hill *(NW3)*
The House *(N1)*
The Junction Tavern *(NW5)*
Landmark
   (Winter Garden) *(NW1)*
Lansdowne *(NW1)\**
Lola's *(N1)*
The Lord Palmerston *(NW5)\**
Mango Room *(NW1)\**
Mesclun *(N16)*
Mosaica *(N22)\**
No 77 Wine Bar *(NW6)*
The Northgate *(N1)\**
Odette's *(NW1)*
The Pumphouse *(N8)*
Queen's Pub & Dining Rm *(NW1)*
The Vine *(NW5)*
Walnut *(NW6)*
The Wells *(NW3)*

### South

The Abbeville *(SW4)*

Archduke Wine Bar *(SE1)*
The Aviary *(SW20)*
Balham Kitchen & Bar *(SW12)*
Bankside *(SE1)*
Beauberry House *(SE21)*
The Blue Pumpkin *(SW17)*
Blueprint Café *(SE1)*
Bread & Roses *(SW4)*
The Bridge *(SW13)*
Buchan's *(SW11)*
Burnt Chair *(TW9)*
Cantina Vinopolis *(SE1)*
Canyon *(TW10)*
The Castle *(SW11)*
Chapter Two *(SE3)*
Chez Bruce *(SW17)**
The County Hall Rest' *(SE1)*
The Depot *(SW14)*
Ditto *(SW18)*
Earl Spencer *(SW18)*
The Fentiman Arms *(SW8)*
The Fire Stables *(SW19)*
Franklins *(SE22)**
The Freemasons *(SW18)*
Garrison *(SE1)**
The Glasshouse *(TW9)**
Greenwich Park *(SE10)*
The Greyhound *(SW11)**
Hampton's Restaurant *(KT8)*
The Hartley *(SE1)*
Inc Bar & Restaurant *(SE10)*
Inside *(SE10)**
Kew Grill *(TW9)*
Lamberts *(SW12)*
The Lavender *(SE11, SW11, SW9)*
The Mason's Arms *(SW8)*
Menier Chocolate Factory *(SE1)*
Mezzanine *(SE1)*
MVH *(SW13)**
Oxo Tower (Rest') *(SE1)*
The Palmerston *(SE22)**
The People's Palace *(SE1)*
Petersham Nurseries *(TW10)*
Phoenix *(SW15)*
Le Pont de la Tour *(SE1)*
Ransome's Dock *(SW11)*
Rapscallion *(SW4)*
Redmond's *(SW14)**
RSJ *(SE1)*
Scoffers *(SW11)*
The Sea Cow *(SE22)**
Shakespeare's Globe *(SE1)*
Sonny's *(SW13)*
The Sun & Doves *(SE5)*
The Trafalgar Tavern *(SE10)*
Tree House *(SW13)*
The Victoria *(SW14)*
The Waterloo
   Fire Station *(SE1)*
The Wharf *(TW11)*
Willie Gunn *(SW18)*

*East*
Addendum *(EC3)*
Bankside *(EC2)*

The Bar & Grill *(EC1)*
Bar Bourse *(EC4)*
Bevis Marks *(EC3)**
Bistrothèque *(E2)*
Café Med *(EC1)*
Cat & Mutton *(E8)*
The Chancery *(EC4)**
The Clerkenwell Dining
   Room *(EC1)*
Club Mangia *(EC4)*
Coach & Horses *(EC1)**
The Crown *(E3)**
The Don *(EC4)**
1802 *(E14)*
The Evangelist *(EC4)*
The Fox *(EC2)**
Frocks *(E9)*
Gow's *(EC2)*
The Green *(EC1)*
The Gun *(E14)**
The Gunmakers *(EC1)*
Hadley House *(E11)*
Home *(EC2)*
Just Gladwins *(EC3)*
Just The Bridge *(EC4)*
Lanes *(E1)*
LMNT *(E8)*
Malmaison *(EC1)*
Medcalf *(EC1)**
Metro *(EC3)*
The Morgan Arms *(E3)**
Moro *(EC1)**
1 Lombard Street *(EC3)*
The Peasant *(EC1)*
Prism *(EC3)*
The Quality Chop House *(EC1)*
Rhodes 24 *(EC2)**
The Rivington Grill *(EC2)**
Searcy's Brasserie *(EC2)*
Smiths (Ground Floor) *(EC1)*
Smiths (Top Floor) *(EC1)*
Terminus *(EC2)*
Throgmorton *(EC2)*
Vic Naylors *(EC1)*
Wapping Food *(E1)*
The Well *(EC1)*
The White Swan *(EC4)**

## BRITISH, TRADITIONAL

*Central*
Boisdale *(SW1)*
Brian Turner *(W1)*
Chimes *(SW1)*
The Endurance *(W1)*
Fortnum's, The Fountain *(W1)*
Fuzzy's Grub *(SW1)**
Gordon's Wine Bar *(WC2)*
Goring Hotel *(SW1)*
Green's *(SW1)*
Greig's *(W1)*
Grenadier *(SW1)*
Dorchester Grill *(W1)*
The Guinea *(W1)**

Odin's (W1)*
Porters English
   Restaurant (WC2)
Rib Room (SW1)
Rules (WC2)
Savoy Grill (WC2)
Shepherd's (SW1)
Wiltons (SW1)

**West**
Bluebird Club & Dining
   Rooms (SW3)
Ffiona's (W8)
Gravy (W4)
Maggie Jones's (W8)
Le Metro (SW3)
Queen's Head (W6)
S & M Café (W10)
The Windsor Castle (W8)

**North**
S & M Café (N1)
St Johns (N19)*

**South**
The Anchor & Hope (SE1)*
Butlers Wharf
   Chop-house (SE1)
Roast (SE1)
Settle Inn (SW11)
The Trafalgar Tavern (SE10)

**East**
Fox & Anchor (EC1)
Fuzzy's Grub (EC4)*
George & Vulture (EC3)
Hope & Sir Loin (EC1)
Ye Olde Cheshire Cheese (EC4)
Paternoster Chop House (EC4)
The Quality Chop House (EC1)
S & M Café (E1)
St John (EC1)*
St John Bread & Wine (E1)*
Simpson's Tavern (EC3)
Sweetings (EC4)*
The Wine Library (EC3)

## DANISH

**West**
Lundum's (SW7)*

## EAST & CENT. EUROPEAN

**Central**
Gay Hussar (W1)
The Wolseley (W1)

**North**
Café Mozart (N6)
Troika (NW1)

## FISH & SEAFOOD

**Central**
Back to Basics (W1)*
Belgo Centraal (WC2)
Bentley's (W1)

Café Fish (W1)
Fishworks (W1)*
Fung Shing (WC2)
Green's (SW1)
Livebait (WC2)
Loch Fyne (WC2)
Manzi's (WC2)
One-O-One (SW1)*
Le Palais du Jardin (WC2)
Quaglino's (SW1)
Randall & Aubin (W1)*
Rib Room (SW1)
J Sheekey (WC2)*
Wheeler's of St James's (SW1)
Wiltons (SW1)
Zilli Fish (W1)

**West**
Bibendum Oyster Bar (SW3)
Big Easy (SW3)
The Cow (W2)*
Deep (SW6)
Fish Hoek (W4)*
Fishworks (W4)*
Ghillies (SW6)
Loch Fyne (SW6)
Lou Pescadou (SW5)
Mandarin Kitchen (W2)*
Poissonnerie de l'Avenue (SW3)*
Stratford's (W8)*
Le Suquet (SW3)*

**North**
Belgo Noord (NW1)
Bradley's (NW3)
Chez Liline (N4)*
Fishworks (N1)*
Pescador Too (NW3)
Sargasso Sea (N21)*

**South**
Balham Kitchen & Bar (SW12)
Fish Club (SW11)*
fish! (SE1)
Gastro (SW4)
Ghillies (SW18)
Livebait (SE1)
Lobster Pot (SE11)*
Loch Fyne (TW2)
Polygon Bar & Grill (SW4)
Le Pont de la Tour
   Bar & Grill (SE1)

**East**
Aquarium (E1)
Chamberlain's (EC3)
The Evangelist (EC4)
Fish Shop (EC1)*
Fishmarket (EC2)
Gow's (EC2)
The Grapes (E14)
Home (EC2)
Rudland Stubbs (EC1)
Sweetings (EC4)*
Vertigo (EC2)
The Well (EC1)
Winkles (E2)*

## FRENCH

### Central

The Admiralty (WC2)
L'Artiste Musclé (W1)
Auberge (W1)
Bellamy's (W1)
Beotys (WC2)
Berkeley Square Café (W1)
Boudin Blanc (W1)
Brasserie Roux (SW1)
Café Bagatelle (W1)
Café Bohème (W1)
Café des Amis du Vin (WC2)
Le Cercle (SW1)
Chez Gérard (SW1, W1, WC2)
The Criterion Grill (W1)
Dover Street (W1)
Drones (SW1)
The Ebury (SW1)
1880 (SW7)*
Elena's L'Etoile (W1)
L'Escargot (W1)
L'Estaminet (WC2)
Foliage (SW1)*
Gabrielles (W1)
La Galette (W1)
Le Gavroche (W1)*
Gordon Ramsay at
  Claridge's (W1)
The Greenhouse (W1)
Incognico (WC2)
Langan's Bistro (W1)
Maggiore's (WC2)*
maze (W1)
Mirabelle (W1)
Mon Plaisir (WC2)
L'Oranger (SW1)
Orrery (W1)
Le Pain Quotidien (W1)*
Le Palais du Jardin (WC2)
Pearl (WC1)
Pétrus (SW1)*
Pied à Terre (W1)
La Poule au Pot (SW1)
Randall & Aubin (W1)*
Le Relais de Venise (W1)
The Ritz (W1)
Roussillon (SW1)*
Sketch (Gallery) (W1)
Sketch (Glade) (W1)
Sketch (Lecture Rm) (W1)
The Square (W1)*
La Trouvaille (W1)
Villandry (W1)
W'sens (SW1)
Windows on the World (W1)

### West

Aubaine (SW3)
Aubergine (SW10)*
Base (SW3)
Belvedere (W8)
Bibendum (SW3)
La Bouchée (SW7)
La Brasserie (SW3)
Brasserie de l'Auberge (SW10)
Brasserie St Quentin (SW3)
Café Crêp' de Hampstead (SW7)
Capital Hotel (SW3)*
Charlotte's Place (W5)
Cheyne Walk Bras' (SW3)
Chez Kristof (W6)
Le Colombier (SW3)
Ealing Park Tavern (W5)
L'Etranger (SW7)*
FireHouse (SW7)
Gordon Ramsay (SW3)*
Langan's Coq d'Or (SW5)
The Ledbury (W11)*
Lou Pescadou (SW5)
Nathalie (SW3)
Notting Hill Brasserie (W11)*
Père Michel (W2)
Poissonnerie de l'Avenue (SW3)*
Racine (SW3)*
Randall & Aubin (SW10)*
Relais de Paris (SW3)
Le Suquet (SW3)*
Tartine (SW3)
Tom Aikens (SW3)
La Trompette (W4)*
Le Vacherin (W4)*
Whits (W8)

### North

The Almeida (N1)
Les Associés (N8)
L'Aventure (NW8)
Base (NW1, NW3)
Bastille (N1)
Bistro Aix (N8)
Bradley's (NW3)
The Bull (N6)
Café Crêp' de Hampstead (NW3)
Café Delancey (NW1)
La Cage Imaginaire (NW3)
Haché (NW1)
Le Mercury (N1)
Morgan M (N7)*
Oslo Court (NW8)*
Petit Auberge (N1)
Le Petit Prince (NW5)
Le Sacré-Coeur (N1)
The Wells (NW3)

### South

Auberge (SE1)
Bar du Musee (SE10)
Le Bouchon Bordelais (SW11)
Brula (TW1)*
La Buvette (TW9)*
Chez Gérard (SE1)
Chez Lindsay (TW10)*
Emile's (SW15)*
The Food Room (SW8)
Gastro (SW4)
Louvaine (SW11)
Ma Cuisine (TW1, TW9)
McClements (TW1)

Morel *(SW4)*
Niksons *(SW11)*
Le Petit Max *(SW11)**
Rick's Café *(SW17)**
Riviera *(SE1)*
Spread Eagle *(SE10)*
Tartine *(TW9)*

### East
Auberge *(EC3)*
Aurora *(EC2)**
Bistrothèque *(E2)*
Bleeding Heart *(EC1)**
Café du Marché *(EC1)**
Cellar Gascon *(EC1)**
Chez Gérard *(EC2, EC3, EC4)*
Club Gascon *(EC1)**
Comptoir Gascon *(EC1)*
Coq d'Argent *(EC3)*
First Edition *(E14)*
The Gun *(E14)**
Luc's Brasserie *(EC3)*
Novelli in the City *(EC4)*
Plateau *(E14)*
Le Rendezvous du Café *(EC1)*
Rosemary Lane *(E1)**
The Royal Exchange *(EC3)*
Le Saint Julien *(EC1)*
South *(EC2)**
Les Trois Garçons *(E1)*

## FUSION

### Central
Archipelago *(W1)*
Asia de Cuba *(WC2)*
Grocer on Warwick Café *(W1)*
Jaan *(WC2)*
Mju *(SW1)**
Nobu *(W1)**
Nobu Berkeley *(W1)*
The Providores *(W1)*
Spoon at Sanderson *(W1)*
Tapa Room (Providores) *(W1)**

### West
Aquasia *(SW10)*
L'Etranger *(SW7)**
I Thai *(W2)*
Levantine *(W2)*

### North
Hoxton Square *(N1)*

### South
Champor-Champor *(SE1)**
Cinnamon Cay *(SW11)**
Silka *(SE1)*
Tsunami *(SW4)**

### East
First Edition *(E14)*
Ubon *(E14)**

## GAME

### Central
Boisdale *(SW1)*
Dorchester Grill *(W1)*
Rules *(WC2)*
Wiltons *(SW1)*

### North
San Daniele *(N5)*

### East
Boisdale in the City *(EC2)*
Gow's *(EC2)*

## GREEK

### Central
Beotys *(WC2)*

### West
As Greek As It Gets *(SW5)**
Costa's Grill *(W8)*
Halepi *(W2)*

### North
Bar Mezé *(N10)**
Daphne *(NW1)*
Halepi *(NW3)*
Lemonia *(NW1)*
The Real Greek *(N1)*
Vrisaki *(N22)**

### South
Bar Mezé *(SW11)**
Real Greek Souvlaki & Bar *(SE1)*

### East
The Real Greek Souvlaki *(EC1)*

## HUNGARIAN

### Central
Gay Hussar *(W1)*

## INTERNATIONAL

### Central
Balans *(W1)*
Bohème Kitchen *(W1)*
Boulevard *(WC2)*
Boxwood Café *(SW1)*
Brahms *(SW1)*
Browns *(W1, WC2)*
Café Emm *(W1)*
Café in the Crypt *(WC2)*
The Castle *(W11)*
Crivelli's Garden *(WC2)*
Dover Street *(W1)*
Eat & Two Veg *(W1)*
Exotika *(WC2)*
Garlic & Shots *(W1)*
Giraffe *(W1)*
Gordon's Wine Bar *(WC2)*
Grumbles *(SW1)*
Hardy's *(W1)*
Michael Moore *(W1)*
Motcombs *(SW1)*

Oriel *(SW1)*
Papageno *(WC2)*
Pomegranates *(SW1)*
Royal Court Bar *(SW1)*
Running Horse *(W1)*
Sarastro *(WC2)*
Savoy Hotel (Banquette) *(WC2)*
Shampers *(W1)*
Star Café *(W1)*
Stock Pot *(SW1, W1)*
Sugar Reef *(W1)*
3G *(W1)*
Tiger Tiger *(SW1)*

### West
Annie's *(W4)*
Balans West *(SW5, W4, W8)*
Beaufort House *(SW3)*
Blakes Hotel *(SW7)*
Blue Kangaroo *(SW6)*
Café Laville *(W2)*
Chelsea Bun Diner *(SW10)*
Chelsea Kitchen *(SW3)*
Coopers Arms *(SW3)*
The Cross Bar *(SW3)*
Electric Brasserie *(W11)*
The Enterprise *(SW3)*
Food@TheMuse *(W11)*
Foxtrot Oscar *(SW3)*
The Gate *(W6)**
Giraffe *(W4, W8)*
Glaisters *(SW10)*
Graze *(W9)*
Lonsdale *(W11)*
Mona Lisa *(SW10)*
The Scarsdale *(W8)*
606 Club *(SW10)*
Sporting Page *(SW10)*
Stock Pot *(SW3)*
The Swag & Tails *(SW7)*
202 *(W11)*
Vesbar *(W12)*
The Waterway *(W9)*
The Windsor Castle *(W8)*
Wine Gallery *(SW10)*
Zinc *(SW6)*

### North
The Arches *(NW6)*
Banners *(N8)*
Browns *(N1)*
The Fox Reformed *(N16)*
Giraffe *(N1, NW3)*
The Haven *(N20)*
Hoxton Apprentice *(N1)*
Toast *(NW3)*
Two Brothers *(N3)**

### South
Alma *(SW18)*
Annie's *(SW13)*
Bread & Roses *(SW4)*
Browns *(SE1, TW9)*
Delfina Studio Café *(SE1)**
Duke of Cambridge *(SW11)*
Giraffe *(SE1, SW11)*

Hudson's *(SW15)*
Laughing Gravy *(SE1)*
The Light House *(SW19)*
Naked Turtle *(SW14)*
Newton's *(SW4)*
Nosh *(TW1)*
Oxo Tower (Bras') *(SE1)*
Putney Station *(SW15)*
The Sequel *(SW4)*
The Ship *(SW18)*
Tate Café *(SE1)*
Tate Restaurant *(SE1)*
White Cross *(TW9)*

### East
Brasserie Rocque *(EC2)*
Browns *(E14, EC2)*
Club Mangia *(EC4)*
$ *(EC1)*
Exmouth Grill *(EC1)*
The Light *(E1)*
Lilly's *(E1)**
Mustards Brasserie *(EC1)*
Throgmorton *(EC2)*
Vivat Bacchus *(EC4)*

## IRISH

### Central
O'Conor Don *(W1)**

## ITALIAN

### Central
Al Duca *(SW1)*
Alloro *(W1)**
Amato *(W1)*
Aperitivo *(W1)*
Bertorelli's *(WC2)*
Bertorelli's *(W1)*
Caffè Caldesi *(W1)*
Caldesi *(W1)*
Camerino *(W1)**
Caraffini *(SW1)**
Carluccio's Caffè *(W1)*
Cecconi's *(W1)*
Ciao Bella *(WC1)*
Cipriani *(W1)*
Como Lario *(SW1)*
Il Convivio *(SW1)**
Cristini *(W2)*
Crivelli's Garden *(WC2)*
Delfino *(W1)*
Diverso *(W1)*
Eddalino *(W1)*
Fiore *(W1)*
5 Cavendish Square *(W1)*
La Fontana *(SW1)*
Getti *(SW1, W1)*
Giardinetto *(W1)*
L'Incontro *(SW1)*
Italian Kitchen *(WC1)*
Latium *(W1)**
Little Italy *(W1)*
Locanda Locatelli *(W1)**

Luigi's *(WC2)*
Mimmo d'Ischia *(SW1)*
Mosaico *(W1)*
Neal Street *(WC2)*
Oliveto *(SW1)*\*
Olivo *(SW1)*\*
Orso *(WC2)*
Pappagallo *(W1)*
Paradiso Olivelli *(W1, WC2)*
Passione *(W1)*\*
Pasta Brown *(WC2)*
Pizza on the Park *(SW1)*
Il Pomodorino *(SW1)*
La Porchetta Pizzeria *(WC1)*
Quirinale *(SW1)*\*
Quo Vadis *(W1)*
Quod *(SW1)*
Rusticana *(W1)*
Sale e Pepe *(SW1)*
Salt Yard *(W1)*\*
Santini *(SW1)*
Sapori *(WC2)*
Sardo *(W1)*\*
Sartoria *(W1)*
Serafino *(W1)*
Signor Sassi *(SW1)*
Signor Zilli *(W1)*
La Spiga *(W1)*
La Spighetta *(W1)*
Strada *(W1, WC2)*
Teca *(W1)*\*
Tomato *(W1)*
Toto's *(SW1)*\*
Uno *(SW1)*
Vasco & Piero's Pavilion *(W1)*\*
Il Vicolo *(SW1)*
Zafferano *(SW1)*\*
Zilli Fish *(W1)*
Zizzi *(W1, WC2)*

**West**
L'Accento Italiano *(W2)*
Aglio e Olio *(SW10)*\*
Al San Vincenzo *(W2)*\*
The Ark *(W8)*
Arturo *(W2)*\*
Assaggi *(W2)*\*
Brunello *(SW7)*
Buona Sera *(SW3)*
Carluccio's Caffè *(SW10, SW7, W5)*
Carpaccio's *(SW3)*
Cibo *(W14)*\*
Da Mario *(SW7)*
Daphne's *(SW3)*
De Cecco *(SW6)*
La Delizia *(SW3)*\*
Edera *(W11)*
Elistano *(SW3)*
Esenza *(W11)*
Est Est Est *(W4)*
Il Falconiere *(SW7)*
La Famiglia *(SW10)*
Frankie's *(SW3)*
Frantoio *(SW10)*
Friends *(SW10)*

The Green Olive *(W9)*
Iniga *(SW3)*
Locanda Ottoemezzo *(W8)*
Loco Locale *(SW6)*
Lucio *(SW3)*\*
Luna Rossa *(W11)*
Made in Italy *(SW3)*\*
Manicomio *(SW3)*
Marechiaro *(SW3)*
Matriciano *(SW6)*
Mediterraneo *(W11)*
Miraggio *(SW6)*\*
Mirto *(SW6)*
Montpeliano *(SW7)*
Monza *(SW3)*
Napulé *(SW6)*
Nuovi Sapori *(SW6)*\*
The Oak *(W2)*\*
Osteria Basilico *(W11)*\*
Osteria dell'Arancio *(SW10)*
Ottolenghi *(W11)*\*
Il Pagliaccio *(SW6)*
Pappa Ciccia *(SW6)*\*
Paradiso Olivelli *(W12)*
Pellicano *(SW3)*
Picasso *(SW3)*
Il Portico *(W8)*
Pucci Pizza *(SW3)*\*
The Red Pepper *(W9)*
Riccardo's *(SW3)*
The River Café *(W6)*\*
San Frediano *(SW3)*
San Lorenzo *(SW3)*
Santa Lucia *(SW10)*
Scalini *(SW3)*\*
Spago *(SW7)*
Strada *(SW5, SW6)*
Timo *(W8)*
Wine Factory *(W11)*
Ziani *(SW3)*
Zizzi *(SW10, SW5, W4)*
Zucca *(W11)*

**North**
Artigiano *(NW3)*
L'Artista *(NW11)*
La Brocca *(NW6)*
Cantina Italia *(N1)*
Carluccio's Caffè *(N1, NW3, NW8)*
Casale Franco *(N1)*
Est Est Est *(N1)*
Fifteen *(N1)*
Florians *(N8)*
Fratelli la Bufala *(NW3)*\*
Marine Ices *(NW3)*
Metrogusto *(N1)*
Ottolenghi *(N1)*\*
Philpotts Mezzaluna *(NW2)*
Pizzeria Oregano *(N1)*
La Porchetta Pizzeria *(N1, N4, NW1)*
Rosmarino *(NW8)*
The Salusbury *(NW6)*
San Carlo *(N6)*
San Daniele *(N5)*

Sardo Canale *(NW1)*
Sarracino *(NW6)*
Strada *(N1, N6, NW1)*
La Superba *(NW1)*
Villa Bianca *(NW3)*
Zizzi *(N3, N6, NW8)*
Zuccato *(NW3)*

### South

A Cena *(TW1)\**
Al Forno *(SW19)*
Antipasto & Pasta *(SW11)*
Antipasto e Pasta *(SW4)*
Arancia *(SE16)\**
Buona Sera *(SW11)*
Cantina del Ponte *(SE1)*
Il Cantuccio di Pulcinella *(SW11)\**
Carluccio's Caffè *(SW15)*
Del Buongustaio *(SW15)*
Enoteca Turi *(SW15)\**
Est Est Est *(SW17, SW19)*
Ferrari's *(SW17)*
La Lanterna *(SE1)*
Loco Locale *(SE3)*
Loco Mensa *(SE1)*
Matilda's *(SW11)*
Murano *(TW9)*
Numero Uno *(SW11)*
Ost. Antica Bologna *(SW11)*
Panzella *(SW11)\**
Pappa Ciccia *(SW15)\**
Pizzeria Castello *(SE1)*
Pomino *(SW17)*
Prego *(TW9)*
Rick's Café *(SW17)\**
Riva *(SW13)*
Riviera *(SE1)*
San Lorenzo Fuoriporta *(SW19)*
Strada *(SW11, SW13, SW4)*
Tentazioni *(SE1)\**
Zizzi *(SW11, TW9)*

### East

Alba *(EC1)*
Bertorelli's *(EC3, EC4)*
Il Bordello *(E1)\**
Caravaggio *(EC3)*
Carluccio's Caffè *(E14, EC1)*
La Figa *(E14)*
1 Blossom Street *(E1)*
E Pellicci *(E2)*
Perc%nto *(EC4)*
La Porchetta Pizzeria *(EC1)*
Quadrato *(E14)*
Refettorio *(EC4)*
Strada *(EC1)*
Taberna Etrusca *(EC4)*
The Zetter *(EC1)*
Zizzi *(E14)*
Zuccato *(EC4)*

## MEDITERRANEAN

### Central

About Thyme *(SW1)*

Connaught (Angela
  Hartnett) *(W1)*
Bistro 1 *(W1, WC2)*
Brahms *(SW1)*
Dover Street *(W1)*
The Fifth Floor (Café) *(SW1)*
Ishtar *(W1)*
Leon *(W1)\**
Mediterranean Kitchen *(WC2)*
Rocket *(W1)*
Salt Yard *(W1)\**
06 St Chad's Place *(WC1)\**
Truc Vert *(W1)*
W'sens *(SW1)*

### West

Aquasia *(SW10)*
The Atlas *(SW6)\**
Cross Keys *(SW3)*
The Grove *(W6)*
Locanda Ottoemezzo *(W8)*
Made in Italy *(SW3)\**
Manicomio *(SW3)*
Mediterranean Kitchen *(SW7, W8)*
Mediterraneo *(W11)*
Meza *(W1)*
Raoul's Café *(W9)*
Snows on the Green *(W6)*
The Swan *(W4)\**
Tom's *(W11)*
Troubadour *(SW5)*
William IV *(NW10)*
Little Bay *(SW6)*

### North

Camden Brasserie *(NW1)*
The Chapel *(NW1)*
Cru *(N1)*
The Little Bay *(NW6)*
Mediterranean Kitchen *(N1)*
The Pumphouse *(N8)*
Queen's Head &
  Artichoke *(NW1)*
The Vine *(NW5)*

### South

Bermondsey Kitchen *(SE1)*
Fish in a Tie *(SW11)*
The Fox & Hounds *(SW11)\**
Little Bay *(SW11)*
Rocket Riverside *(SW15)*
El Vergel *(SE1)\**
The Wharf *(TW11)*

### East

Bonds *(EC2)*
Cantaloupe *(EC2)*
The Eagle *(EC1)*
Eyre Brothers *(EC2)\**
Flâneur *(EC1)\**
The Light *(E1)*
The Little Bay *(EC1)*
The Peasant *(EC1)*
Portal *(EC1)*
Le Saint Julien *(EC1)*

## ORGANIC

**Central**
Hamburger Union *(W1, WC2)*
Leon *(W1)**

**West**
Babes 'n' Burgers *(W11)*

**North**
The Duke of Cambridge *(N1)**

**South**
The Hartley *(SE1)*
Tandoori Nights *(SE22)**

**East**
The Crown *(E3)**
Smiths (Dining Rm) *(EC1)*
Story Deli *(E1)**

## POLISH

**West**
Daquise *(SW7)*
Lowiczanka *(W6)*
Ognisko Polskie *(SW7)*
Patio *(W12)*
Wódka *(W8)*

**North**
Zamoyski *(NW3)*

**South**
Baltic *(SE1)*

## PORTUGUESE

**West**
Lisboa Patisserie *(W10)*
Tugga *(SW3)*

**North**
Pescador Too *(NW3)*

**South**
Bar Estrela *(SW8)*
Café Portugal *(SW8)*

**East**
Portal *(EC1)*

## RUSSIAN

**West**
Nikita's *(SW10)*

**North**
Troika *(NW1)*

**East**
Potemkin *(EC1)*

## SCANDINAVIAN

**Central**
Garbo's *(W1)*

**West**
Lundum's *(SW7)**

**South**
Glas *(SE1)*

**East**
Lightship *(E1)*

## SCOTTISH

**Central**
Albannach *(WC2)*
Boisdale *(SW1)*

**South**
Buchan's *(SW11)*

**East**
Boisdale of Bishopsgate *(EC2)*

## SPANISH

**Central**
Cigala *(WC1)*
Fino *(W1)**
Goya *(SW1)*
Navarro's *(W1)*
El Pirata *(W1)*
La Rueda *(W1)*
Salt Yard *(W1)**
La Tasca *(WC2)*

**West**
El Blasõn *(SW3)*
Cambio de Tercio *(SW5)**
La Copita *(W12)*
Galicia *(W10)**
Lomo *(SW10)*
Meza *(W1)*
La Rueda *(SW6)*
La Tasca *(W4, W5)*
Tendido Cero *(SW5)**

**North**
Don Pepe *(NW8)*
La Tasca *(N1)*

**South**
Barcelona Tapas *(SE22)*
don Fernando's *(TW9)*
El Rincón Latino *(SW4)*
La Finca *(SE11)*
La Mancha *(SW15)*
Meson don Felipe *(SE1)*
Rebato's *(SW8)**
Rick's Café *(SW17)**
La Rueda *(SW4)*
Tapas Brindisa *(SE1)**

**East**
Barcelona Tapas *(E1, EC3, EC4)*
Cantaloupe *(EC2)*
Eyre Brothers *(EC2)**
Leadenhall Tapas Bar *(EC3)*
Meson los Barilles *(E1)**
Moro *(EC1)**
La Tasca *(E14, EC2)*

## STEAKS & GRILLS

**Central**
Black & Blue *(W1)*
Bodean's *(W1)*

Chez Gérard (SW1, W1, WC2)
Christopher's (WC2)
Gaucho Grill (W1, WC2)
The Guinea (W1)*
Ishtar (W1)
Quaglino's (SW1)
Rowley's (SW1, W1)
Smollensky's (WC2)
Texas Embassy Cantina (SW1)
Wolfe's (WC2)

### West
Black & Blue (SW7, W8)
El Gaucho (SW3, SW7)*
Gaucho Grill (SW3)
Notting Grill (W11)
Popeseye (W14)*
Rôtisserie Jules (SW7, W11)
Smollensky's (W6)
Sophie's Steakhouse (SW10)

### North
Black & Blue (NW3)
Camden Brasserie (NW1)
Gaucho Grill (NW3)
Haché (NW1)

### South
Bermondsey Kitchen (SE1)
Black & Blue (SE1)
Bodean's (SW4)
Chez Gérard (SE1)
Kew Grill (TW9)
La Pampa (SW11)*
Polygon Bar & Grill (SW4)
Pont de la Tour Bar & Grill (SE1)
Popeseye (SW15)*
Smollensky's (TW1)

### East
Arkansas Café (E1)
Chez Gérard (EC2, EC3, EC4)
Christopher's In The City (EC3)
Epicurean Pizza Lounge (EC1)
Fox & Anchor (EC1)
Gaucho Grill (E14, EC3)
Hope & Sir Loin (EC1)
Lilly's (E1)*
Missouri Grill (EC3)*
Santa Maria de Buen Ayre (E8)
Simpson's Tavern (EC3)
Smiths (Ground Floor) (EC1)
Smiths (Dining Rm) (EC1)
Smiths (Top Floor) (EC1)
Smollensky's (E1, E14)

## SWISS

### Central
St Moritz (W1)*

## VEGETARIAN

### Central
Al Hamra (W1)
Blue Lagoon (SW1)
Chiang Mai (W1)*

Food for Thought (WC2)*
India Club (WC2)
The Lanesborough (SW1)
Malabar Junction (WC1)
Masala Zone (W1)
Mildred's (W1)*
Red Veg (W1)
Woodlands (SW1, W1)*

### West
Blah! Blah! Blah! (W12)*
Blue Elephant (SW6)*
Blue Lagoon (W14)
The Gate (W6)*
Gordon Ramsay (SW3)*
Masala Zone (SW5)
Woodlands (W4)*

### North
Chutneys (NW1)
Diwana B-P House (NW1)
Geeta (NW6)*
Iznik (N5)
Jashan (HA0, N8)*
Little Earth Cafe (NW3)*
Manna (NW3)
Masala Zone (N1)
Rani (N3)*
Rasa (N16)*
Sabras (NW10)*
Sakonis (HA0)*
Sedir (N1)
Vijay (NW6)*

### South
Kastoori (SW17)*
McClements (TW1)
Le Pont de la Tour (SE1)
Sree Krishna (SW17)*

### East
Carnevale (EC1)
The Place Below (EC2)*
Sri Siam City (EC2)

## AFTERNOON TEA

### Central
Brasserie Roux (SW1)
The Fifth Floor (Café) (SW1)
Fortnum's, The Fountain (W1)
The Lanesborough (SW1)
Pâtisserie Valerie (SW1, W1)
Richoux (W1)
The Ritz (W1)
Royal Academy (W1)
Sketch (Parlour) (W1)
Villandry (W1)
The Wolseley (W1)
Yauatcha (W1)*

### West
Daquise (SW7)
Pâtisserie Valerie (SW3, W8)
Richoux (SW3)
The Tea Palace (W11)

### North
Richoux (NW8)

## BURGERS, ETC

### Central
Black & Blue (W1)
Boxwood Café (SW1)
Eagle Bar Diner (W1)
Ed's Easy Diner (W1, WC2)
Fine Burger Company (W1)
Hamburger Union (W1, WC2)
Hard Rock Café (W1)
Joe Allen (WC2)
Kettners (W1)
Maxwell's (WC2)
Planet Hollywood (W1)
Rainforest Café (W1)
Red Veg (W1)
Savoy Hotel (Banquette) (WC2)
Tootsies (W1)
Wolfe's (WC2)

### West
Babes 'n' Burgers (W11)
Big Easy (SW3)
Black & Blue (SW7, W8)
Ed's Easy Diner (SW3)
Electric Brasserie (W11)
Foxtrot Oscar (SW3)
Gourmet Burger Kitchen (SW6, W2, W4)*
Henry J Beans (SW3)
Joe's Café (SW3)
Lucky Seven (W2)
Notting Grill (W11)
PJ's (SW3)
Sticky Fingers (W8)
Tootsies (SW6, SW7, W11, W4)

### North
Black & Blue (NW3)
Ed's Easy Diner (NW3)
Fine Burger Company (N1, N10)
Gourmet Burger Kitchen (NW3, NW6)*
Haché (NW1)
Maxwell's (NW3)
No 77 Wine Bar (NW6)
Tootsies (NW3)

### South
Black & Blue (SE1)
Dexter's Grill (SW17)
Fine Burger Company (SW12)
Gourmet Burger Kitchen (SW11, SW15)*
Real Burger World (SW11)*
Tootsies (SW11, SW15, SW19, SW4)

### East
Arkansas Café (E1)
The Bar & Grill (EC1)
$ (EC1)
Smiths (Dining Rm) (EC1)

## CRÊPES

### Central
La Galette (W1)

### West
Café Crêp' de Hampstead (SW7)

### North
Café Crêp' de Hampstead (NW3)

### South
Chez Lindsay (TW10)*

## FISH & CHIPS

### Central
Fryer's Delight (WC1)
Golden Hind (W1)*
Harry Ramsden's (W1)
North Sea Fish (WC1)
Seafresh (SW1)

### West
Geale's (W8)

### North
Nautilus (NW6)*
Seashell (NW1)
Toff's (N10)*
Two Brothers (N3)*

### South
Brady's (SW18)*
Fish Club (SW11)*
Olley's (SE24)*
The Sea Cow (SE22, SW4)*

### East
Faulkner's (E8)*

## ICE CREAM

### North
Marine Ices (NW3)

## PIZZA

### Central
Delfino (W1)
Fire & Stone (WC2)
Gourmet Pizza Co. (W1)
Kettners (W1)
Mash (W1)
Oliveto (SW1)*
Paradiso Olivelli (W1, WC1, WC2)
Pizza on the Park (SW1)
La Porchetta Pizzeria (WC1)
Rocket (W1)
Sapori (WC2)
La Spiga (W1)
La Spighetta (W1)
Strada (W1, WC2)
Tomato (W1)
Zizzi (W1, WC2)

### West
(Ciro's) Pizza Pomodoro (SW3)
Basilico (SW6)
Buona Sera (SW3)

Da Mario (SW7)
La Delizia (SW3)*
Friends (SW10)
Made in Italy (SW3)*
Osteria Basilico (W11)*
Paradiso Olivelli (W12)
Pucci Pizza (SW3)*
Spago (SW7)
Strada (SW5, SW6)
Wine Factory (W11)
Zizzi (SW10, SW5, W4)
Zucca (W11)

### North
Basilico (N1, NW3)
La Brocca (NW6)
Cantina Italia (N1)
Furnace (N1)
Marine Ices (NW3)
Pizzeria Oregano (N1)
Porchetta Pizzeria (N1, N4, NW1)
Strada (N1, N6, NW1)
Zizzi (N3, N6, NW8)

### South
Al Forno (SW19)
Amano Café (SE1)*
Basilico (SW11, SW14)
Buona Sera (SW11)
Eco (SW4, SW9)*
Firezza (SW11)*
Gourmet Pizza Co. (SE1)
La Lanterna (SE1)
Paradiso Olivelli (SE1)
Pizza Metro (SW11)*
Pizzeria Castello (SE1)
Rocket Riverside (SW15)
Strada (SW11, SW13, SW4)
Zero Degrees (SE3)
Zizzi (SW11, TW9)

### East
Bar Capitale (EC2, EC4)*
Il Bordello (E1)*
Epicurean Pizza Lounge (EC1)
Gourmet Pizza Co. (E14)
(Ciro's) Pizza Pomodoro (EC2)
La Porchetta Pizzeria (EC1)
Scuzi (E14, EC3)
Strada (EC1)
Zizzi (E14)

## SANDWICHES, CAKES, ETC

### Central
Amato (W1)
Apostrophe (W1, WC2)*
Baker & Spice (SW1)
Bar Italia (W1)
Benugo (W1)*
Crussh (SW1, W1)
La Fromagerie Café (W1)*
Fuzzy's Grub (SW1)*
Konditor & Cook (W1, WC1)*
Maison Bertaux (W1)*
Monmouth Coffee Co (WC2)*

Le Pain Quotidien (W1)*
Pâtisserie Valerie (SW1, W1)
Paul (W1, WC2)
Richoux (W1)
Royal Academy (W1)
Sketch (Parlour) (W1)

### West
Aubaine (SW3)
Baker & Spice (SW3)
Benugo (SW7)*
Bluebird Café (SW3)
Chez Kristof, Deli (W6)*
Crussh (W12, W8)
Joe's Café (SW3)
Lisboa Patisserie (W10)
Pâtisserie Valerie (SW3, W8)
Richoux (SW3)
Tom's (W11)
Troubadour (SW5)

### North
Baker & Spice (NW6)
Café Crêperie de
  Hampstead (NW3)
Chamomile (NW3)
Richoux (NW8)

### South
Boiled Egg (SW11)
Konditor & Cook (SE1)*
Monmouth Coffee Co (SE1)*

### East
Apostrophe (EC2, EC4)*
Benugo (EC1)*
Brick Lane Beigel Bake (E1)*
Crussh (E14, EC3, EC4)
Fuzzy's Grub (EC4)*
Pâtisserie Valerie (E1)

## ARGENTINIAN

### Central
Gaucho Grill (W1, WC2)

### West
El Gaucho (SW3, SW7)*
Gaucho Grill (SW3)

### North
Gaucho Grill (NW3)

### South
La Pampa (SW11)*

### East
Gaucho Grill (E14, EC3)
Santa Maria de Buen Ayre (E8)

## BRAZILIAN

### West
Rodizio Rico (W2)

### North
Rodizio Rico (N1)

## CUBAN

**Central**
Floridita (W1)

**North**
Cuba Libre (N1)
Cube & Star (N1)

## MEXICAN/TEXMEX

**Central**
Café Pacifico (WC2)
La Perla (W1, WC2)
Texas Embassy Cantina (SW1)

**West**
Crazy Homies (W2)
La Perla (SW6)
Taqueria (W11)*
Texas Lone Star (SW7)

**North**
Mestizo (NW1)*

## PERUVIAN

**South**
Fina Estampa (SE1)

## SOUTH AMERICAN

**Central**
Destino (W1)
Floridita (W1)

**West**
Cactus Blue (SW3)
1492 (SW6)

**North**
La Piragua (N1)
Sabor (N1)*

**South**
El Vergel (SE1)*

**East**
Armadillo (E8)*

## AFRO-CARIBBEAN

**Central**
Calabash (WC2)
Mr Jerk (W1)*

**West**
Mr Jerk (W2)*

**North**
Cottons (NW1)
The Green (NW2)
Mango Room (NW1)*

**East**
Coco (EC1)

## ETHIOPIAN

**West**
Demera (W12)*

**North**
Tobia (NW3)*

## MOROCCAN

**Central**
Mamounia (W1)
Momo (W1)
Occo (W1)*
Original Tajines (W1)

**West**
Adams Café (W12)
Aziz (SW6)
Moroccan Tagine (W10)
Pasha (SW7)

## NORTH AFRICAN

**Central**
Mamounia (W1)
Souk (WC2)

**West**
Azou (W6)

**East**
Moro (EC1)*

## SOUTH AFRICAN

**West**
Fish Hoek (W4)*

**South**
Chakalaka (SW15)

## TUNISIAN

**West**
Adams Café (W12)

## EGYPTIAN

**North**
Ali Baba (NW1)*

## ISRAELI

**North**
Solly's Exclusive (NW11)

## KOSHER

**Central**
Reubens (W1)
Six-13 (W1)

**North**
Harry Morgan's (NW8)*
Kaifeng (NW4)*
Solly's Exclusive (NW11)

**East**
Bevis Marks (EC3)*

### LEBANESE

**Central**
Al Hamra (W1)
Al Sultan (W1)
Beiteddine (SW1)
Fairuz (W1)*
Fakhreldine (W1)
Ishbilia (SW1)*
Levant (W1)
Mamounia (W1)
Maroush (W1)*
Noura (SW1, W1)
Ranoush (SW1)*

**West**
Al Bustan (SW7)
Al-Waha (W2)
Beirut Express (W2)*
Café Maroush (W2)*
Chez Marcelle (W14)*
Fairuz (W2)*
Fresco (W2)*
Maroush (SW3)*
Ranoush (SW3, W2, W8)*

### MIDDLE EASTERN

**Central**
Gaby's (WC2)
Levant (W1)

**West**
Abu Zaad (W12)*
Aziz (SW6)
Levantine (W2)
Shish (W2)

**North**
Shish (NW2)
Solly's Exclusive (NW11)

**East**
Shish (EC1)

### PERSIAN

**West**
Alounak (W14)
Kandoo (W2)
Mohsen (W14)*
Yas (W14)
Yas on the Park (W2)

**South**
Dish Dash (SW12)*

### TURKISH

**Central**
Efes Restaurant (W1)
Ishtar (W1)
Kazan (SW1)
Ozer (W1)
Sofra (W1, WC2)

**North**
Gallipoli (N1)

Istanbul Iskembecisi (N16)
Iznik (N5)
Pasha (N1)
Sedir (N1)
Sofra (NW8)

**South**
EV (SE1)
Tas (SE1)
Tas Pide (SE1)

**East**
Haz (E1)*
Mangal (E8)*
Savarona (EC2)
Sofra (EC1)
Tas Pide (EC1)

### AFGHANI

**North**
Afghan Kitchen (N1)

### BURMESE

**West**
Mandalay (W2)*

### CHINESE

**Central**
China Tang (W1)
The Chinese Experience (W1)*
Chuen Cheng Ku (W1)
ECapital (W1)
Fung Shing (WC2)*
Golden Dragon (W1)
Hakkasan (W1)
Harbour City (W1)
Hunan (SW1)*
Imperial China (WC2)*
Jade Garden (W1)
Jenny Lo's (SW1)*
Joy King Lau (WC2)*
Kai Mayfair (W1)*
Ken Lo's Memories (SW1)*
Laureate (W1)
Mekong (SW1)
Mr Chow (SW1)
Mr Kong (WC2)*
New Culture Revolution (WC1)
New Mayflower (W1)*
New World (W1)
Poons (WC2)
Princess Garden (W1)*
Royal China (W1)*
Shanghai Blues (WC1)
Taman gang (W1)
Wong Kei (W1)
Yauatcha (W1)*
Yming (W1)*
Zen Central (W1)*

**West**
Choys (SW3)
The Four Seasons (W2)*

Good Earth *(SW3)*\*
Ken Lo's Memories *(W8)*\*
Made in China *(SW10)*\*
Mandarin Kitchen *(W2)*\*
Mao Tai *(SW3, SW6)*\*
Mr Wing *(SW5)*\*
New Culture Rev'n *(SW3, W11)*
Royal China *(W2)*\*
Stick & Bowl *(W8)*
Yi-Ban *(SW6)*\*

### North
Good Earth *(NW7)*\*
Gung-Ho *(NW6)*\*
Kaifeng *(NW4)*\*
New Culture Rev'n *(N1, NW1)*
OQO Bar *(N1)*\*
Phoenix Palace *(NW1)*\*
Royal China *(NW8)*\*
Sakonis *(HA0)*\*
Singapore Garden *(NW6)*
Weng Wah House *(NW3)*
ZeNW3 *(NW3)*\*

### South
Dalchini *(SW19)*
Evo *(SW4)*
Four Regions *(SE1, TW9)*
Royal China *(SW15)*\*

### East
Imperial City *(EC3)*\*
Royal China *(E14)*\*
Shanghai *(E8)*\*
Yi-Ban *(E16)*\*

## CHINESE, DIM SUM

### Central
The Chinese Experience *(W1)*\*
Chuen Cheng Ku *(W1)*
dim T *(W1)*
Golden Dragon *(W1)*
Hakkasan *(W1)*
Harbour City *(W1)*
Imperial China *(WC2)*\*
Jade Garden *(W1)*
Joy King Lau *(WC2)*\*
New World *(W1)*
Ping Pong *(W1)*\*
Royal China *(W1)*\*
Shanghai Blues *(WC1)*
Yauatcha *(W1)*\*

### West
Royal China *(W2)*\*

### North
dim T café *(NW3)*
Phoenix Palace *(NW1)*\*
Royal China *(NW8)*\*

### South
O'Zon *(TW1)*
Royal China *(SW15)*\*

### East
Drunken Monkey *(E1)*
Royal China *(E14)*\*

Shanghai *(E8)*\*
Yi-Ban *(E16)*\*

## FRENCH-VIETNAMESE

### Central
Bam-Bou *(W1)*\*
Opium *(W1)*

## INDIAN

### Central
Amaya *(SW1)*\*
Benares *(W1)*\*
Café Lazeez *(W1)*
Chai Pani *(W1)*
Chor Bizarre *(W1)*
Chowki *(W1)*\*
The Cinnamon Club *(SW1)*\*
Curryleaf *(W1)*
Deya *(W1)*\*
Gopal's of Soho *(W1)*\*
India Club *(WC2)*
Malabar Junction *(WC1)*
Masala Zone *(W1)*
Mela *(WC2)*
Mint Leaf *(SW1)*\*
Moti Mahal *(WC2)*
La Porte des Indes *(W1)*
Rasa Samudra *(W1)*\*
Red Fort *(W1)*\*
Soho Spice *(W1)*
Tamarind *(W1)*\*
Veeraswamy *(W1)*
Woodlands *(SW1, W1)*\*
Yatra *(W1)*

### West
Anarkali *(W6)*
Bombay Bicycle Club *(W11)*\*
Bombay Brasserie *(SW7)*\*
Bombay Palace *(W2)*\*
Brilliant *(UB2)*\*
Café Lazeez *(SW7)*
Chutney Mary *(SW10)*\*
Five Hot Chillies *(HA0)*\*
Ginger *(W2)*
Haandi *(SW3)*\*
kare kare *(SW5)*\*
Khan's *(W2)*\*
Khan's of Kensington *(SW7)*
Khyber Pass *(SW7)*
Love India *(SW3)*
Madhu's *(UB1)*\*
Malabar *(W8)*\*
Masala Zone *(SW5)*
Memories of India *(SW7)*
Noor Jahan *(SW5, W2)*\*
The Painted Heron *(SW10)*\*
Rasoi Vineet Bhatia *(SW3)*\*
Shikara *(SW3)*
Standard Tandoori *(W2)*
Star of India *(SW5)*\*
Tandoori Lane *(SW6)*
Vama *(SW10)*\*

Woodlands (W4)*
Zaika (W8)*

### North
Anglo Asian Tandoori (N16)*
Bombay Bicycle Club (NW3)*
Chutneys (NW1)
Diwana B-P House (NW1)
Eriki (NW3)*
Geeta (NW6)*
Great Nepalese (NW1)*
Jashan (HA0, N8)*
Kovalam (NW6)*
Masala Zone (N1)
The Parsee (N19)*
Rani (N3)*
Rasa (N16)*
Sabras (NW10)*
Sakonis (HA0)*
Vijay (NW6)*
Zamzama (NW1)

### South
Babur Brasserie (SE23)*
Bengal Clipper (SE1)
Bombay Bicycle Club (SW12)*
Dalchini (SW19)
Hot Stuff (SW8)*
Indian Ocean (SW17)*
Just India (SW15)
Kastoori (SW17)*
Ma Goa (SW15)*
Mirch Masala (SW16, SW17, UB1)*
Nanglo (SW12)*
The Painted Heron (SE11)*
Sarkhel's (SW14, SW18)*
Silka (SE1)
Sree Krishna (SW17)*
Tandoori Nights (SE22)*
3 Monkeys (SE24)

### East
Café Spice Namaste (E1)*
Curryleaf (EC1)
Kasturi (EC3)
Lahore Kebab House (E1)*
Mehek (EC2)*
New Tayyabs (E1)*
Rajasthan (EC3)*

## INDIAN, SOUTHERN

### Central
India Club (WC2)
Malabar Junction (WC1)
Quilon (SW1)*
Ragam (W1)*
Rasa (W1)*
Rasa Maricham (WC1)*
Woodlands (SW1, W1)*

### West
Sagar (W6)*
Woodlands (W4)*

### North
Chutneys (NW1)

Geeta (NW6)*
Kovalam (NW6)*
Rani (N3)*
Rasa (N16)*
Rasa Travancore (N16)*
Sabras (NW10)*
Vijay (NW6)*

### South
Kastoori (SW17)*
Sree Krishna (SW17)*

## INDONESIAN

### Central
Melati (W1)
Trader Vics (W1)

### South
Nancy Lam's Enak Enak (SW11)

## JAPANESE

### Central
Abeno (WC1)
Abeno Too (WC2)
Benihana (W1)
Chisou (W1)*
Defune (W1)*
Edokko (WC1)*
Feng Sushi (W1)
Gili Gulu (WC2)
Gonbei (WC1)*
Grocer on Warwick Café (W1)
Hazuki (WC2)
Ikeda (W1)
Ikkyu (W1)
Itsu (W1)
Kulu Kulu (W1, WC2)*
Matsuri (SW1, WC1)*
Michiaki (W1)
Mitsukoshi (SW1)*
Miyama (W1)*
Mju (SW1)*
Nobu (W1)*
Nobu Berkeley (W1)
Roka (W1)*
Sakura (W1)*
Satsuma (W1)
Shogun (W1)*
Sumosan (W1)*
Taman gang (W1)
Taro (W1)
Ten Ten Tei (W1)
Tokyo Diner (WC2)
Umu (W1)
Wagamama (SW1, W1, WC1, WC2)
Yo! Sushi (SW1, W1, WC1)
Yoshino (W1)*

### West
Benihana (SW3)
L'Etranger (SW7)*
Feng Sushi (SW10, W11, W8)
Inaho (W2)*
Itsu (SW3)

Kisso (SW5)
Kulu Kulu (SW7)*
Nozomi (SW3)
Sushi-Hiro (W5)*
Wagamama (W8)
Yo! Sushi (SW6, W2)
Zuma (SW7)*

**North**
Benihana (NW3)
Bu San (N7)*
Café Japan (NW11)*
Jin Kichi (NW3)*
Sushi-Say (NW2)*
Wagamama (N1, NW1)
Wakaba (NW3)*
Yo! Sushi (N1, NW3)
Yuzu (NW6)*
ZeNW3 (NW3)*

**South**
Feng Sushi (SE1)
Fujiyama (SW9)*
Inshoku (SE1)
Tsunami (SW4)*
Wagamama (SE1, SW15)
Yo! Sushi (SE1)

**East**
City Miyama (EC4)*
Itsu (E14)
K10 (EC2)*
Kurumaya (EC4)
Miyabi (EC2)*
Moshi Moshi (E14, EC2)
Noto (EC2)
Pham Sushie (EC1)*
Tatsuso (EC2)*
Tokyo City (EC2)*
Ubon (E14)*
Wagamama (E14, EC2, EC3, EC4)
Yo! Sushi (EC1)

## KOREAN

**Central**
Koba (W1)*

**West**
Wizzy (SW6)*

**North**
Bu San (N7)*

**East**
Young Bin (EC2)

## MALAYSIAN

**Central**
Melati (W1)

**West**
Awana (SW3)
Mawar (W2)
Nyonya (W11)

**North**
Café de Maya (NW3)

Singapore Garden (NW6)
**South**
Champor-Champor (SE1)*

**East**
Ekachai (EC2)*
Singapura (EC2, EC3, EC4)

## PAKISTANI

**Central**
Salloos (SW1)*

**South**
Mirch Masala (SW16, SW17, UB1)*

**East**
Lahore Kebab House (E1)*
New Tayyabs (E1)*

## PAN-ASIAN

**Central**
Cocoon (W1)
dim T (W1)
Grocer on Warwick Café (W1)
Hare & Tortoise (WC1)*
Just Oriental (SW1)
Katana (WC2)
Mongolian Barbecue (WC2)
Noodle Noodle (SW1)
Pan-Asian Canteen (SW1)
Pengelley's (SW1)
The Penthouse (WC2)
Le Soufflé (W1)*

**West**
E&O (W11)*
Eight Over Eight (SW3)*
Hare & Tortoise (W14, W5)*
Jim Thompson's (SW6)
Uli (W11)*
Zimzun (SW6)

**North**
dim T café (NW3)
Jim Thompson's (N21)
Oriental City (NW9)
Tiger Lil's (N1)

**South**
The Banana Leaf Canteen (SW11)
Hare & Tortoise (SW15)*
Mongolian Barbecue (SW19)
Nancy Lam's Enak Enak (SW11)
Tiger Lil's (SW4)

**East**
Apium (EC1)
Cicada (EC1)*
Gt Eastern Dining Rm (EC2)*
Pacific Oriental (EC2)
Satu Bar & Kitchen (EC2)

## THAI

**Central**
Blue Jade (SW1)
Blue Lagoon (SW1)

Busaba Eathai *(W1, WC1)**
Chada *(W1)*
Chiang Mai *(W1)**
Crazy Bear *(W1)*
Mango Tree *(SW1)**
Mekong *(SW1)*
Nahm *(SW1)*
Page in Pimlico *(SW1)*
Patara *(W1)**
Sri Thai Soho *(W1)**
Thai Café *(SW1)*
Thai Pot *(WC2)*
Thai Square *(SW1, W1, WC2)*

### West
Bangkok *(SW7)**
Bedlington Café *(W4)*
Ben's Thai *(W9)**
Blue Elephant *(SW6)**
Blue Lagoon *(W14)*
Busabong *(SW10)*
Café 209 *(SW6)*
Churchill Arms *(W8)**
Esarn Kheaw *(W12)**
Fat Boy's *(W5)*
Hammersmith Café *(W6)*
Latymers *(W6)**
Old Parr's Head *(W14)*
The Papaya Tree *(W8)*
Patara *(SW3)**
Sabai Sabai *(W6)*
Silks & Spice *(W4)*
Sugar Hut *(SW6)*
Tawana *(W2)**
The Thai *(SW7)*
Thai Bistro *(W4)*
Thai Noodle Bar *(SW10)*
Thai Square *(SW7)*
The Walmer Castle *(W11)*
Yelo Thai Canteen *(W11)*

### North
Café de Maya *(NW3)*
Isarn *(N1)*
Silks & Spice *(NW1)*

Thai Square *(N1)*
Yelo *(N1)*
Yum Yum *(N16)*

### South
Amaranth *(SW18)**
Chada *(SW11)*
Fat Boy's *(TW1, TW8, W4)*
Kwan Thai *(SE1)**
The Pepper Tree *(SW4)**
Talad Thai *(SW15)**
Thai Corner Café *(SE22)*
Thai Elephant *(TW10)*
Thai Garden *(SW11)*
Thai on the River *(SW11)*
Thai Square *(SW15)*
Thailand *(SE14)**
The Wharf *(TW11)*

### East
Ekachai *(EC2)**
Elephant Royale *(E14)*
Gt Eastern Dining Rm *(EC2)**
Silks & Spice *(EC4)*
Sri Siam City *(EC2)*
Sri Thai *(EC4)*
Thai Square *(EC4)*
Thai Square City *(EC3)*

## VIETNAMESE

### Central
Bam-Bou *(W1)**
Mekong *(SW1)*
Opium *(W1)*

### West
Nam Long *(SW5)*

### North
Huong-Viet *(N1)**
Viet-Anh *(NW1)*

### East
Cây Tre *(EC1)**
Sông Quê *(E2)**
Viet Hoa *(E2)*

# AREA OVERVIEWS

## CENTRAL

### Soho, Covent Garden & Bloomsbury
### (Parts of W1, all WC2 and WC1)

| | | | |
|---|---|---|---|
| **£70+** | Lindsay House | *British, Modern* | ③③② |
| | Savoy Grill | *British, Traditional* | ③②③ |
| | Asia de Cuba | *Fusion* | ④④③ |
| **£60+** | Alastair Little | *British, Modern* | ③③⑤ |
| | Silk | " | – – – |
| | Pearl | *French* | ③④④ |
| | Matsuri | *Japanese* | ②②④ |
| **£50+** | Christopher's | *American* | ④④④ |
| | Adam Street | *British, Modern* | ③②② |
| | Atlantic Bar & Grill | " | ⑤⑤④ |
| | Indigo | " | ③②③ |
| | The Ivy | " | ③②① |
| | Refuel | " | ⑤④④ |
| | Simpsons-in-the-Strand | " | ④③③ |
| | Rules | *British, Traditional* | ③③① |
| | J Sheekey | *Fish & seafood* | ①②② |
| | The Admiralty | *French* | ③③④ |
| | The Criterion Grill | " | ⑤⑤② |
| | Jaan | *Fusion* | ③②④ |
| | Little Italy | *Italian* | ④④④ |
| | Neal Street | " | ④④④ |
| | Quo Vadis | " | ④④④ |
| | Floridita | *Cuban* | ⑤⑤③ |
| | The Penthouse | *Pan-Asian* | ⑤⑤② |
| **£40+** | Joe Allen | *American* | ④④② |
| | Axis | *British, Modern* | ③②④ |
| | Bank Aldwych | " | ④④④ |
| | Circus | " | ③③③ |
| | Le Deuxième | " | ④③④ |
| | French House | " | ③④② |
| | Homage | " | ③③④ |
| | The Perseverance | " | ③④③ |
| | The Portrait | " | ④④② |
| | Livebait | *Fish & seafood* | ④④④ |
| | Manzi's | " | ③④④ |
| | Zilli Fish | " | ③③③ |
| | Beotys | *French* | ④③③ |
| | Café des Amis du Vin | " | – – – |
| | Chez Gérard | " | ④④④ |
| | L'Escargot | " | ③②③ |
| | L'Estaminet | " | ④③③ |
| | Incognico | " | – – – |
| | Maggiore's | " | ②②① |
| | Mon Plaisir | " | ③③② |
| | Le Palais du Jardin | " | ③④③ |
| | La Trouvaille | " | ③①② |
| | Savoy Hotel (Banquette) | *International* | ④④⑤ |
| | Luigi's | *Italian* | ⑤④④ |
| | Orso | " | ④③③ |
| | Signor Zilli | " | ③③③ |

| | | | | |
|---|---|---|---|---|
| | Vasco & Piero's Pavilion | " | ❷❶❸ |
| | Albannach | Scottish | ❸④④ |
| | Cigala | Spanish | ❸❸④ |
| | Gaucho Grill | Steaks & grills | ❸④④ |
| | St Moritz | Swiss | ❷❸❷ |
| | Planet Hollywood | Burgers, etc | ⑤④④ |
| | Opium | French-Vietnamese | ⑤⑤❸ |
| | Moti Mahal | Indian | ④❷❸ |
| | Red Fort | " | ❷❸❸ |
| | Patara | Thai | ❶❷❸ |
| £35+ | TGI Friday's | American | ⑤⑤⑤ |
| | Aurora | British, Modern | ❸❸❶ |
| | Café du Jardin | " | ④❸④ |
| | 115 at Hodgson's | " | ④④❷ |
| | British Museum | " | ⑤④❷ |
| | Tuttons | " | ④④❸ |
| | Gay Hussar | Hungarian | ④❷❶ |
| | Bohème Kitchen | International | ④④❷ |
| | Papageno | " | ④❷❶ |
| | Sarastro | " | ⑤⑤❶ |
| | Sugar Reef | " | ⑤⑤⑤ |
| | Bertorelli's | Italian | ⑤④④ |
| | Italian Kitchen | " | ❸❸❸ |
| | Fung Shing | Chinese | ❷❸⑤ |
| | Imperial China | " | ❷❷❷ |
| | Shanghai Blues | " | ④④❷ |
| | Yauatcha | " | ❶❸❷ |
| | Café Lazeez | Indian | ❸④❸ |
| | Rasa Maricham | Indian, Southern | ❶❷❸ |
| | Katana | Pan-Asian | ❸❸④ |
| | Sri Thai Soho | Thai | ❷❷❸ |
| £30+ | Bodean's | American | ❸④④ |
| | Maxwell's | " | ④❸❸ |
| | Smollensky's | " | ⑤⑤④ |
| | Belgo Centraal | Belgian | ④④❸ |
| | Andrew Edmunds | British, Modern | ❷❶❶ |
| | Ha! Ha! | " | ④❶❶ |
| | The Endurance | British, Traditional | ④④④ |
| | Loch Fyne | Fish & seafood | ④④④ |
| | Café Bohème | French | ④❸❶ |
| | Randall & Aubin | " | ❷❷❶ |
| | Balans | International | ⑤❸❸ |
| | Boulevard | " | ④④❸ |
| | Browns | " | ⑤④④ |
| | Shampers | " | ❸❶❷ |
| | Aperitivo | Italian | ❸❸❸ |
| | Crivelli's Garden | " | ④⑤④ |
| | Pasta Brown | " | ⑤④⑤ |
| | Rusticana | " | ❸❶❸ |
| | Sapori | " | ④❸❷ |
| | Strada | " | ④❸❸ |
| | Tomato | " | ❸❷④ |
| | Mediterranean Kitchen | Mediterranean | ⑤④④ |
| | 06 St Chad's Place | " | ❷❸❸ |
| | Meza | Spanish | ④❸❸ |
| | Rainforest Café | Burgers, etc | ⑤⑤④ |

| | Name | Cuisine | Rating |
|---|---|---|---|
| | Wolfe's | " | ③④③ |
| | Kettners | Pizza | ④③❶ |
| | La Spiga | " | ③④④ |
| | Café Pacifico | Mexican/TexMex | ⑤④④ |
| | La Perla | " | ④④③ |
| | The Chinese Experience | Chinese | ②②③ |
| | ECapital | " | ③②④ |
| | New World | " | ③④④ |
| | Yming | " | ❶❶③ |
| | Malabar Junction | Indian | ③②③ |
| | Mela | " | ③③③ |
| | Soho Spice | " | ④④④ |
| | Abeno Too | Japanese | ③③④ |
| | Edokko | " | ②②③ |
| | Grocer on Warwick Café | " | ③②③ |
| | Ten Ten Tei | " | ③③⑤ |
| | Chiang Mai | Thai | ②④⑤ |
| | Thai Pot | " | ③③④ |
| | Thai Square | " | ④④③ |
| £25+ | The Easton | Australian | ③④③ |
| | Cork & Bottle | British, Modern | ⑤④❶ |
| | Smithy's | " | ④③④ |
| | Porters English Restaurant | British, Traditional" | ⑤④⑤ |
| | Garlic & Shots | International | ④④④ |
| | Ciao Bella | Italian | ③②② |
| | Zizzi | " | ④④③ |
| | La Tasca | Spanish | ⑤④③ |
| | Mildred's | Vegetarian | ②④③ |
| | North Sea Fish | Fish 'n' chips | ③②⑤ |
| | Fire & Stone | Pizza | ④②③ |
| | Paradiso Olivelli | " | ④④④ |
| | Gaby's | Middle Eastern | ④④④ |
| | Sofra | Turkish | ④③④ |
| | Chuen Cheng Ku | Chinese | ③③③ |
| | Harbour City | " | ③②③ |
| | Jade Garden | " | ③④④ |
| | Laureate | " | ③②③ |
| | New Mayflower | " | ②④④ |
| | Ping Pong | Chinese, Dim sum | ②❶❶ |
| | Gopal's of Soho | Indian | ②④④ |
| | Gonbei | Japanese | ②④④ |
| | Hazuki | " | ③②③ |
| | Itsu | " | ③③④ |
| | Satsuma | " | ③②④ |
| | Yo! Sushi | " | ④④④ |
| | Melati | Malaysian | ④③④ |
| | Mongolian Barbecue | Pan-Asian | ⑤⑤⑤ |
| | Busaba Eathai | Thai | ②③② |
| £20+ | Café Emm | International | ④④③ |
| | Café in the Crypt | " | ④⑤③ |
| | Exotika | " | ③②⑤ |
| | Gordon's Wine Bar | " | ⑤③❶ |
| | Star Café | " | ③③③ |
| | Amato | Italian | ③②③ |
| | La Porchetta Pizzeria | " | ③③③ |
| | Ed's Easy Diner | Burgers, etc | ④③② |

| | | | |
|---|---|---|---|
| | Hamburger Union | " | ③③④ |
| | Harry Ramsden's | Fish & chips | ④④⑤ |
| | Pâtisserie Valerie | Sandwiches, cakes, etc | ③④③ |
| | Calabash | Afro-Caribbean | ④④⑤ |
| | Souk | North African | ⑤⑤❷ |
| | Golden Dragon | Chinese | ③④⑤ |
| | Joy King Lau | " | ❷④④ |
| | Mr Kong | " | ❷③⑤ |
| | New Culture Revolution | " | ③③④ |
| | Poons | " | ④④④ |
| | Chowki | Indian | ❷③③ |
| | Masala Zone | " | ③③③ |
| | Gili Gulu | Japanese | ④⑤④ |
| | Kulu Kulu | " | ❷④④ |
| | Taro | " | ③③④ |
| | Wagamama | " | ③③④ |
| | Hare & Tortoise | Pan-Asian | ❷③④ |
| £15+ | Stock Pot | International | ④④④ |
| | Bistro 1 | Mediterranean | ④③④ |
| | Leon | " | ❷❷③ |
| | Food for Thought | Vegetarian | ❷④④ |
| | Konditor & Cook | Sandwiches, cakes, etc | ❶③④ |
| | Paul | " | ③⑤④ |
| | Mr Jerk | Afro-Caribbean | ❶③③ |
| | Wong Kei | Chinese | ④⑤⑤ |
| | India Club | Indian | ④④⑤ |
| | Tokyo Diner | Japanese | ③③④ |
| £10+ | Apostrophe | Sandwiches, cakes, etc | ❷❷③ |
| | Bar Italia | " | ④❷❶ |
| | Monmouth Coffee Company | " | ❶❷③ |
| £5+ | Red Veg | Vegetarian | ③⑤⑤ |
| | Fryer's Delight | Fish & chips | ③④⑤ |
| | Maison Bertaux | Sandwiches, cakes, etc | ❷③③ |

## Mayfair & St James's (Parts of W1 and SW1)

| | | | |
|---|---|---|---|
| £130+ | Sketch (Lecture Rm) | French | ⑤⑤④ |
| £110+ | Le Gavroche | French | ❷❶❷ |
| £100+ | Umu | Japanese | ④④④ |
| £80+ | G Ramsay at Claridges | French | ③❷③ |
| | The Greenhouse | " | ③③③ |
| | The Ritz | " | ④❷❶ |
| | Windows on the World | " | ⑤④❷ |
| | Nobu | Japanese | ❷④④ |
| | Nobu Berkeley | " | – – – |
| £70+ | Dorchester Grill | British, Traditional | ③❶❷ |
| | Wiltons | " | ③③③ |
| | L'Oranger | French | ③③③ |
| | The Square | " | ❷❷④ |
| | Connaught (Angela Hartnett) | Mediterranean | ③③③ |
| | Hakkasan | Chinese | ③④❷ |
| | Taman gang | " | ④④❶ |

| | | | Rating |
|---|---|---|---|
| **£60+** | Le Soufflé | British, Modern | 2 0 3 |
| | Bentley's | Fish & seafood | – – – |
| | Wheeler's of St James's | " | 3 3 4 |
| | Dover Street | French | 5 5 3 |
| | Mirabelle | " | 3 3 2 |
| | Sketch (Gallery) | " | 5 5 4 |
| | Cipriani | " | 5 5 4 |
| | Trader Vics | Indonesian | 5 4 2 |
| | Ikeda | Japanese | 3 3 4 |
| | Matsuri | " | 2 2 4 |
| | Sumosan | " | 1 3 4 |
| **£50+** | Bellamy's | British, Modern | 3 3 3 |
| | Berkeley Square Café | " | 3 2 4 |
| | Brian Turner | " | 4 4 4 |
| | Le Caprice | " | 2 0 0 |
| | Embassy | " | 4 4 5 |
| | Hush | " | 4 3 2 |
| | Nicole's | " | 4 3 4 |
| | Patterson's | " | 2 2 3 |
| | Quaglino's | " | 5 5 5 |
| | Six-13 | " | 3 4 4 |
| | The Wolseley | " | 3 3 2 |
| | Green's | British, Traditional | 3 3 2 |
| | Greig's | " | 4 4 4 |
| | maze | French | 4 4 4 |
| | Diverso | Italian | 4 3 4 |
| | Giardinetto | " | – – – |
| | Sartoria | " | 5 5 5 |
| | Teca | " | 2 2 4 |
| | The Guinea | Steaks & grills | 2 3 3 |
| | Mamounia | Moroccan | 3 4 3 |
| | Kai Mayfair | Chinese | 2 0 2 |
| | Princess Garden | " | 2 2 4 |
| | Benares | Indian | 2 2 3 |
| | Mint Leaf | " | 2 3 2 |
| | Tamarind | " | 2 2 3 |
| | Benihana | Japanese | 4 4 4 |
| | Mitsukoshi | " | 2 2 5 |
| | Miyama | " | 2 2 5 |
| | Shogun | " | 1 2 4 |
| | Cocoon | Pan-Asian | 3 4 2 |
| **£40+** | The Avenue | British, Modern | 4 4 4 |
| | Inn the Park | " | 4 5 3 |
| | Just St James | " | 4 4 4 |
| | Langan's Brasserie | " | 4 3 2 |
| | Rhodes W1 | " | – – – |
| | Zinc | " | 5 5 5 |
| | Boudin Blanc | French | 3 3 2 |
| | Brasserie Roux | " | 3 3 4 |
| | Chez Gérard | " | 4 4 4 |
| | Gabrielles | " | 3 4 3 |
| | Alloro | Italian | 2 2 2 |
| | Fiore | " | 4 2 4 |
| | Mosaico | " | 3 2 4 |
| | Pappagallo | " | 3 2 3 |
| | Serafino | " | 3 2 4 |

| | Name | Cuisine | Ratings |
|---|---|---|---|
| | Il Vicolo | " | ❸❸④ |
| | Truc Vert | Mediterranean | ❸⑤④ |
| | Gaucho Grill | Steaks & grills | ❸④④ |
| | Rowley's | " | ④④④ |
| | Destino | South American | ④④❶ |
| | Momo | Moroccan | ④④❷ |
| | Al Hamra | Lebanese | ❸④④ |
| | Fakhreldine | " | ❸❷❸ |
| | Levant | Middle Eastern | ④④❶ |
| | Zen Central | Chinese | ❷❸④ |
| | Chor Bizarre | Indian | ❸❸❷ |
| | Veeraswamy | " | — — — |
| | Yatra | " | ❸❷❸ |
| | Quilon | Indian, Southern | ❷❷❸ |
| | Patara | Thai | ❶❷❸ |
| £35+ | Automat | American | ❸❸❷ |
| | 43 South Molton | British, Modern | ❸❸④ |
| | The Little Square | " | ④❸❸ |
| | Sotheby's Café | " | ❷❶❷ |
| | Fortnum's, The Fountain | British, Traditional | ④❸❸ |
| | Café Fish | Fish & seafood | ④④⑤ |
| | Sketch (Glade) | French | — — — |
| | Tiger Tiger | International | ⑤⑤④ |
| | Al Duca | Italian | ❸❸④ |
| | Getti | " | ⑤④⑤ |
| | Il Pomodorino | " | ⑤④④ |
| | Quod | " | ⑤④④ |
| | Sketch (Parlour) | Sandwiches, cakes, etc | ④④❸ |
| | Al Sultan | Lebanese | ❸④④ |
| | Noura | " | ❸❷④ |
| | Rasa | Indian | ❶❷❸ |
| | Chisou | Japanese | ❷❷⑤ |
| | Yoshino | " | ❷❷④ |
| £30+ | Broadway Bar & Grill | American | ❸❸❸ |
| | L'Artiste Musclé | French | ④④④ |
| | Browns | International | ⑤④④ |
| | Strada | Italian | ④❸❸ |
| | Rocket | Mediterranean | ❸❸❶ |
| | El Pirata | Spanish | ④❸❸ |
| | Hard Rock Café | Burgers, etc | ④❸❷ |
| | Delfino | Pizza | ❸④④ |
| | Richoux | Sandwiches, cakes, etc | ④④❸ |
| | Thai Square | Thai | ④④❸ |
| £25+ | Running Horse | International | ④❸④ |
| | Gourmet Pizza Co. | Pizza | ❸④④ |
| | Royal Academy | Sandwiches, cakes, etc | ④⑤④ |
| | Ishtar | Turkish | ❸❸④ |
| | Sofra | " | ④❸④ |
| | Woodlands | Indian | ❷❷④ |
| | Itsu | Japanese | ❸❸④ |
| | Sakura | " | ❷④④ |
| | Yo! Sushi | " | ④④④ |
| | Busaba Eathai | Thai | ❷❸❷ |
| £20+ | Pâtisserie Valerie | Sandwiches, cakes, etc | ❸④❸ |

|  |  |  |  |
|---|---|---|---|
|  | Wagamama | Japanese | ❸❸④ |
|  | Noodle Noodle | Pan-Asian | ❸❸④ |
| £15+ | Stock Pot | International | ④④④ |
| £10+ | Benugo | Sandwiches, cakes, etc | ❷④④ |
| £5+ | Crussh | Sandwiches, cakes, etc | ❸❷④ |
|  | Fuzzy's Grub | " | ❷❷❷ |

## Fitzrovia & Marylebone (Part of W1)

|  |  |  |  |
|---|---|---|---|
| £70+ | Pied à Terre | French | – – – |
|  | Spoon at Sanderson | Fusion | ⑤⑤④ |
| £60+ | Orrery | French | ❸❷❸ |
|  | Defune | Japanese | ❷④⑤ |
| £50+ | Oscar | British, Modern | ⑤⑤④ |
|  | The Providores | Fusion | ❸④④ |
|  | Caldesi | Italian | ❸④④ |
|  | 5 Cavendish Square | " | ④❸❸ |
|  | Locanda Locatelli | " | ❷❷❷ |
|  | Passione | " | ❷❸❸ |
|  | La Porte des Indes | Indian | ❸④❷ |
| £40+ | Blandford Street | British, Modern | ④❸④ |
|  | CVO Firevault | " | ④④❶ |
|  | Mash | " | ⑤⑤④ |
|  | Odin's | British, Traditional | ❷❶❶ |
|  | Back to Basics | Fish & seafood | ❶❷④ |
|  | Fishworks | " | ❷❸④ |
|  | Elena's L'Etoile | French | ❸❷❷ |
|  | Villandry | " | ④④④ |
|  | Archipelago | Fusion | ❸❶❶ |
|  | Hardy's | International | ❸❷❸ |
|  | Michael Moore | " | ❸❸④ |
|  | Caffè Caldesi | Italian | ❸④④ |
|  | Camerino | " | ❷❷❸ |
|  | Eddalino | " | ❸❷④ |
|  | Latium | " | ❷❷❸ |
|  | Sardo | " | ❷❸❸ |
|  | Fino | Spanish | ❷❷❸ |
|  | Reubens | Kosher | ④④❸ |
|  | Maroush | Lebanese | ❷④④ |
|  | Deya | Indian | ❶❷④ |
|  | Roka | Japanese | ❷④❸ |
|  | Crazy Bear | Thai | ❸❷❶ |
|  | Bam-Bou | Vietnamese | ❷❸❶ |
| £35+ | Galvin | British, Modern | – – – |
|  | The Union Café | " | ④④④ |
|  | Café Bagatelle | French | ⑤④❶ |
|  | Bertorelli's | Italian | ⑤④④ |
|  | Getti | " | ⑤④⑤ |
|  | La Spighetta | " | – – – |
|  | Garbo's | Scandinavian | ④❸⑤ |
|  | Black & Blue | Steaks & grills | ❸❸④ |
|  | Occo | Moroccan | ❷④❸ |
|  | Fairuz | Lebanese | ❷❸④ |

| | | | |
|---|---|---|---|
| | Royal China | *Chinese* | ❶④④ |
| | Rasa Samudra | *Indian* | ❶❷❸ |
| | Koba | *Japanese* | ❷❶❸ |
| | Michiaki | *"* | ❸④④ |
| £30+ | Ha! Ha! | *British, Modern* | ④④④ |
| | RIBA Café | *"* | ④❸❶ |
| | Auberge | *French* | ⑤⑤④ |
| | Langan's Bistro | *"* | ④❷❷ |
| | Tapa Room (Providores) | *Fusion* | ❷❷❷ |
| | O'Conor Don | *Irish* | ❷❷❷ |
| | Strada | *Italian* | ④❸❸ |
| | Salt Yard | *Mediterranean* | ❶❸❸ |
| | La Rueda | *Spanish* | ④❸❸ |
| | Tootsies | *Burgers, etc* | ④④④ |
| | La Perla | *Mexican/TexMex* | ④④❸ |
| | Original Tajines | *Moroccan* | ❸❸❷ |
| | Chai Pani | *Indian* | ❸❷④ |
| | Ragam | *Indian, Southern* | ❶❶⑤ |
| | Abeno | *Japanese* | ❸❷❸ |
| £25+ | La Galette | *French* | ❸④④ |
| | Le Relais de Venise | *"* | – – – |
| | Eat & Two Veg | *International* | ⑤④❸ |
| | Giraffe | *"* | ④❷❸ |
| | Carluccio's Caffè | *Italian* | ④④❸ |
| | Zizzi | *"* | ④④❸ |
| | Navarro's | *Spanish* | ❸❷❷ |
| | Eagle Bar Diner | *Burgers, etc* | ❸④❷ |
| | Paradiso Olivelli | *Pizza* | ④④④ |
| | La Fromagerie Café | *Sandwiches, cakes, etc* | ❶❷❷ |
| | Efes II | *Turkish* | ④❸❸ |
| | Ozer | *"* | ④❸❸ |
| | Sofra | *"* | ④❸④ |
| | Curryleaf | *Indian* | ④④④ |
| | Woodlands | *"* | ❷❷④ |
| | Ikkyu | *Japanese* | ❸❸❸ |
| | Yo! Sushi | *"* | ④④④ |
| | dim T | *Pan-Asian* | ④④❸ |
| | Chada | *Thai* | ❸❷④ |
| £20+ | Fine Burger Company | *Burgers, etc* | ❸❸④ |
| | Le Pain Quotidien | *Sandwiches, cakes, etc* | ❷④❷ |
| | Pâtisserie Valerie | *"* | ❸④❸ |
| | Wagamama | *Japanese* | ❸❸④ |
| £15+ | Golden Hind | *Fish & chips* | ❷❷④ |
| | Paul | *Sandwiches, cakes, etc* | ❸⑤④ |
| £10+ | Apostrophe | *Sandwiches, cakes, etc* | ❷❷❸ |
| | Benugo | *"* | ❷④④ |

## Belgravia, Pimlico, Victoria & Westminster (SW1, except St James's)

| Price | Name | Cuisine | Rating |
|---|---|---|---|
| £90+ | The Lanesborough | British, Modern | ④❷❷ |
| £80+ | Pétrus | French | ❷❷❷ |
| £70+ | Rib Room | British, Traditional | ④④④ |
| | One-O-One | Fish & seafood | ❷❸⑤ |
| | Mju | Fusion | ❷❷④ |
| | Nahm | Thai | ❸④④ |
| £60+ | Foliage | French | ❷❶❷ |
| | Roussillon | " | ❶❶❸ |
| | Santini | Italian | ④④④ |
| | Toto's | " | ❷❷❶ |
| | Mr Chow | Chinese | ④④④ |
| £50+ | The Fifth Floor | British, Modern | ④④⑤ |
| | Goring Hotel | British, Traditional | ❸❶❷ |
| | W'sens | French | ④④④ |
| | Boxwood Café | International | ❸❸④ |
| | L'Incontro | Italian | ❸❸④ |
| | Mimmo d'Ischia | " | ④❸④ |
| | Signor Sassi | " | ❸❷❷ |
| | Zafferano | " | ❶❷❷ |
| | Amaya | Indian | ❶❸❷ |
| | The Cinnamon Club | " | ❷❸❸ |
| £40+ | Atrium | British, Modern | ⑤⑤④ |
| | Bank Westminster | " | ④❸❸ |
| | Ebury Street Wine Bar | " | ④❸❸ |
| | Messanges | " | ❸❷④ |
| | Tate Britain | " | ④④❷ |
| | Shepherd's | British, Traditional | ④❷❷ |
| | Chez Gérard | French | ④④④ |
| | Drones | " | ④❸④ |
| | The Ebury | " | ④④❸ |
| | La Poule au Pot | " | ❸❷❶ |
| | Motcombs | International | ④❷❸ |
| | Pomegranates | " | ④④❸ |
| | Caraffini | Italian | ❷❶❷ |
| | Como Lario | " | ❸❸❸ |
| | Il Convivio | " | ❷❶❸ |
| | Olivo | " | ❷❸④ |
| | Quirinale | " | ❶❶❸ |
| | Sale e Pepe | " | ❸❷❸ |
| | The Fifth Floor (Café) | Mediterranean | ⑤⑤④ |
| | Boisdale | Scottish | ④④④ |
| | Ken Lo's Memories | Chinese | ❷❷❸ |
| | Pengelley's | Pan-Asian | ❸④④ |
| | Mango Tree | Thai | ❷❸④ |
| £35+ | The Contented Vine | British, Modern | ④❸④ |
| | Grenadier | British, Traditional | ④④❷ |
| | Le Cercle | French | ❶❷❷ |
| | Royal Court Bar | International | ⑤④❸ |
| | La Fontana | Italian | ❸❷❸ |
| | Pizza on the Park | " | ④④❷ |

| | | | | | |
|---|---|---|---|---|---|
| | Uno | " | ④ | ④ | ④ |
| | About Thyme | Mediterranean | ⑤ | ④ | ④ |
| | Oliveto | Pizza | ❷ | ❸ | ④ |
| | Baker & Spice | Sandwiches, cakes, etc | ❸ | ⑤ | ④ |
| | Texas Embassy Cantina | Mexican/TexMex | ④ | ④ | ❸ |
| | Beiteddine | Lebanese | ❸ | ❷ | ④ |
| | Ishbilia | " | ❷ | ❷ | ④ |
| | Noura | " | ❸ | ❷ | ④ |
| | Hunan | Chinese | ❶ | ❶ | ④ |
| | Salloos | Pakistani | ❶ | ④ | ④ |
| £30+ | Footstool | British, Modern | ⑤ | ⑤ | ❸ |
| | Grumbles | International | ④ | ④ | ❸ |
| | Oriel | " | ⑤ | ⑤ | ❸ |
| | Goya | Spanish | ④ | ❷ | ④ |
| | Kazan | Turkish | ❸ | ❷ | ❸ |
| | Just Oriental | Pan-Asian | ❸ | ❷ | ❷ |
| £25+ | Chimes | British, Traditional | ⑤ | ④ | ④ |
| | Seafresh | Fish & chips | – | – | – |
| | Ranoush | Lebanese | ❷ | ④ | ④ |
| | Feng Sushi | Japanese | ❸ | ❸ | ④ |
| | Yo! Sushi | " | ④ | ④ | ④ |
| | Pan-Asian Canteen | Pan-Asian | ❸ | ❷ | ❸ |
| | Blue Jade | Thai | ④ | ❶ | ④ |
| | Blue Lagoon | " | ❸ | ❸ | ④ |
| | Page in Pimlico | " | ❸ | ❷ | ❸ |
| | Thai Café | " | ❸ | ④ | ④ |
| £20+ | Brahms | International | ④ | ❸ | ④ |
| | Pâtisserie Valerie | Sandwiches, cakes, etc | ❸ | ④ | ❸ |
| | Jenny Lo's | Chinese | ❷ | ❷ | ④ |
| | Wagamama | Japanese | ❸ | ❸ | ④ |
| | Mekong | Vietnamese | ❸ | ❷ | ④ |
| £5+ | Crussh | Sandwiches, cakes, etc | ❸ | ❷ | ④ |

## WEST

### Chelsea, South Kensington, Kensington, Earl's Court & Fulham (SW3, SW5, SW6, SW7, SW10 & W8)

| | | | |
|---|---|---|---|
| £100+ | Blakes Hotel | *International* | ④③❶ |
| £90+ | Aubergine | *French* | ❶②③ |
| | Gordon Ramsay | *"* | ❶❶② |
| £70+ | Capital Hotel | *French* | ❶②③ |
| | Tom Aikens | *"* | ③②③ |
| | Brunello | *Italian* | ④④④ |
| | Rasoi Vineet Bhatia | *Indian* | ❶②③ |
| £60+ | Clarke's | *British, Modern* | ❶❶③ |
| | 1880 | *"* | ❶②③ |
| | Bibendum | *French* | ③②② |
| | L'Etranger | *Fusion* | ②③③ |
| | Nozomi | *Japanese* | – – – |
| | Zuma | *"* | ❶③❶ |
| £50+ | Babylon | *British, Modern* | ④④② |
| | Bluebird | *"* | ⑤⑤⑤ |
| | The Collection | *"* | ④④③ |
| | The Tenth | *"* | ④②② |
| | Bluebird Club | *British, Traditional* | ③③③ |
| | Deep | *Fish & seafood* | ③④⑤ |
| | Poissonnerie de l'Avenue | *"* | ②②③ |
| | Belvedere | *French* | ③②❶ |
| | Cheyne Walk Bras' | *"* | ③④② |
| | Aquasia | *Fusion* | ④④④ |
| | Daphne's | *Italian* | ④③② |
| | Montpeliano | *"* | ④④④ |
| | San Lorenzo | *"* | ④④③ |
| | Scalini | *"* | ②②② |
| | Locanda Ottoemezzo | *Mediterranean* | ③②② |
| | Bombay Brasserie | *Indian* | ②③② |
| | Chutney Mary | *"* | ②②② |
| | Benihana | *Japanese* | ④④④ |
| £40+ | Big Easy | *American* | ④④③ |
| | PJ's | *"* | ④④③ |
| | Abingdon Road | *British, Modern* | – – – |
| | Admiral Codrington | *"* | ③④② |
| | Bistrot 190 | *"* | ④⑤③ |
| | Dan's | *"* | ④②② |
| | The Farm | *"* | ③④③ |
| | Kensington Place | *"* | ③③④ |
| | Launceston Place | *"* | ④③② |
| | Whits | *"* | ③②④ |
| | Maggie Jones's | *British, Traditional* | ③③❶ |
| | Lundum's | *Danish* | ②❶❶ |
| | Bibendum Oyster Bar | *Fish & seafood* | ③③③ |
| | Ghillies | *"* | ③④③ |
| | Le Suquet | *"* | ②④③ |
| | La Brasserie | *French* | ④④③ |

| | | | |
|---|---|---|---|
| | Brasserie St Quentin | " | ❸❷❸ |
| | Le Colombier | " | ❸❷❷ |
| | FireHouse | " | ❸❷❸ |
| | Nathalie | " | ❸⓪⑤ |
| | Racine | " | ❷⓪❸ |
| | Zinc | International | ⑤⑤⑤ |
| | The Ark | Italian | ④④④ |
| | Carpaccio's | " | ④④❷ |
| | La Famiglia | " | ❸❷❸ |
| | Frankie's | " | ④④❸ |
| | Iniga | " | ④④❸ |
| | Lucio | " | ❷⓪❷ |
| | Monza | " | ❸❷❸ |
| | Pellicano | " | ❸❷④ |
| | Il Portico | " | ❸⓪❸ |
| | San Frediano | " | ❸❷❸ |
| | Timo | " | – – – |
| | Cross Keys | Mediterranean | ❸④❷ |
| | Manicomio | " | ❸❸❸ |
| | Wódka | Polish | ❸❷❷ |
| | Nikita's | Russian | ⑤❸❷ |
| | El Blasõn | Spanish | ④❸④ |
| | Cambio de Tercio | " | ❷❸❸ |
| | Gaucho Grill | Steaks & grills | ❸④④ |
| | Aubaine | Sandwiches, cakes, etc | ④⑤❷ |
| | Pasha | Moroccan | ④④❶ |
| | Maroush | Lebanese | ❷④④ |
| | Ken Lo's Memories | Chinese | ❷❷❸ |
| | Mr Wing | " | ❷❷❷ |
| | The Painted Heron | Indian | ❶⓪❸ |
| | Vama | " | ❶❷❸ |
| | Zaika | " | ❷❸❸ |
| | Awana | Malaysian | – – – |
| | Eight Over Eight | Pan-Asian | ❶❸❷ |
| | Blue Elephant | Thai | ❷❷❶ |
| | Patara | " | ❶❷❸ |
| | Sugar Hut | " | ④❸❶ |
| £35+ | Sticky Fingers | American | ④④④ |
| | TGI Friday's | " | ⑤⑤⑤ |
| | The Abingdon | British, Modern | ❸❷❷ |
| | The Anglesea Arms | " | ④❸❸ |
| | Joe's Café | " | ❸④❷ |
| | Lots Road | " | ❸❸❸ |
| | The Mall Tavern | " | ❸❸❸ |
| | The Pen | " | ❸❸❸ |
| | The Pig's Ear | " | ❸❷❷ |
| | Ffiona's | British, Traditional | ❸⓪❶ |
| | Lou Pescadou | Fish & seafood | ❸❷④ |
| | Stratford's | " | ❷⓪❸ |
| | Base | French | ❸❸④ |
| | La Bouchée | " | ④④❷ |
| | Brasserie de l'Auberge | " | ❸❸④ |
| | Langan's Coq d'Or | " | ❸❸❸ |
| | Relais de Paris | " | ④④④ |
| | The Cross Bar | International | ❸❸④ |
| | The Enterprise | " | ④❸❷ |

| | | |
|---|---|---|
| Foxtrot Oscar | " | ⑤④⑤ |
| 606 Club | " | ⑤④❶ |
| The Swag & Tails | " | ❸❷❷ |
| De Cecco | Italian | ❸❷❸ |
| Elistano | " | ④❸❸ |
| Il Falconiere | " | ④④④ |
| Frantoio | " | ❸❷❷ |
| Loco Locale | " | ④④❸ |
| Matriciano | " | ④④④ |
| Mirto | " | ❸❶④ |
| Osteria dell'Arancio | " | ❸❸❷ |
| Ziani | " | ❸❷❷ |
| Polish Club (Ognisko Polskie) | Polish | ❸❷❷ |
| Tugga | Portuguese | ❸❸❷ |
| Black & Blue | Steaks & grills | ❸❸④ |
| Friends | Pizza | ④④④ |
| Baker & Spice | Sandwiches, cakes, etc | ❸⑤④ |
| Bluebird Café | " | ⑤⑤④ |
| Cactus Blue | South American | ④④❸ |
| 1492 | " | ❸④❸ |
| Al Bustan | Lebanese | ❸❸④ |
| Aziz | Middle Eastern | ❸❷❶ |
| Good Earth | Chinese | ❶❷④ |
| Made in China | " | ❷❷④ |
| Mao Tai | " | ❷❸❸ |
| Café Lazeez | Indian | ❸④❸ |
| Star of India | " | ❷❸④ |
| Kisso | Japanese | ❸❸❸ |
| **£30+**  Brinkley's | British, Modern | ④❸❷ |
| The Builder's Arms | " | ④④❶ |
| Harwood Arms | " | ❸❸❷ |
| The Ifield | " | ❸❷❷ |
| Le Metro | " | ❸❸❸ |
| The Phoenix | " | ④❸❷ |
| The Salisbury Tavern | " | ❸❸❸ |
| Vingt-Quatre | " | ④❸④ |
| White Horse | " | ❸❸❸ |
| Loch Fyne | Fish & seafood | ④④④ |
| Randall & Aubin | French | ❷❷❶ |
| Tartine | " | ❸❸❷ |
| Balans | International | ⑤❸❸ |
| Beaufort House | " | ④❷❷ |
| Glaisters | " | ④❸❷ |
| The Scarsdale | " | ④❸❶ |
| Da Mario | Italian | ❸❸❸ |
| Made in Italy | " | ❷⑤❸ |
| Marechiaro | " | ❸⑤④ |
| Miraggio | " | ❷❷❷ |
| Napulé | " | ❸⑤❸ |
| Nuovi Sapori | " | ❷❶❸ |
| Riccardo's | " | ❸❸❷ |
| Santa Lucia | " | ❸⑤④ |
| Strada | " | ④❸❸ |
| Mediterranean Kitchen | Mediterranean | ⑤④④ |
| La Rueda | Spanish | ④❸❸ |
| El Gaucho | Steaks & grills | ❷④④ |

| | | | |
|---|---|---|---|
| | Sophie's Steakhouse | " | ③③❶ |
| | Tootsies | Burgers, etc | ④④④ |
| | (Ciro's) Pizza Pomodoro | Pizza | ④④❷ |
| | Richoux | Sandwiches, cakes, etc | ④④❸ |
| | Troubadour | " | ⑤④❶ |
| | La Perla | Mexican/TexMex | ④④❸ |
| | Choys | Chinese | ④❷❸ |
| | Haandi | Indian | ❷❸④ |
| | kare kare | " | ❷❷❸ |
| | Love India | " | – – – |
| | Malabar | " | ❷❷❸ |
| | Noor Jahan | " | ❷❷④ |
| | Wizzy | Korean | ❷④❸ |
| | Jim Thompson's | Pan-Asian | ④④❷ |
| | Bangkok | Thai | ❷❷⑤ |
| | Busabong | " | ❸❷④ |
| | The Papaya Tree | " | ❸④⑤ |
| | The Thai | " | ❸❸④ |
| | Thai Square | " | ④④❸ |
| | Nam Long | Vietnamese | ⑤⑤❸ |
| £25+ | Abbaye | Belgian | ④④④ |
| | Joe's Brasserie | British, Modern | ④❸❸ |
| | The Oratory | " | ④④❸ |
| | Blue Kangaroo | International | ④❸❷ |
| | Coopers Arms | " | ❸❷❷ |
| | Giraffe | " | ④❷❸ |
| | Sporting Page | " | ❸❸❷ |
| | The Windsor Castle | " | ❸④❶ |
| | Wine Gallery | " | ④❸❷ |
| | Aglio e Olio | Italian | ❷❷❸ |
| | Buona Sera | " | ❸❸❷ |
| | Carluccio's Caffè | " | ④④❸ |
| | Il Pagliaccio | " | ④❷❶ |
| | Pappa Ciccia | " | ❷❷❸ |
| | Picasso | " | ④④❸ |
| | Pucci Pizza | " | ❷④❷ |
| | Spago | " | ❸④❸ |
| | Zizzi | " | ④④❸ |
| | The Atlas | Mediterranean | ❷❸❷ |
| | Daquise | Polish | ④④④ |
| | Lomo | Spanish | ④④❸ |
| | Tendido Cero | " | ❷❶❷ |
| | Henry J Beans | Burgers, etc | ④④❷ |
| | Geale's | Fish & chips | ④④⑤ |
| | Basilico | Pizza | ❸④④ |
| | La Delizia | " | ❷④❸ |
| | Texas Lone Star | Mexican/TexMex | ④❸④ |
| | Ranoush | Lebanese | ❷④④ |
| | Yi-Ban | Chinese | ❷❸❷ |
| | Khan's of Kensington | Indian | ❸❷④ |
| | Khyber Pass | " | ❸❷④ |
| | Memories of India | " | ❸❷④ |
| | Shikara | " | ❸❸④ |
| | Feng Sushi | Japanese | ❸❸④ |
| | Itsu | " | ❸❸④ |
| | Yo! Sushi | " | ④④④ |

| | | | |
|---|---|---|---|
| | Zimzun | *Pan-Asian* | ❸❷❸ |
| | Thai Noodle Bar | *Thai* | ❸❷❸ |
| £20+ | Little Bay | *Mediterranean* | ❸❷❷ |
| | As Greek As It Gets | *Greek* | ❶④⑤ |
| | Chelsea Bun Diner | *International* | ❸❸④ |
| | Mona Lisa | " | ❸❶④ |
| | Rôtisserie Jules | *Steaks & grills* | ❸❷⑤ |
| | Ed's Easy Diner | *Burgers, etc* | ④❸❷ |
| | Gourmet Burger Kitchen | " | ❷④④ |
| | Pâtisserie Valerie | *Sandwiches, cakes, etc* | ❸④❸ |
| | New Culture Rev'n | *Chinese* | ❸❸④ |
| | Masala Zone | *Indian* | ❸❸❸ |
| | Tandoori Lane | " | ④❸④ |
| | Kulu Kulu | *Japanese* | ❷④④ |
| | Wagamama | " | ❸❸④ |
| £15+ | Costa's Grill | *Greek* | ④❷❸ |
| | Stock Pot | *International* | ④④④ |
| | Café Crêperie | *Crêpes* | ❸⑤④ |
| | Stick & Bowl | *Chinese* | ❸❸⑤ |
| | Café 209 | *Thai* | ❸❸❶ |
| | Churchill Arms | " | ❷④❷ |
| £10+ | Chelsea Kitchen | *International* | ④❸❸ |
| | Benugo | *Sandwiches, cakes, etc* | ❷④④ |
| £5+ | Crussh | *Sandwiches, cakes, etc* | ❸❷④ |

## Notting Hill, Holland Park, Bayswater, North Kensington & Maida Vale (W2, W9, W10, W11)

| | | | |
|---|---|---|---|
| £60+ | I Thai | *Fusion* | – – – |
| £50+ | The Ledbury | *French* | ❷❶❷ |
| | Assaggi | *Italian* | ❶❶❸ |
| £40+ | Beach Blanket Babylon | *British, Modern* | ⑤⑤❶ |
| | Island | " | ❸❸❸ |
| | Julie's | " | ⑤④❶ |
| | Julie's Wine Bar | " | ④❸❶ |
| | Notting Hill Brasserie | " | ❷❶❶ |
| | The Tea Palace | " | ④❸④ |
| | Electric Brasserie | *International* | ❸④❷ |
| | Graze | " | – – – |
| | Al San Vincenzo | *Italian* | ❷❷❸ |
| | Arturo | " | ❷❷❸ |
| | Edera | " | ④❷④ |
| | Esenza | " | ❸④④ |
| | The Green Olive | " | ❸❸❸ |
| | Osteria Basilico | " | ❷❸❷ |
| | Notting Grill | *Steaks & grills* | ❸④❸ |
| | Café Maroush | *Lebanese* | ❷④④ |
| | E&O | *Pan-Asian* | ❶❷❶ |
| £35+ | Harlem | *American* | ④⑤④ |
| | TGI Friday's | " | ⑤⑤⑤ |
| | First Floor | *British, Modern* | ❸❸❶ |
| | Formosa Dining Room | " | ❸❸❷ |
| | The Frontline Club | " | ④❷❸ |

| | | | |
|---|---|---|---|
| | The Ladbroke Arms | " | ❷❸❷ |
| | The Waterway | " | ❸⑤❸ |
| | The Cow | Fish & seafood | ❷④❷ |
| | Père Michel | French | ❸❸④ |
| | Food@TheMuse | International | – – – |
| | Lonsdale | " | ⑤⑤④ |
| | L'Accento Italiano | Italian | ❸❷❸ |
| | Cristini | " | ❸❷④ |
| | Luna Rossa | " | ④⑤④ |
| | Mediterraneo | " | ❸❸❸ |
| | The Oak | " | ❷❸❷ |
| | Ottolenghi | " | ❶❸❷ |
| | Zucca | " | ④❸④ |
| | Crazy Homies | Mexican/TexMex | ❸❷❷ |
| | Fairuz | Lebanese | ❷❸④ |
| | Levantine | Middle Eastern | ④④❸ |
| | Royal China | Chinese | ❶④④ |
| | Bombay Bicycle Club | Indian | ❷❷❸ |
| | Bombay Palace | " | ❶❶❸ |
| £30+ | Lucky Seven | American | ❸④❷ |
| | Paradise, Kensal Green | British, Modern | ④④❷ |
| | Raoul's Café | " | ❸⑤❸ |
| | Ruby Lounge & Sequoia Bar | " | – – – |
| | The Vale | " | ❷❶❸ |
| | The Westbourne | " | ❸⑤❷ |
| | Halepi | Greek | ❸❷④ |
| | 202 | International | ④❷❶ |
| | The Red Pepper | Italian | ❸④④ |
| | Wine Factory | " | ④❷❸ |
| | Tootsies | Burgers, etc | ④④④ |
| | Rodizio Rico | Brazilian | ④④④ |
| | Al-Waha | Lebanese | ④❸④ |
| | Ginger | Indian | ❸❸④ |
| | Noor Jahan | " | ❷❷④ |
| £25+ | The Prince Bonaparte | British, Modern | ❷④❸ |
| | The Castle | British, Traditional | ❸④❸ |
| | Café Laville | International | ④❸❷ |
| | Galicia | Spanish | ❷❸❷ |
| | Tom's | Sandwiches, cakes, etc | ❸❸❸ |
| | Taqueria | Mexican/TexMex | ❶④❸ |
| | Ranoush | Lebanese | ❷④④ |
| | Yas on the Park | Persian | ❸❸④ |
| | Mandarin Kitchen | Chinese | ❶④④ |
| | Feng Sushi | Japanese | ❸❸④ |
| | Inaho | " | ❶⑤⑤ |
| | Yo! Sushi | " | ④④④ |
| | Nyonya | Malaysian | ❸❸④ |
| | Uli | Pan-Asian | ❷❶❷ |
| | Tawana | Thai | ❷❷⑤ |
| | The Walmer Castle | " | ❸④❷ |
| £20+ | S & M Café | British, Traditional | ÃÃÃ |
| | Rôtisserie Jules | Steaks & grills | ❸❷⑤ |
| | Gourmet Burger Kitchen | Burgers, etc | ❷④④ |
| | Babes 'n' Burgers | " | ❸⑤④ |
| | Beirut Express | Lebanese | ❶④④ |

| | | | Ratings |
|---|---|---|---|
| | Shish | Middle Eastern | ④❷❸ |
| | Kandoo | Persian | ❸❷④ |
| | The Four Seasons | Chinese | ❶⑤⑤ |
| | New Culture Rev'n | " | ❸❸④ |
| | Standard Tandoori | Indian | ❸④④ |
| | Mawar | Malaysian | ❸④⑤ |
| | Ben's Thai | Thai | ❷④❸ |
| | Yelo Thai Canteen | " | ❸❷❷ |
| £15+ | Mr Jerk | Afro-Caribbean | ❶❸❸ |
| | Moroccan Tagine | Moroccan | ❸❸❸ |
| | Fresco | Lebanese | ❷❷④ |
| | Mandalay | Burmese | ❶❶④ |
| | Khan's | Indian | ❷④④ |
| £5+ | Lisboa Patisserie | Sandwiches, cakes, etc | ❸④④ |

## Hammersmith, Shepherd's Bush, Olympia, Chiswick & Ealing (W4, W5, W6, W12, W14)

| | | | Ratings |
|---|---|---|---|
| £60+ | The River Café | Italian | ❷❸❸ |
| £40+ | Fish Hoek | Fish & seafood | ❶❷④ |
| | Fishworks | " | ❷❸④ |
| | Charlotte's Place | French | ❸❷❸ |
| | La Trompette | " | ❶❶❷ |
| | Cibo | Italian | ❷❸❸ |
| | Popeseye | Steaks & grills | ❷❸⑤ |
| £35+ | The Brackenbury | British, Modern | ❷❷❷ |
| | The Burlington | " | ❸❸④ |
| | Bush Bar & Grill | " | ④④❸ |
| | Café Med | " | ④④❸ |
| | Devonshire House | " | ❸❷❸ |
| | Gravy | " | ❸④❸ |
| | Pissarro's | " | ④❸❶ |
| | The Rocket | " | ❸❸❸ |
| | Sam's Brasserie | " | – – – |
| | Snows on the Green | " | ❸❷❸ |
| | Chez Kristof | French | ❸❸❷ |
| | Le Vacherin | " | ❷❸④ |
| | The Grove | Mediterranean | ④❸❸ |
| £30+ | Smollensky's | American | ⑤⑤④ |
| | The Anglesea Arms | British, Modern | ❶④❷ |
| | The Bollo House | " | ④④❸ |
| | Cotto | " | ❷❷④ |
| | Ealing Park Tavern | " | ❸❷❷ |
| | The Havelock Tavern | " | ❶⑤❷ |
| | Hole in the Wall | " | ❸❸❷ |
| | Seven Stars | " | ④❸❷ |
| | The Thatched House | " | ❸❸❷ |
| | Annie's | International | ④❶❶ |
| | Balans | " | ⑤❸❸ |
| | The Swan | Mediterranean | ❷❷❷ |
| | The Gate | Vegetarian | ❶❷❷ |
| | Tootsies | Burgers, etc | ④④④ |

|  |  |  |  |
|---|---|---|---|
|  | Yas | Persian | ❸❸④ |
|  | Brilliant | Indian | ❷❷④ |
|  | Silks & Spice | Thai | ❸❸❸ |
| £25+ | The Crown & Sceptre | British, Modern | ❸④❷ |
|  | Dove | " | ④❸❶ |
|  | The Pilot | " | ❸❸④ |
|  | Stone Mason's Arms | " | ❸❸❷ |
|  | Whole Hog Canteen | " | ❸❷❸ |
|  | Queen's Head | British, Traditional | ④❸❸ |
|  | Giraffe | International | ④❷❸ |
|  | Vesbar | " | ④❸❸ |
|  | Carluccio's Caffè | Italian | ④④❸ |
|  | Est Est Est | " | – – – |
|  | Zizzi | " | ④④❸ |
|  | Lowiczanka | Polish | ❸❷❸ |
|  | Patio | " | ④❶❷ |
|  | La Copita | Spanish | ❸④④ |
|  | La Tasca | " | ⑤④❸ |
|  | Blah! Blah! Blah! | Vegetarian | ❷❸④ |
|  | Paradiso Olivelli | Pizza | ④④④ |
|  | Adams Café | Moroccan | ❸❷❷ |
|  | Azou | North African | ❸❸❸ |
|  | Mohsen | Persian | ❷❷④ |
|  | Anarkali | Indian | ❸❸④ |
|  | Madhu's | " | ❶❷❸ |
|  | Woodlands | " | ❷❷④ |
|  | Sushi-Hiro | Japanese | ❶❷④ |
|  | Blue Lagoon | Thai | ❸❸④ |
|  | Esarn Kheaw | " | ❶❸④ |
|  | Fat Boy's | " | ❸❸❸ |
|  | Thai Bistro | " | ❸❷④ |
| £20+ | Gourmet Burger Kitchen | Burgers, etc | ❷④④ |
|  | Demera | Ethiopian | ❷④④ |
|  | Chez Marcelle | Lebanese | ❶❷⑤ |
|  | Alounak | Persian | ❸④④ |
|  | Mirch Masala | Indian | ❶④④ |
|  | Sagar | Indian, Southern | ❶❶④ |
|  | Hare & Tortoise | Pan-Asian | ❷❸④ |
|  | Bedlington Café | Thai | ❸④④ |
|  | Latymers | " | ❷❸⑤ |
|  | Sabai Sabai | " | ❸❸⑤ |
| £15+ | Chez Kristof (Deli) | Sandwiches, cakes, etc | ❷❸❸ |
|  | Abu Zaad | Middle Eastern | ❷❸④ |
|  | Hammersmith Café | Thai | ❸❸⑤ |
|  | Old Parr's Head | " | ❸❷④ |
| £10+ | Bush Garden Café | Organic | ❷❸❷ |
| £5+ | Crussh | Sandwiches, cakes, etc | ❸❷④ |

## NORTH

### Hampstead, West Hampstead, St John's Wood, Regent's Park, Kilburn & Camden Town (NW postcodes)

| Price | Restaurant | Cuisine | Ratings |
|---|---|---|---|
| £60+ | Landmark (Winter Gdn) | British, Modern | ④❸❷ |
| £50+ | Odette's | British, Modern | ❸❸❶ |
|  | Benihana | Japanese | ④④④ |
| £40+ | Bradley's | British, Modern | ④④④ |
|  | The Engineer | " | ❸④❸ |
|  | Globe Restaurant | " | ④❷④ |
|  | The Wells | " | ❸④❸ |
|  | L'Aventure | French | ❸❸❷ |
|  | Oslo Court | " | ❷❶❸ |
|  | Artigiano | Italian | ④❸❸ |
|  | Rosmarino | " | ④④❸ |
|  | Sardo Canale | " | ❸❷❸ |
|  | Villa Bianca | " | ④❸❷ |
|  | Gaucho Grill | Steaks & grills | ❸④④ |
|  | Kaifeng | Chinese | ❷❷❸ |
|  | Wakaba | Japanese | ❷❸⑤ |
| £35+ | Café Med | British, Modern | ④④❸ |
|  | Lansdowne | " | ❷❸❷ |
|  | Queen's Pub & Dining Rm | " | ④❸④ |
|  | Base | French | ❸❸④ |
|  | Toast | International | ④❷❷ |
|  | Philpotts Mezzaluna | Italian | ❸❸④ |
|  | The Salusbury | " | ❸❸❸ |
|  | Camden Brasserie | Mediterranean | ④❸④ |
|  | Queen's Head & Artichoke | " | ❸❷❸ |
|  | Black & Blue | Steaks & grills | ❸❸④ |
|  | Baker & Spice | Sandwiches, cakes, etc | ❸⑤④ |
|  | Cottons | Afro-Caribbean | ❸④④ |
|  | Good Earth | Chinese | ❶❷④ |
|  | Royal China | " | ❶④④ |
|  | ZeNW3 | " | ❷❸❸ |
|  | Bombay Bicycle Club | Indian | ❷❷❸ |
|  | Yuzu | Japanese | ❶❷④ |
| £30+ | Maxwell's | American | ④❸❸ |
|  | Belgo Noord | Belgian | ④④❸ |
|  | The Belsize | British, Modern | ④❷④ |
|  | The Chapel | " | ④❸④ |
|  | Freemasons Arms | " | ④④❸ |
|  | The Green | " | ❸❸❸ |
|  | The Greyhound | " | ④④④ |
|  | The Highgate | " | ④④④ |
|  | The Hill | " | ④④❷ |
|  | The Junction Tavern | " | ❸❷❷ |
|  | The Vine | " | ④⑤❸ |
|  | Walnut | " | ❸❸④ |
|  | La Cage Imaginaire | French | ④❷❷ |
|  | Halepi | Greek | ❸❷④ |
|  | The Arches | International | ④❷❷ |
|  | Sarracino | Italian | ❷❷❸ |
|  | Strada | " | ④❸❸ |

| | | | |
|---|---|---|---|
| | La Superba | " | ❸❷❸ |
| | Zuccato | " | ④❸④ |
| | Pescador Too | Portuguese | ❸❷❸ |
| | Don Pepe | Spanish | ❸①❷ |
| | Manna | Vegetarian | ④❸❸ |
| | Tootsies | Burgers, etc | ④④④ |
| | Seashell | Fish & chips | ❸④⑤ |
| | Richoux | Sandwiches, cakes, etc | ④④❸ |
| | Mango Room | Afro-Caribbean | ❷④❷ |
| | Solly's Exclusive | Israeli | ④④❸ |
| | Gung-Ho | Chinese | ❷❷❷ |
| | Weng Wah House | " | ❸❷❸ |
| | Eriki | Indian | ❷❸❸ |
| | Jin Kichi | Japanese | ❶❷④ |
| | Sushi-Say | " | ❷①⑤ |
| | Singapore Garden | Malaysian | ❸❷❸ |
| | Silks & Spice | Thai | ❸❸❸ |
| £25+ | Crown & Goose | British, Modern | ❸❷❷ |
| | The Garden Café | " | ❸❷❷ |
| | The Lord Palmerston | " | ❷④❷ |
| | No 77 Wine Bar | " | ④④❷ |
| | Lemonia | Greek | ④❶❶ |
| | Giraffe | International | ④❷❸ |
| | L'Artista | Italian | ④❷❷ |
| | La Brocca | " | ❸❷❷ |
| | Carluccio's Caffè | " | ④④❸ |
| | Fratelli la Bufala | " | ❶❷❸ |
| | Marine Ices | " | ❸❷❷ |
| | Zizzi | " | ④④❸ |
| | William IV | Mediterranean | ❸❸❸ |
| | Zamoyski | Polish | ④❸❷ |
| | Troika | Russian | ④④❸ |
| | Nautilus | Fish & chips | ❶❶④ |
| | Basilico | Pizza | ❸④④ |
| | Mestizo | Mexican/TexMex | ❷❷④ |
| | Tobia | Ethiopian | ❷❸④ |
| | Sofra | Turkish | ④❸④ |
| | Phoenix Palace | Chinese | ❶❸❸ |
| | Vijay | Indian | ❶❶❸ |
| | Café Japan | Japanese | ❶❷④ |
| | Yo! Sushi | " | ④④④ |
| | dim T café | Pan-Asian | ④④❸ |
| £20+ | Haché | French | ❸❸④ |
| | Le Petit Prince | " | ❸❸❸ |
| | Daphne | Greek | ❸❷❷ |
| | La Porchetta Pizzeria | Italian | ❸❸❸ |
| | The Little Bay | Mediterranean | ❸❷❷ |
| | Ed's Easy Diner | Burgers, etc | ④❸❷ |
| | Gourmet Burger Kitchen | " | ❷④④ |
| | Ali Baba | Egyptian | ❷❷⑤ |
| | Harry Morgan's | Kosher | ❷❸❸ |
| | Shish | Middle Eastern | ④❷❸ |
| | New Culture Revolution | Chinese | ❸❸④ |
| | Chutneys | Indian | ④④④ |
| | Five Hot Chillies | " | ❶❷❷ |
| | Great Nepalese | " | ❷❷⑤ |

| | | | Rating |
|---|---|---|---|
| | Jashan | " | ②①④ |
| | Sabras | " | ❶④⑤ |
| | Zamzama | " | ③③❸ |
| | Kovalam | Indian, Southern | ②❷⑤ |
| | Wagamama | Japanese | ❸③④ |
| | Oriental City | Pan-Asian | ③④⑤ |
| | Café de Maya | Thai | ❸②④ |
| £15+ | Little Earth Cafe | Vegetarian | ②❸④ |
| | Café Crêp de Hampst. | Crêpes | ❸⑤④ |
| | Chamomile | Sandwiches, cakes, etc | ❸②④ |
| | Diwana B-P House | Indian | ③④⑤ |
| | Geeta | " | ②❶⑤ |
| | Sakonis | " | ❶④⑤ |
| | Viet-Anh | Vietnamese | ❸❶⑤ |

## Hoxton, Islington, Highgate, Crouch End, Stoke Newington, Muswell Hill & Finchley (N postcodes)

| | | | Rating |
|---|---|---|---|
| £70+ | Fifteen | Italian | ⑤⑤⑤ |
| £40+ | Frederick's | British, Modern | ❸③❷ |
| | The House | " | ❸③❸ |
| | Lola's | " | ❸③❸ |
| | Fishworks | Fish & seafood | ②❸④ |
| | Sargasso Sea | " | ②②❷ |
| | The Almeida | French | ❸②❸ |
| | Bistro Aix | " | ❸④❸ |
| | Morgan M | " | ❶③④ |
| | Metrogusto | Italian | ❸❶② |
| | Cru | Mediterranean | ④④❸ |
| £35+ | The Bull | British, Modern | – – – |
| | The Drapers Arms | " | ❸④❸ |
| | The Duke of Cambridge | " | ②❸❸ |
| | Fig | " | ④❸❸ |
| | Mosaica | " | ❶②② |
| | The Real Greek | Greek | ④⑤④ |
| | Casale Franco | Italian | ④❸② |
| | Ottolenghi | " | ❶❸② |
| | San Carlo | " | ④❸② |
| | Cube & Star | Cuban | ❸❸② |
| | Rasa Travancore | Indian, Southern | ❶②❸ |
| £30+ | The Barnsbury | British, Modern | ❸❸② |
| | The Elk in the Woods | " | ④④② |
| | Ha! Ha! | " | ④④④ |
| | The Haven | " | ❸❸② |
| | Mesclun | " | ④④④ |
| | The Northgate | " | ②②② |
| | The Pumphouse | " | – – – |
| | St Johns | British, Traditional | ②②❶ |
| | Chez Liline | Fish & seafood | ②②④ |
| | Les Associés | French | ❸❸❸ |
| | Bastille | " | ❸④❸ |
| | Hoxton Square | Fusion | ④④❸ |
| | Banners | International | ❸②❶ |
| | Browns | " | ⑤④④ |

| | | | |
|---|---|---|---|
| | The Fox Reformed | " | ④❸❷ |
| | Hoxton Apprentice | " | ④❸❷ |
| | Cantina Italia | Italian | ❸❸❸ |
| | Florians | " | ④❸❸ |
| | Strada | " | ④❸❸ |
| | Mediterranean Kitchen | Mediterranean | ⑤④④ |
| | Furnace | Pizza | ❸④❸ |
| | Rodizio Rico | Brazilian | ④④④ |
| | Cuba Libre | Cuban | ④④④ |
| | Sabor | South American | ❷❶❷ |
| | Pasha | Turkish | ④❸❸ |
| | OQO Bar | Chinese | ❷❷❷ |
| | The Parsee | Indian | ❷❸⑤ |
| | Jim Thompson's | Pan-Asian | ④④❷ |
| | Tiger Lil's | " | ④④④ |
| | Isarn | Thai | ❸❸④ |
| | Thai Square | " | ④④❸ |
| £25+ | Café Mozart | East & Cent. European | ❸❷❶ |
| | Petit Auberge | French | ❸④❸ |
| | Le Sacré-Coeur | " | ❸❸❸ |
| | Bar Mezé | Greek | ❷❸④ |
| | Vrisaki | " | ❷❷❸ |
| | Giraffe | International | ④❷❸ |
| | Carluccio's Caffè | Italian | ④④❸ |
| | Est Est Est | " | – – – |
| | Pizzeria Oregano | " | ❸❸④ |
| | San Daniele | " | ❸❶❷ |
| | Zizzi | " | ④④❸ |
| | La Tasca | Spanish | ⑤④❸ |
| | Toff's | Fish & chips | ❷❶④ |
| | Two Brothers | " | ❷❷④ |
| | Basilico | Pizza | ❸④④ |
| | Sedir | Turkish | ❸❸④ |
| | Yo! Sushi | Japanese | ④④④ |
| £20+ | S & M Café | British, Traditional | ❸❸❸ |
| | Le Mercury | French | ④❷❶ |
| | La Porchetta Pizzeria | Italian | ❸❸❸ |
| | Fine Burger Company | Burgers, etc | ❸❸④ |
| | La Piragua | South American | ❸④❷ |
| | Gallipoli | Turkish | ❸❸❸ |
| | Istanbul Iskembecisi | " | ❸④④ |
| | Iznik | " | ④❸❷ |
| | New Culture Rev'n | Chinese | ❸❸④ |
| | Anglo Asian Tandoori | Indian | ❷❶❷ |
| | Jashan | " | ❷❶④ |
| | Masala Zone | " | ❸❸❸ |
| | Rani | " | ❷❷❸ |
| | Rasa | " | ❶❷❷ |
| | Wagamama | Japanese | ❸❸④ |
| | Bu San | Korean | ❷❸⑤ |
| | Yelo | Thai | ❸❷❷ |
| | Yum Yum | " | – – – |
| | Huong-Viet | Vietnamese | ❶④❸ |
| £15+ | Afghan Kitchen | Afghani | ❸⑤④ |

## SOUTH

### South Bank (SE1)

| | | | Rating |
|---|---|---|---|
| £60+ | Oxo Tower (Rest') | British, Modern | ⑤⑤❷ |
| | Le Pont de la Tour | " | ④④❸ |
| £50+ | The County Hall Rest' | British, Modern | ⑤④④ |
| | Butlers Wharf Chop-house | British, Traditional | ⑤④④ |
| £40+ | Blueprint Café | British, Modern | ④④❷ |
| | Cantina Vinopolis | " | ④④❸ |
| | The People's Palace | " | – – – |
| | Livebait | Fish & seafood | ④④④ |
| | Chez Gérard | French | ④④④ |
| | Oxo Tower (Bras') | International | ⑤⑤❸ |
| | Tentazioni | Italian | ❷❷④ |
| | Le Pont de la Tour Bar & Grill | Steaks & grills | ④④❸ |
| £35+ | Garrison | British, Modern | ❷④❷ |
| | Mezzanine | " | ⑤⑤⑤ |
| | RSJ | " | ❸❷⑤ |
| | fish! | Fish & seafood | ❸❸④ |
| | Riviera | French | ④④❸ |
| | Champor-Champor | Fusion | ❶❷❶ |
| | Delfina Studio Café | International | ❶❶❷ |
| | Laughing Gravy | " | ❸❸❷ |
| | Tate Restaurant | " | ④④❷ |
| | Cantina del Ponte | Italian | ⑤⑤⑤ |
| | Loco Mensa | " | ④④❸ |
| | Baltic | Polish | ❸❸❷ |
| | Glas | Scandinavian | ❸❷④ |
| | Black & Blue | Steaks & grills | ❸❸④ |
| | Fina Estampa | Peruvian | ④❸④ |
| | Kwan Thai | Thai | ❷❷❸ |
| £30+ | Archduke Wine Bar | British, Modern | ⑤④❸ |
| | The Hartley | " | ❸④❷ |
| | Menier Chocolate Factory | " | ④❷❷ |
| | Shakespeare's Globe | " | ⑤④❷ |
| | The Waterloo Fire Station | " | ⑤⑤④ |
| | The Anchor & Hope | British, Traditional | ❷❸❸ |
| | Auberge | French | ⑤⑤④ |
| | Browns | International | ⑤④④ |
| | Tate Café | " | ④④❸ |
| | La Lanterna | Italian | ❸❷❸ |
| | Bermondsey Kitchen | Mediterranean | ④❸❸ |
| | Tapas Brindisa | Spanish | ❷❸❷ |
| | Four Regions | Chinese | ❸❸④ |
| £25+ | Bankside | British, Modern | ④❸❸ |
| | Real Greek Souvlaki & Bar | Greek | ⑤⑤④ |
| | Giraffe | International | ④❷❸ |
| | Amano Café | Pizza | ❷❷❷ |
| | Gourmet Pizza Co. | " | ❸④④ |
| | Paradiso Olivelli | " | ④④④ |
| | Pizzeria Castello | " | ❸❷❸ |

| | | | |
|---|---|---|---|
| | EV | Turkish | ④❷❷ |
| | Tas | " | ❸②❸ |
| | Tas Pide | " | ❸②❷ |
| | Bengal Clipper | Indian | ❸❸❷ |
| | Silka | " | ❸④④ |
| | Feng Sushi | Japanese | ❸❸④ |
| | Yo! Sushi | " | ④④④ |
| £20+ | Meson don Felipe | Spanish | ④④❶ |
| | Inshoku | Japanese | ❸❸❸ |
| | Wagamama | " | ❸❸④ |
| £15+ | Konditor & Cook | Sandwiches, cakes, etc | ❶❸④ |
| | El Vergel | South American | ❶❶❷ |
| £10+ | Monmouth Coffee Company | Sandwiches, cakes, etc | ❶❷❸ |

## Greenwich, Lewisham & Blackheath
### (All SE postcodes, except SE1)

| | | | |
|---|---|---|---|
| £40+ | Beauberry House | British, Modern | – – – |
| | Franklins | " | ❷❷❷ |
| | Lobster Pot | Fish & seafood | ❶❷❸ |
| | Bar du Musee | French | ⑤④❷ |
| | Spread Eagle | " | ❸❷❷ |
| | The Painted Heron | Indian | ❶❶❸ |
| £35+ | Chapter Two | British, Modern | ❸❸❸ |
| | Greenwich Park | " | ⑤❸④ |
| | Inc Bar & Restaurant | " | ④❷❷ |
| | Inside | " | ❷❸④ |
| | The Palmerston | " | ❶❸❸ |
| | Loco Locale | Italian | ④④❸ |
| £30+ | The Trafalgar Tavern | British, Traditional | ④④❷ |
| | Babur Brasserie | Indian | ❷❶❷ |
| | 3 Monkeys | " | ❸❸❸ |
| £25+ | The Lavender | British, Modern | ④❸❷ |
| | The Sun & Doves | " | ❸④❷ |
| | Arancia | Italian | ❷❷❷ |
| | Barcelona Tapas | Spanish | ④❸❸ |
| | La Finca | " | ④④❷ |
| | Olley's | Fish & chips | ❶❷④ |
| | Zero Degrees | Pizza | ❸❷❷ |
| | Tandoori Nights | Indian | ❶❶❷ |
| | Thailand | Thai | ❶❷④ |
| £20+ | The Sea Cow | British, Modern | ❷❸④ |
| | Thai Corner Café | Thai | ❸❸❸ |

## Battersea, Brixton, Clapham, Wandsworth
## Barnes, Putney & Wimbledon
### (All SW postcodes south of the river)

| | | | |
|---|---|---|---|
| £50+ | Chez Bruce | British, Modern | ❶❶❷ |
| £40+ | MVH | British, Modern | ❷❷❷ |
| | Ransome's Dock | " | ❸❷❸ |
| | Redmond's | " | ❷❶④ |

| | | | |
|---|---|---|---|
| | Sonny's | " | ❸❸❸ |
| | The Victoria | " | ❸④❷ |
| | Ghillies | Fish & seafood | ❸④❸ |
| | Le Bouchon Bordelais | French | ⑤④④ |
| | Morel | " | ❸④⑤ |
| | The Light House | International | ❸❷④ |
| | Naked Turtle | " | ④④④ |
| | Enoteca Turi | Italian | ❷❷❸ |
| | Riva | " | ❸❸④ |
| | San Lorenzo Fuoriporta | " | ❸④④ |
| | Popeseye | Steaks & grills | ❷❸⑤ |
| | La Pampa | Argentinian | ❷④❸ |
| | Chakalaka | South African | ❸❸④ |
| | Thai on the River | Thai | ❸❸❷ |
| £35+ | Harlem | American | ④⑤④ |
| | Cinnamon Cay | Australian | ❷❷❸ |
| | Balham Kitchen & Bar | British, Modern | ④④❷ |
| | The Bridge | " | ④❷❸ |
| | Buchan's | " | ❸❷❷ |
| | The Depot | " | ⑤⑤❷ |
| | Ditto | " | ❸❷❷ |
| | The Fire Stables | " | ④④❷ |
| | The Greyhound | " | ❷❷❸ |
| | Lamberts | " | ❶❶❷ |
| | Phoenix | " | ❸❷❸ |
| | Rapscallion | " | ❸❸❷ |
| | Willie Gunn | " | ④④❸ |
| | The Food Room | French | ❸❷④ |
| | Gastro | " | ④⑤❸ |
| | Niksons | " | ④④❸ |
| | Duke of Cambridge | International | ④④❸ |
| | The Sequel | " | ④❸❸ |
| | Del Buongustaio | Italian | ⑤⑤⑤ |
| | Ost. Antica Bologna | " | ④④④ |
| | Pomino | " | ⑤④④ |
| | Polygon Bar & Grill | Steaks & grills | ⑤⑤⑤ |
| | Bombay Bicycle Club | Indian | ❷❷❸ |
| | Nancy Lam's Enak Enak | Indonesian | ❸④④ |
| | Tsunami | Japanese | ❶❷❸ |
| £30+ | Bodean's | American | ❸④④ |
| | The Abbeville | British, Modern | ❸④❷ |
| | The Aviary | " | ❸❷❸ |
| | Earl Spencer | " | ❸④❸ |
| | The Fentiman Arms | " | ❸❸❷ |
| | The Freemasons | " | ❸❷❷ |
| | The Mason's Arms | " | ❸④❸ |
| | Scoffers | " | ④❸❷ |
| | Tree House | " | ④④❸ |
| | Fish Club | Fish & seafood | ❷❷④ |
| | Emile's | French | ❷❶❷ |
| | Louvaine | " | ④❷❸ |
| | Le Petit Max | " | ❷❷❸ |
| | Annie's | International | ④❶❶ |
| | Hudson's | " | ④❷❸ |
| | Newton's | " | ④④❸ |
| | The Ship | " | ④⑤❷ |

| | | | |
|---|---|---|---|
| | Antipasto e Pasta | *Italian* | ❸①❸ |
| | Matilda's | " | ④⑤❸ |
| | Numero Uno | " | ❸②❷ |
| | Panzella | " | ❷❷❸ |
| | Rick's Café | " | ❷❷❷ |
| | Strada | " | ④❷❸ |
| | Rocket Riverside | *Mediterranean* | ❸❸① |
| | La Mancha | *Spanish* | ❸❷❷ |
| | La Rueda | " | ④❷❸ |
| | Tootsies | *Burgers, etc* | ④④④ |
| | Dish Dash | *Persian* | ❷❷❷ |
| | Royal China | *Chinese* | ❷❸④ |
| | Just India | *Indian* | ④❷④ |
| | Ma Goa | " | ❷❷❸ |
| | Tiger Lil's | *Pan-Asian* | ④④④ |
| | Thai Square | *Thai* | ④④❸ |
| £25+ | The Blue Pumpkin | *British, Modern* | ④④❸ |
| | The Castle | " | ❸❸❸ |
| | The Lavender | " | ④❸❷ |
| | Settle Inn | *British, Traditional* | ❸❸❸ |
| | Bar Mezé | *Greek* | ❷❸④ |
| | Alma | *International* | ❸④❷ |
| | Bread & Roses | " | ④❸❷ |
| | Giraffe | " | ④❷❸ |
| | Putney Station | " | ④④④ |
| | Antipasto & Pasta | *Italian* | ❸④❸ |
| | Buona Sera | " | ❸❸❷ |
| | Il Cantuccio di Pulcinella | " | ❷①❸ |
| | Carluccio's Caffè | " | ④④❸ |
| | Est Est Est | " | – – – |
| | Ferrari's | " | ④❸④ |
| | Pappa Ciccia | " | ❷❷❸ |
| | Zizzi | " | ④④❸ |
| | The Fox & Hounds | *Mediterranean* | ❷❷❷ |
| | El Rincón Latino | *Spanish* | ❸①① |
| | Rebato's | " | ❷①① |
| | Dexter's Grill | *Burgers, etc* | ④❸❸ |
| | Al Forno | *Pizza* | ❸❷❷ |
| | Basilico | " | ❸④④ |
| | Eco | " | ❷④❸ |
| | Pizza Metro | " | ❷❷❷ |
| | Dalchini | *Chinese* | ❸❷④ |
| | Evo | " | ④❸④ |
| | Sarkhel's | *Indian* | ❷❷❸ |
| | The Banana Leaf Canteen | *Pan-Asian* | ❸❸❸ |
| | Mongolian Barbecue | " | ⑤⑤⑤ |
| | Chada | *Thai* | ❸❷④ |
| | Talad Thai | " | ❷❷④ |
| £20+ | Fish in a Tie | *Mediterranean* | ❸❷❷ |
| | Little Bay | " | ❸❷❷ |
| | Bar Estrela | *Portuguese* | ❸④❷ |
| | Café Portugal | " | ❸❷❸ |
| | Fine Burger Company | *Burgers, etc* | ❸❸④ |
| | Gourmet Burger Kitchen | " | ❷④④ |
| | Brady's | *Fish & chips* | ❷❷❸ |
| | Sea Cow | " | ❷❸④ |

| | | | Ratings |
|---|---|---|---|
| | Firezza | *Pizza* | ❶❷④ |
| | Boiled Egg & Soldiers | *Sandwiches, cakes, etc* | ④④④ |
| | Indian Ocean | *Indian* | ❷❷❸ |
| | Kastoori | *"* | ❶❶④ |
| | Mirch Masala SW16 | *"* | ❶④④ |
| | Nanglo | *"* | ❷❷④ |
| | Wagamama | *Japanese* | ❸❸④ |
| | Hare & Tortoise | *Pan-Asian* | ❷❸④ |
| | Amaranth | *Thai* | ❶❶❷ |
| | Thai Garden | *"* | ❸❸❸ |
| £15+ | Sree Krishna | *Indian* | ❶❶④ |
| | Fujiyama | *Japanese* | ❷④❸ |
| | The Pepper Tree | *Thai* | ❶❷❸ |
| £10+ | Real Burger World | *Burgers, etc* | ❷❸⑤ |
| | Hot Stuff | *Indian* | ❷❷❸ |

## Outer western suburbs
### Kew, Richmond, Twickenham, Teddington

| | | | Ratings |
|---|---|---|---|
| £60+ | McClements | *French* | ❸④⑤ |
| £50+ | Petersham Nurseries | *British, Modern* | ❸④❶ |
| £40+ | Burnt Chair | *British, Modern* | ❸❷④ |
| | Canyon | *"* | ⑤⑤❸ |
| | The Glasshouse | *"* | ❶❷❸ |
| | The Wharf | *"* | ④❸❷ |
| | A Cena | *Italian* | ❷❷❷ |
| | Kew Grill | *Steaks & grills* | ❸❸④ |
| £35+ | Hampton's Restaurant | *British, Modern* | ④❷❸ |
| | Brula | *French* | ❷❶❷ |
| | Chez Lindsay | *"* | ❷❷❸ |
| | Murano | *Italian* | ④❸❸ |
| | Prego | *"* | ❸④❸ |
| £30+ | Smollensky's | *American* | ⑤⑤④ |
| | Loch Fyne | *Fish & seafood* | ④④④ |
| | La Buvette | *French* | ❷❷❷ |
| | Ma Cuisine | *"* | ❸❸❸ |
| | Tartine | *"* | ❸❸❷ |
| | Browns | *International* | ⑤④④ |
| | Nosh | *"* | ④❸④ |
| | Four Regions | *Chinese* | ❸❸④ |
| £25+ | Zizzi | *Italian* | ④④❸ |
| | don Fernando's | *Spanish* | ❸❸❷ |
| | O'Zon | *Chinese, Dim sum* | ❸❷❸ |
| | Fat Boy's | *Thai* | ❸❸❸ |
| | Thai Elephant | *"* | ❸❸❸ |
| £20+ | White Cross | *International* | ④④❸ |

# EAST

## Smithfield & Farringdon (EC1)

| | | | |
|---|---|---|---|
| £50+ | Smiths (Top Floor) | British, Modern | ❸❸❷ |
| | Club Gascon | French | ❶❷❷ |
| £40+ | The Bar & Grill | British, Modern | ❸❸④ |
| | The Clerkenwell Dining Rm | " | ④❸④ |
| | Malmaison | " | ❸❸❷ |
| | Moro | " | ❶❷❷ |
| | St John | British, Traditional | ❶❷❸ |
| | Fish Shop | Fish & seafood | ❷❸④ |
| | Rudland Stubbs | " | ④④④ |
| | Bleeding Heart | French | ❷❷❶ |
| | Café du Marché | " | ❷❷❶ |
| | Cellar Gascon | " | ❷❸❷ |
| | The Zetter | Italian | ❸❸❸ |
| | Flâneur | Mediterranean | ❷❸❷ |
| | Portal | " | – – – |
| £35+ | Café Med | British, Modern | ④④❸ |
| | The Peasant | " | ④④④ |
| | The Quality Chop House | " | ❸❸❸ |
| | Vic Naylors | " | ④❸❷ |
| | The Well | " | ❸❸❸ |
| | Le Rendezvous du Café | French | ❸❸④ |
| | Alba | Italian | ❸❷④ |
| | Potemkin | Russian | ❸❷④ |
| | Hope & Sir Loin | Steaks & grills | ❸④⑤ |
| | Smiths (Dining Rm) | " | ❸④❸ |
| £30+ | Coach & Horses | British, Modern | ❷❸❸ |
| | The Green | " | ❸❸❸ |
| | The Gunmakers | " | ❸④❸ |
| | Medcalf | " | ❷❸❷ |
| | Le Saint Julien | French | ❸❸❸ |
| | $ | International | ④❷④ |
| | Exmouth Grill | " | ④④④ |
| | Mustards Brasserie | " | ④❷❸ |
| | Strada | Italian | ④❸❸ |
| | Carnevale | Vegetarian | ❸❷④ |
| | Epicurean Pizza Lounge | Pizza | – – – |
| | Coco | Afro-Caribbean | ④❷❷ |
| | Cicada | Pan-Asian | ❷❸❷ |
| £25+ | Abbaye | Belgian | ④④④ |
| | Fox & Anchor | British, Traditional | ❸❸❸ |
| | Comptoir Gascon | French | – – – |
| | The Real Greek Souvlaki | Greek | ⑤⑤④ |
| | Carluccio's Caffè | Italian | ④④❸ |
| | The Eagle | Mediterranean | ❸④❷ |
| | Sofra | Turkish | ④❸④ |
| | Tas Pide | " | ❸❷❷ |
| | Curryleaf | Indian | ④④④ |
| | Yo! Sushi | Japanese | ④④④ |
| | Cây Tre | Vietnamese | ❶❷④ |
| £20+ | Smiths (Ground Floor) | British, Modern | ④④❷ |

|  | | | |
|---|---|---|---|
| | La Porchetta Pizzeria | Italian | ❸❸❸ |
| | The Little Bay | Mediterranean | ❸❷❷ |
| | Shish | Middle Eastern | ④❷❸ |
| | Pham Sushie | Japanese | ❶❷④ |
| | Apium | Pan-Asian | ④④④ |
| £10+ | Benugo | Sandwiches, cakes, etc | ❷④④ |

## The City (EC2, EC3, EC4)

| £80+ | Tatsuso | Japanese | ❷❸④ |
|---|---|---|---|
| £60+ | 1 Lombard Street | British, Modern | ❸❸❸ |
| | Prism | " | ④④④ |
| | Aurora | French | ❷❷❸ |
| | Bonds | Mediterranean | ❸④④ |
| £50+ | Christopher's In The City | American | – – – |
| | Just Gladwins | British, Modern | ❸④④ |
| | Rhodes 24 | " | ❷❷❷ |
| | Paternoster Chop House | British, Traditional | ④④④ |
| | Chamberlain's | Fish & seafood | ④④④ |
| | Fishmarket | " | ④④⑤ |
| | Coq d'Argent | French | ④④❸ |
| | Refettorio | Italian | ❸④④ |
| £40+ | Missouri Grill | American | ❷❶④ |
| | Bar Bourse | British, Modern | ④④④ |
| | The Chancery | " | ❷❷④ |
| | The Don | " | ❷❷❷ |
| | The Rivington Grill | " | ❷❷❸ |
| | Searcy's Brasserie | " | ④❸④ |
| | Terminus | " | ④④⑤ |
| | Gow's | Fish & seafood | ④❸④ |
| | Sweetings | " | ❷❷❷ |
| | Vertigo | " | ④❸❶ |
| | Chez Gérard | French | ④④④ |
| | Novelli in the City | " | ④④④ |
| | The Royal Exchange | " | ④④❷ |
| | Vivat Bacchus | International | ❸❶❸ |
| | Caravaggio | Italian | ⑤⑤⑤ |
| | Perc%nto | " | ④④④ |
| | Boisdale of Bishopsgate | Scottish | ④❸❸ |
| | Eyre Brothers | Spanish | ❷❸④ |
| | Gaucho Grill | Steaks & grills | ❸④④ |
| | Bevis Marks | Kosher | ❷❷❸ |
| | City Miyama | Japanese | ❶❷⑤ |
| | Pacific Oriental | Pan-Asian | ❸④⑤ |
| £35+ | Home | British, Modern | ❷❷❷ |
| | Just The Bridge | " | ④④❸ |
| | The White Swan | " | ❷❷❸ |
| | George & Vulture | British, Traditional | ⑤④❷ |
| | Ye Olde Cheshire Cheese | " | ④④❶ |
| | Luc's Brasserie | French | ④④④ |
| | Bertorelli's | Italian | ⑤④④ |
| | Taberna Etrusca | " | ④❸④ |
| | Cantaloupe | Spanish | ❸④❸ |

| | | | |
|---|---|---|---|
| | Imperial City | *Chinese* | ❷❷❷ |
| | Miyabi | *Japanese* | ❷④⑤ |
| | Sri Siam City | *Thai* | ❸❷④ |
| £30+ | The Princess | *Australian* | – – – |
| | The Fox | *British, Modern* | ❷④❷ |
| | Throgmorton | *"* | ④❸❸ |
| | Auberge | *French* | ⑤⑤④ |
| | South | *"* | ❷❷④ |
| | Brasserie Rocque | *International* | ⑤④④ |
| | Browns | *"* | ⑤④④ |
| | Zuccato | *Italian* | ④❸④ |
| | Bar Capitale | *Pizza* | ❷❷④ |
| | (Ciro's) Pizza Pomodoro | *"* | ④④❷ |
| | Scuzi | *"* | ④⑤❸ |
| | Savarona | *Turkish* | ❸❸❸ |
| | Mehek | *Indian* | ❷❷❸ |
| | Tokyo City | *Japanese* | ❷④④ |
| | Singapura | *Malaysian* | ④❸❸ |
| | Gt Eastern Dining Room | *Pan-Asian* | ❷❷❷ |
| | Silks & Spice | *Thai* | ❸❸❸ |
| | Sri Thai | *"* | ❸❷❷ |
| | Thai Square | *"* | ④④❸ |
| £25+ | Bankside | *British, Modern* | ④❸❸ |
| | The Evangelist | *"* | ④❸❸ |
| | Barcelona Tapas | *Spanish* | ④❸❸ |
| | Leadenhall Tapas Bar | *"* | ④④④ |
| | La Tasca | *"* | ⑤④❸ |
| | Kasturi | *Indian* | ❸❸❸ |
| | Rajasthan | *"* | ❷❷④ |
| | K10 | *Japanese* | ❶❸❸ |
| | Kurumaya | *"* | ④④⑤ |
| | Noto | *"* | ❸❸⑤ |
| | Young Bin | *Korean* | ❸❸⑤ |
| | Satu Bar & Kitchen | *Pan-Asian* | ❸④❷ |
| | Ekachai | *Thai* | ❷❸④ |
| £20+ | Simpson's Tavern | *British, Traditional* | ④❸❶ |
| | The Wine Library | *"* | ⑤❷❶ |
| | Moshi Moshi | *Japanese* | ④④④ |
| | Wagamama | *"* | ❸❸④ |
| £15+ | Club Mangia | *British, Modern* | ❸❸❸ |
| | The Place Below | *Vegetarian* | ❷④④ |
| £10+ | Apostrophe | *Sandwiches, cakes, etc* | ❷❷❸ |
| £5+ | Crussh | *Sandwiches, cakes, etc* | ❸❷④ |
| | Fuzzy's Grub | *"* | ❷❷❸ |

## East End & Docklands (All E postcodes)

| | | | |
|---|---|---|---|
| £80+ | Ubon | *Japanese* | ❷④④ |
| £60+ | Plateau | *French* | ④④❸ |
| | Les Trois Garçons | *"* | ④❸❶ |
| | Quadrato | *Italian* | ❸❷④ |
| £40+ | The Gun | *British, Modern* | ❷❸❷ |

*sign up for the survey at www.hardens.com*

| | | | |
|---|---|---|---|
| | Lanes | " | ❸❷❸ |
| | The Morgan Arms | " | ❷❹❷ |
| | Wapping Food | " | ❸❸❷ |
| | St John Bread & Wine | British, Traditional | ❷❷❸ |
| | Aquarium | Fish & seafood | ④④④ |
| | First Edition | French | ④④④ |
| | Rosemary Lane | " | ❷❷④ |
| | 1 Blossom Street | Italian | ④④④ |
| | Lightship | Scandinavian | ④④❶ |
| | Gaucho Grill | Steaks & grills | ❸④④ |
| £35+ | The Crown | British, Modern | ❷④❷ |
| | 1802 | " | ❸④❷ |
| | Frocks | " | ④④❸ |
| | Hadley House | " | ❸❸④ |
| | The Grapes | Fish & seafood | ❸❸❶ |
| | Winkles | " | ❶❷⑤ |
| | Bistrothèque | French | ❸❷❷ |
| | The Light | International | ④④④ |
| | Il Bordello | Italian | ❷❶❷ |
| | Royal China | Chinese | ❶④④ |
| | Café Spice Namaste | Indian | ❷❷❸ |
| £30+ | Smollensky's | American | ⑤⑤④ |
| | Cat & Mutton | British, Modern | ④④❸ |
| | Browns | International | ⑤④④ |
| | La Figa | Italian | ❸❷❸ |
| | Lilly's | Steaks & grills | ❷❷❷ |
| | Scuzi | Pizza | ④⑤❸ |
| | Armadillo | South American | ❷❶❷ |
| | Elephant Royale | Thai | ❸❷❷ |
| £25+ | LMNT | British, Modern | ❸❸❶ |
| | Carluccio's Caffè | Italian | ④④❸ |
| | Zizzi | " | ④④❸ |
| | Barcelona Tapas | Spanish | ④❸❸ |
| | Meson los Barilles | " | ❷❸④ |
| | La Tasca | " | ⑤④❸ |
| | Faulkner's | Fish & chips | ❷❷④ |
| | Gourmet Pizza Co. | Pizza | ❸④④ |
| | Santa Maria de Buen Ayre | Argentinian | ❸❷④ |
| | Haz | Turkish | ❷❷❸ |
| | Shanghai | Chinese | ❷❷❸ |
| | Yi-Ban | " | ❷❸❷ |
| | Itsu | Japanese | ❸❸④ |
| | Sông Quê | Vietnamese | ❶④⑤ |
| £20+ | S & M Café | British, Traditional | ❸❸❸ |
| | Arkansas Café | Steaks & grills | ❸❸❸ |
| | Pâtisserie Valerie | Sandwiches, cakes, etc | ❸④❸ |
| | Drunken Monkey | Chinese, Dim sum | ❸❸❸ |
| | Moshi Moshi | Japanese | ④④④ |
| | Wagamama | " | ❸❸④ |
| | Viet Hoa | Vietnamese | ❸④④ |
| £15+ | Story Deli | Organic | ❶④❷ |
| | Mangal | Turkish | ❶❷❸ |
| | Lahore Kebab House | Indian | ❷⑤⑤ |
| | New Tayyabs | Pakistani | ❶❸❸ |

| £10+ | E Pellicci | *Italian* | ❸④❶ |
| £5+ | Crussh | *Sandwiches, cakes, etc* | ❸❷④ |
| £1+ | Brick Lane Beigel Bake | *Sandwiches, cakes, etc* | ❶❸④ |

# MAPS

## MAP 1 – LONDON OVERVIEW

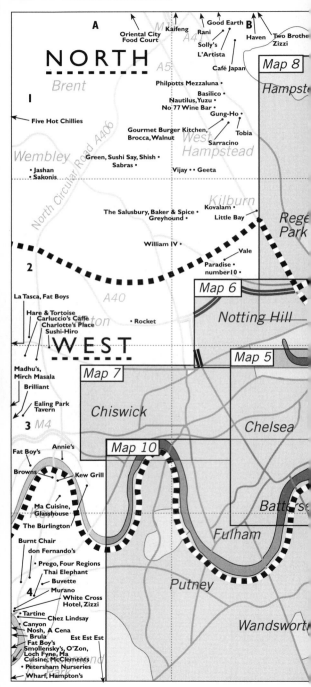

**A**

M1

Kaifeng

Good Earth

Rani

**B**

Oriental City
Food Court

A4

Solly's

Haven

Two Brothers

Zizzi

L'Artista

# NORTH

A5

Café Japan

Map 8

*Brent*

Hampste...

**1**

Philpotts Mezzaluna

Basilico

Nautilus, Yuzu

No 77 Wine Bar

*West*

← Five Hot Chillies

Gung-Ho

*Wembley*

North Circular Road A406

Gourmet Burger Kitchen,
Brocca, Walnut

Tobia

*Hampstead*

Sarracino

Green, Sushi Say, Shish

• Jashan

Sabras

• Sakonis

Vijay • • Geeta

*Kilburn*

The Salusbury, Baker & Spice

Kovalam

*Rege...*

Greyhound •

Little Bay

*Park*

William IV •

Vale

**2**

Paradise •

number10 •

Map 6

*A40*

La Tasca, Fat Boys

*ton*

*Notting Hill*

• Rocket

Hare & Tortoise
Carluccio's Caffè
Charlotte's Place
Sushi-Hiro

Map 5

# WEST

Map 7

Madhu's,
Mirch Masala

Map 10

**Brilliant**

*Chiswick*

*Chelsea*

Ealing Park
Tavern

**3** M4

Fat Boy's

Annie's

Browns

Kew Grill

*Batters...*

Ma Cuisine,
Glasshouse

The Burlington

*Fulham*

Burnt Chair

don Fernando's

• Prego, Four Regions

*Putney*

*Wandswort...*

Thai Elephant

• Buvette

**4** Murano

White Cross
Hotel, Zizzi

• Tartine

Chez Lindsay

Canyon

Nosh, A Cena

Brula

Fat Boy's

Smollensky's, O'Zon,

Loch Fyne, Ma

Cuisine, McClements

Est Est Est

• Petersham Nurseries

← Wharf, Hampton's

## MAP 1 – LONDON OVERVIEW

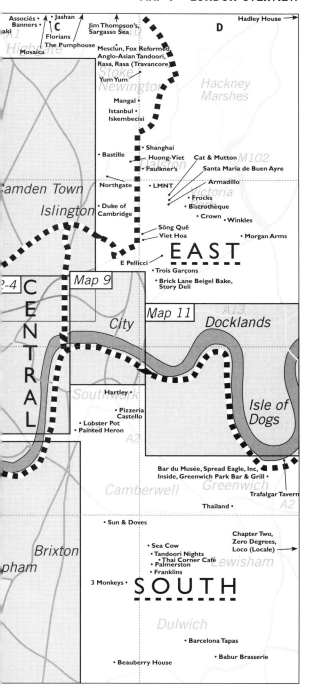

Associés •
Banners •
• Jashan
aki
A1
Highgate
• Mosaica
Florians
C
The Pumphouse
Jim Thompson's,
Sargasso Sea
D
Hadley House →

Mesclun, Fox Reformed,
Anglo-Asian Tandoori,
Rasa, Rasa (Travancore)
Stoke
Newington
Hackney
Marshes

Yum Yum

Mangal •

Istanbul •
Iskembecisi

• Bastille

• Shanghai
Dalston
• Huong-Viet
• Faulkner's
Cat & Mutton
Santa Maria de Buen Ayre
M102

Northgate

• LMNT
Victoria
Armadillo
• Frocks
• Bistrothèque
• Crown • Winkles

• Duke of
Cambridge

Sông Quê
Viet Hoa

• Morgan Arms

Camden Town

Islington

E A S T

E Pellicci •

2-4
C
E
N
T
R
A
L

Map 9
City

• Trois Garçons
• Brick Lane Beigel Bake,
Story Deli

Map 11
Docklands
A13

Hartley •

Southwark

• Pizzeria
Castello
• Lobster Pot
• Painted Heron

Isle of
Dogs

A2

Bar du Musée, Spread Eagle, Inc,
Inside, Greenwich Park Bar & Grill •
Greenwich
Trafalgar Tavern

Camberwell

Thailand •

A2

• Sun & Doves

Brixton
pham

• Sea Cow
• Tandoori Nights
• Thai Corner Café
• Palmerston
• Franklins

Chapter Two,
Zero Degrees,
Loco (Locale) →
Lewisham

3 Monkeys •

S O U T H

Dulwich

• Barcelona Tapas

• Babur Brasserie

• Beauberry House

## MAP 2 – WEST END OVERVIEW

**A**

- Ali Baba
- Phoenix Palace
- Base •

BAKER ST.

Marylebone Road

REGENTS PARK

**MARYLEBONE**

- Orrery
- Eat & Two Veg
- Galette
- Getti
- Zizzi
- Ishtar • Original Tajines
- Galvin
- Michiaki
- Garbo's, Occo •
- Reubens
- Royal China
- La Spighetta, Giraffe

• Odin's, Langan's Bistro
Fishworks, Pain Quotidien
• Strada
Pâtisserie Valerie (at Sagne)
Providores & Tapa Room
Paul
Blandford Street, Fairuz, Michael Moore
Woodlands, Golden Hind,
Caffè Caldesi, Relais deVenise

• Hardy's

**B**

- Archipelago, •
- Sardo
GT. PORTLAND ST

- Efes II • • Villandry • Ragam
- RIBA Cafe

- Back to Basics •
- • Efes
- Ha!Ha! • • Salt Yard

*See Map 3*

**LOCANDA LOCATELLI**

- Cristini •
- Maroush III •
- Chai Pani •
- Deya
- Rhodes W1 •
MARBLE ARCH
- Porte des Indes

Oxford Street

**BOND ST.**

Grosvenor Square

Oxford Stree
OXFOR
CIRCU

New Bond Street

Regent Street

Old Bond Street

**2**

- Taman gang •

Park Lane

**MAYFAIR**

Berkeley Square

St James's

Piccadilly

GREEN PARK

**3**

*See Map 5*

**Hyde Park**

Knightsbridge

KNIGHTSBRIDGE

Green Park

HYDE PARK CORNER Constitution Hill

Grosvenor Place

**Buckingham Palace**

**BELGRAVIA**

Belgrave Square

Sloane Street

Pont Street

- • Nahm

- Mango Tree, Noura •
- • Goya
Noodle Noodle •

- Quilon, Bank Westmi

- • Goring

**4**

- Santini •

- • Chez Gérard

VICTORIA

- Jenny Lo's • • Ken Lo's Memories
- Goya
- Olivo •
- Boisdale

- Baker & Spice •
- Mimmo d'Ischia •
- Oliveto •
- Ebury Street Wine Bar •

Eaton Square

Eccleston

Buckingham Palace Road

Belgrave Road

Vauxhall Bridge Road

- Seafresh, Kazan, About Thyme •

- • Noodle

- Page in

SLOANE SQ.

- Convivio •
- Feng Sushi •

- • Blue Jade

- Chimes, Mekong, Grumbles

## MAP 2 – WEST END OVERVIEW

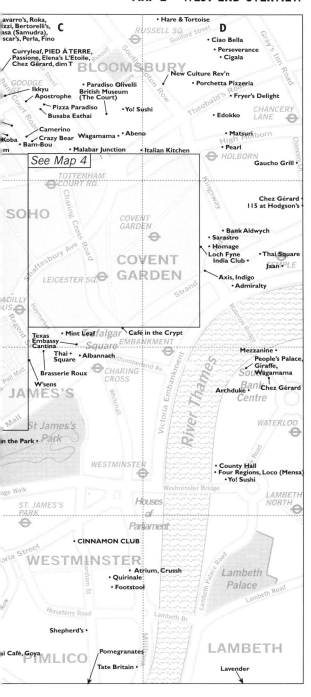

**C**

avarro's, Roka,
zzi, Bertorelli's,
asa (Samudra),
scar's, Perla, Fino

Curryleaf, PIED À TERRE,
Passione, Elena's L'Etoile,
Chez Gérard, dim T

*GOODGE*
Ikkyu
Apostrophe
• Pizza Paradiso
Busaba Eathai

Camerino
Crazy Bear
Koba • Bam-Bou
m
• Malabar Junction

BLOOMSBURY

• Paradiso Olivelli
British Museum
(The Court)

• Yo! Sushi

Wagamama • • Abeno

• Italian Kitchen

*RUSSELL SQ.*

• Hare & Tortoise

**D**

*Guilford Street*

• Ciao Bella
• Perseverance
• Cigala

New Culture Rev'n
• Porchetta Pizzeria
• Fryer's Delight

• Edokko

*CHANCERY
LANE*

• Matsuri
• Pearl
*HOLBORN*
Gaucho Grill •

*See Map 4*

SOHO

*TOTTENHAM
COURT RD.*

COVENT
GARDEN

COVENT
GARDEN

*LEICESTER SQ.*

*Strand*

Chez Gérard •
115 at Hodgson's

• Bank Aldwych
• Sarastro
• Homage
Loch Fyne
India Club • • Thai Square
Jaan •

• Axis, Indigo
• Admiralty

*ADILLY
US*

Texas
Embassy
Cantina

Thai •
Square • Albannach

Brasserie Roux
W'sens

JAMES'S

n the Park •

• Mint Leaf
*Trafalgar
Square*

*EMBANKMENT*

*Northumberland Av.*

CHARING
CROSS

*Whitehall*

*St James's
Park*

WESTMINSTER

*age Walk*

ST. JAMES'S
PARK

*oria Street*

WESTMINSTER

• CINNAMON CLUB

• Atrium, Crussh
• Quirinale
• Footstool

*Horseferry Road*

Shepherd's •

i Café, Goya
PIMLICO

Pomegranates

Tate Britain •

• Café in the Crypt

*River Thames*

Mezzanine •
People's Palace,
Giraffe,
Wagamama
Chez Gérard
Archduke •

*SOU
Bank
Centre*

*WATERLOO*

• County Hall
• Four Regions, Loco (Mensa)
• Yo! Sushi

*LAMBETH
NORTH*

*Houses
of
Parliament*

*Westminster Bridge*

Lambeth
Palace

*Lambeth Road*

*Lambeth Br.*

LAMBETH

Lavender

# MAP 3 – MAYFAIR, ST JAMES'S & WEST SOHO

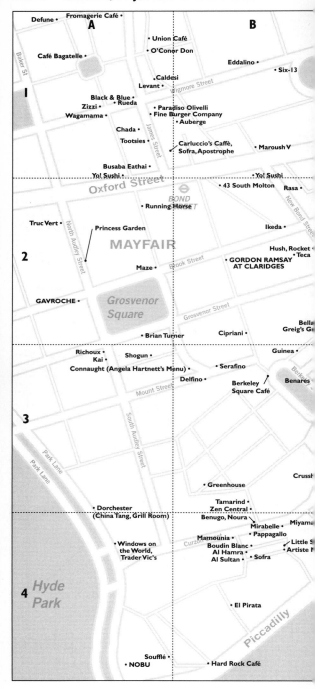

Defune •
Fromagerie Café •

**A**

**B**

Café Bagatelle •

• Union Café

• O'Conor Don

Eddalino •

• Six-13

•Caldesi

Levant •

*Wigmore Street*

**1**

Black & Blue •

• Rueda

Zizzi •

Wagamama •

• Paradiso Olivelli
• Fine Burger Company
• Auberge

Chada •

Tootsies •

• Carluccio's Caffè,
Sofra, Apostrophe

• Maroush V

Busaba Eathai •

Yo! Sushi •

• Yo! Sushi

**Oxford Street**

• 43 South Molton

Rasa •

• Running Horse

*BOND*

Truc Vert •

Princess Garden

Ikeda •

*North Audley Street*

**MAYFAIR**

Hush, Rocket •
Teca

**2**

Maze •

*Brook Street*

• GORDON RAMSAY
AT CLARIDGES

**GAVROCHE** •

*Grosvenor
Square*

*Grosvenor Street*

Bella
Greig's G

• Brian Turner

Cipriani •

Richoux •

Kai •

Shogun •

Guinea •

Connaught (Angela Hartnett's Menu) •

• Serafino

Benarès

Delfino •

Berkeley
Square Café

*Mount Street*

**3**

*South Audley Street*

Crush

• Greenhouse

*Park Lane*

*Park Lane*

Tamarind •
Zen Central •

• Dorchester
(China Tang, Grill Room)

Benugo, Noura •

Miyama

Mirabelle •

Mamounia • • Pappagallo

• Windows on
the World,
Trader Vic's

Boudin Blanc •
Al Hamra •
Al Sultan •

• Little S
• Artiste N

*Curzo*

• Sofra

*Hyde
Park*

**4**

• El Pirata

*Piccadilly*

Soufflé •

• NOBU

• Hard Rock Café

# MAP 3 – MAYFAIR, ST JAMES'S & WEST SOHO

**MAP 4 – EAST SOHO, CHINATOWN & COVENT GARDEN**

**A**

**B**

New Oxford Street

Dy

HAKKASAN •

• Eagle Bar Diner

Oxford Street

**1**

TOTTENHAM CT. RD

Soho St

Charing Cross Road

Soho Square

• Gay Hussar

SOHO

Mon

• Patara

Shaftesbury Avenue

• Hamburger Union
• Quo Vadis

Monmouth Coffee Compar

**2**

• Gopal's
of Soho
• Red Fort

Dean St

Frith St

• Bertorelli's
Escargot •
• Garlic & Shots

Amato

Taro •

Deca •

• Mela

• Sri Thai Soho
Stock Pot

Tomato
Alastair Little •
Chiang Mai •
• Signor Zilli

• Café Emm
• Little Italy
• Bar Italia

Ed's •

• Café Bohème
Bohème Kitchen & Bar

Cambridge
CIRCUS

Café
Lazeez •

Balans •

• Maison Bertaux

Gili Gulu

Pâtisserie
Valerie

Kettners •
Yming •

Rusticana •

Balans •

• French House
• Lindsay House

• Konditor & Cook

• New World

Souk •

IVY •

Shaftesbury Avenue

Chinese Experience

• Jade Garden

• Harbour City

Ed's, Abeno Too

**3**

New Mayflower •
Laureate •

• ECapital

CHINATOWN

Wardour Street

Gerrard St

Mr Kong •
Fung Shing •

Lisle Street

Wong Kei •

• Golden Dragon

• Café Fish

Chuen Cheng Ku •

• Manzi's

• Joy King Lau
• Poons

• Tokyo Diner
• Imperial China

Charing Cross Road

Cranbourn St

Brown
Beot

LEICEST
SQ

• J SHE

Cork & Bottle •

• Gaby's

Penthouse •

Leicester
Square

Planet Hollywood

Coventry St

• TGI Friday's

• Wagamama

**4**

• Tiger Tiger

• Wagamama

Haymarket

• Stock Pot
• Woodlands

Whitcomb Street

Quod, •
Yo! Sushi

• Blue Lagoon

Crivelli's Garden

K

Portrait •

• Broadway Bar & Grill

# MAP 4 – EAST SOHO, CHINATOWN & COVENT GARDEN

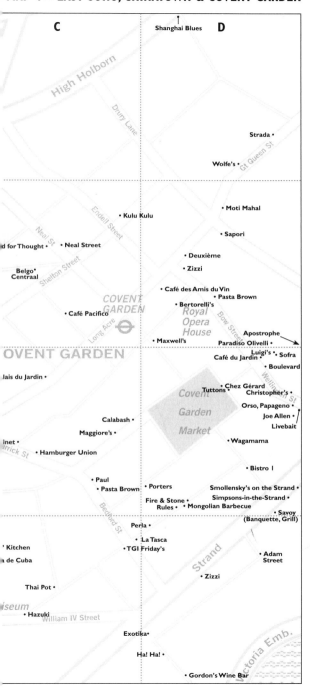

**C**

**D**

Shanghai Blues

High Holborn

Drury Lane

Strada •

Wolfe's • Gt Queen St

• Moti Mahal

• Kulu Kulu

Eridell Street

Neal St

d for Thought • • Neal Street

• Sapori

Shelton Street

Belgo •
Centraal

• Deuxième

• Zizzi

COVENT
GARDEN

• Café des Amis du Vin

• Pasta Brown

Royal
Opera
House

• Bertorelli's

• Café Pacifico

Long Acre

Bow Street

Apostrophe

**OVENT GARDEN**

Paradiso Olivelli •

• Maxwell's

Luigi's • • Sofra

Café du Jardin •

lais du Jardin •

Covent

• Boulevard

Wellington St

• Chez Gérard

Tuttons •

Christopher's •

Garden

Orso, Papageno •

Calabash •

Joe Allen •

Maggiore's •

Market

Livebait

inet •

• Wagamama

arrick St • Hamburger Union

• Bistro 1

• Paul
• Pasta Brown • Porters

Smollensky's on the Strand •

Bedford St

Fire & Stone •
Rules • • Mongolian Barbecue

Simpsons-in-the-Strand •

• Savoy
(Banquette, Grill)

Perla •

• La Tasca

' Kitchen

•TGI Friday's

Strand

a de Cuba

• Adam
Street

Thai Pot •

• Zizzi

iseum

• Hazuki

William IV Street

Exotika•

Victoria Emb.

Ha! Ha! •

• Gordon's Wine Bar

# MAP 5 – KNIGHTSBRIDGE, CHELSEA & SOUTH KENSINGT

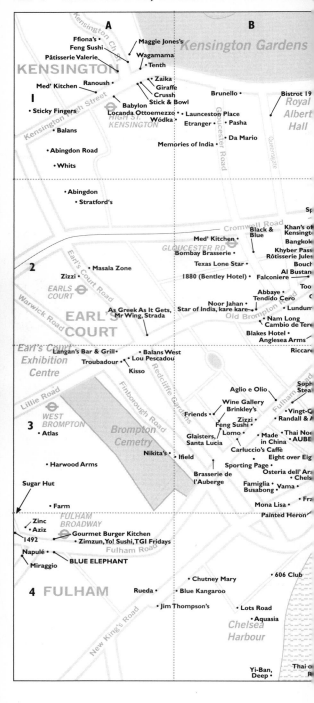

**A**

**B**

Kensington Gardens

Ffiona's •
Feng Sushi •
Pâtisserie Valerie •

**KENSINGTON**

Maggie Jones's •
Wagamama •
• Tenth

Med' Kitchen •  Ranoush •

• Sticky Fingers

• Zaika
Giraffe
Crussh
Stick & Bowl

Brunello •

Bistrot 19

*Royal Albert Hall*

Babylon
Locanda Ottoemezzo • •
Wódka

Launceston Place •
Etranger • • Pasha
• Da Mario

**HIGH ST. KENSINGTON**

• Balans

• Abingdon Road

Memories of India •

• Whits

• Abingdon
• Stratford's

Sp

Cromwell Road

Khan's of Kensingt

Med' Kitchen •
Bombay Brasserie •

Black & Blue

GLOUCESTER RD.

Bangkok

Khyber Pass
Rôtisserie Jules

**2**

• Masala Zone

Zizzi •

Texas Lone Star •

1880 (Bentley Hotel) •  Falconiere •

Bouch
Al Bustan

Too

EARLS COURT

Abbaye •
Tendido Cero

**EARL'S COURT**

As Greek As It Gets,
Mr Wing, Strada

Noor Jahan •
Star of India, kare kare •

Lundun

• Nam Long
Cambio de Tere

Warwick Road

Old Brompt

Blakes Hotel •
Anglesea Arms •

Riccare

*Earl's Court Exhibition Centre*

Langan's Bar & Grill •  • Balans West
• Lou Pescadou
Troubadour •
Kisso •

Lillie Road

Aglio e Olio •

Soph
Stea

WEST BROMPTON

Wine Gallery •
Brinkley's
Friends •

Vingt-Q
• Randall & A

**3**

• Atlas

*Brompton Cemetery*

Zizzi •
Feng Sushi •
Lomo •

Glaisters, •
Santa Lucia

Nikita's •

• Ifield

• Made
in China

Thai No
• AUBE

Carluccio's Caffè

Eight over Eig

• Harwood Arms

Sporting Page •

Osteria dell' Ara
• Chels

Brasserie de
l'Auberge

Famiglia •
Busabong

• Vama

Sugar Hut

Mona Lisa •

• Fra

Painted Heron

• Farm

*FULHAM BROADWAY*

Zinc •
• Aziz

Gourmet Burger Kitchen

1492

• Zimzun, Yo! Sushi, TGI Fridays

Napulé •

Fulham Road

**BLUE ELEPHANT**

Miraggio •

**4 FULHAM**

Rueda •

• Chutney Mary

• 606 Club

• Blue Kangaroo

• Jim Thompson's

• Lots Road

New King's Road

• Aquasia

*Chelsea Harbour*

Yi-Ban,
Deep •

Thai
R

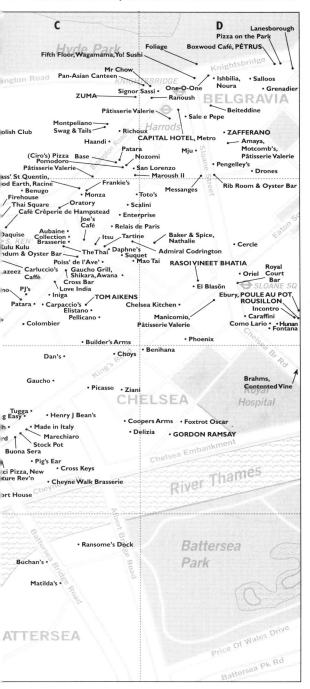

**C**

**D**

Hyde Park

Lanesborough
Pizza on the Park
Boxwood Café, PÉTRUS
Foliage

Fifth Floor, Wagamama, Yo! Sushi

Knightsbridge

ngton Road

Mr Chow

Pan-Asian Canteen

KNIGHTSBRIDGE

• Ishbilia, • Salloos
Noura

ZUMA

Signor Sassi •

One-O-One

• Grenadier

Ranoush

BELGRAVIA

Pâtisserie Valerie

Beiteddine

• Sale e Pepe

olish Club

Montpeliano
Swag & Tails

Harrods

CAPITAL HOTEL, Metro

• ZAFFERANO

• Richoux

— Amaya,
Motcomb's,
Pâtisserie Valerie

Haandi

(Ciro's) Pizza
Pomodoro

Base

Patara

Nozomi

Mju •

Pâtisserie Valerie

San Lorenzo

• Pengelley's

• Drones

ass' St Quentin,
od Earth, Racine

Maroush II

Rib Room & Oyster Bar

• Benugo

Frankie's

Messanges

Firehouse

• Monza

• Toto's

Thai Square

Oratory

• Scalini

Café Crêperie de Hampstead
Joe's
Café

• Enterprise

Daquise

Aubaine •
Collection •
Brasserie •

• Relais de Paris

Itsu

Tartine

Baker & Spice,
Nathalie

Kulu Kulu

Daphne's

ndum & Oyster Bar

The Thai

Suquet

Admiral Codrington

• Cercle

Poiss' de l'Ave' •

• Mao Tai

azeez

Carluccio's
Caffè

Gaucho Grill,
Shikara, Awana •

RASOI VINEET BHATIA

Royal
Court
Bar

no

PJ's

Love India

Cross Bar

• Oriel

SLOANE SQ

• Iniga

TOM AIKENS

• El Blasón

Ebury, POULE AU POT
ROUSILLON

Patara •

• Carpaccio's

Chelsea Kitchen •

Incontro

Elistano •

• Caraffini

Pellicano •

Manicomio,
Pâtisserie Valerie

Como Lario • • Hunan
• Fontana

• Colombier

• Builder's Arms

• Phoenix

Dan's •

• Choys

• Benihana

King's Road

Chelsea Br Rd

Gaucho •

• Picasso

• Ziani

CHELSEA

Brahms,
Contented Vine

Royal
Hospital

Tugga •
g Easy •

• Henry J Bean's

• Coopers Arms • Foxtrot Oscar

h •

• Made in Italy

• Delizia

• GORDON RAMSAY

rd •

Marechiaro
Stock Pot

Buona Sera

Chelsea Embankment

• Pig's Ear

ci Pizza, New
ture Rev'n

• Cross Keys

River Thames

• Cheyne Walk Brasserie

rt House

Cheyne

ATTERSEA

• Ransome's Dock

Battersea
Park

Buchan's •

Matilda's •

Albert Bridge Road

Battersea Bridge Road

ATTERSEA

Price Of Wales Drive

Battersea Pk Rd

## MAP 6 – NOTTING HILL & BAYSWATER

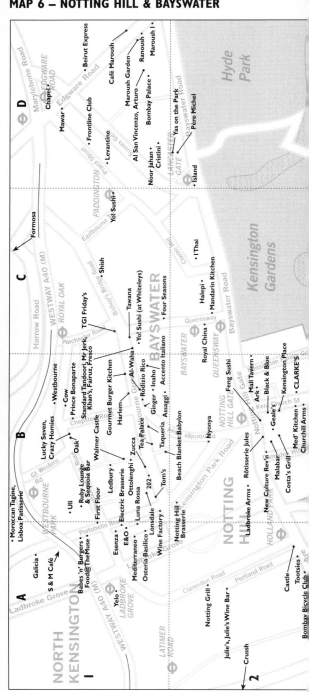

**MAP 7 – HAMMERSMITH & CHISWICK**

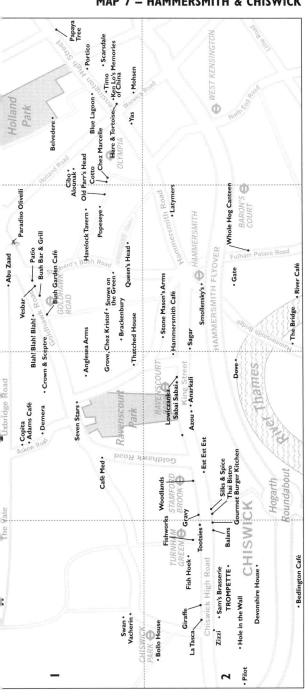

# MAP 8 – HAMPSTEAD, CAMDEN TOWN & ISLINGTON

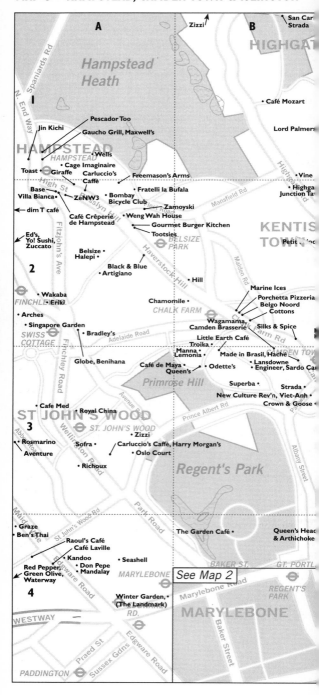

Zizzi

San Car
Strada

**A**

**B**

HIGHGAT

*Hampstead
Heath*

HIGHGAT

Spaniards Rd

N. End Way

**1**

Café Mozart

Lord Palmers

Jin Kichi

Pescador Too

Gaucho Grill, Maxwell's

HAMPSTEAD

Vine

Wells

Toast

Cage Imaginaire

Giraffe

Carluccio's

Caffè

Freemason's Arms

Highga
Junction Ta

Base

Villa Bianca

ZeNW3

High St

Fratelli la Bufala

Mansfield Rd

dim T café

Bombay
Bicycle Club

Zamoyski

Café Crêperie
de Hampstead

Weng Wah House

KENTIS

Gourmet Burger Kitchen

TOWN

Petit,, In

Ed's,
Yo! Sushi,
Zuccato

Tootsies

BELSIZE
PARK

**2**

Belsize
Halepi

Fitzjohn's Ave

Haverstock Hill

Black & Blue

Artigiano

Hill

Marine Ices

Wakaba
Eriki

Porchetta Pizzeria
Belgo Noord

FINCHLEY

Cottons

Arches

Chamomile

Malden Rd

Silks & Spice

Singapore Garden

CHALK FARM

Wagamama,
Camden Brasserie

Farm Rd

SWISS
COTTAGE

Bradley's

Adelaide Road

Little Earth Café

EN TOW

Globe, Benihana

Troika

Manna
Lemonia

Made in Brasil, Haché

Finchley Road

Café de Maya

Odette's

Lansdowne
Engineer, Sardo Ca

Queen's

*Primrose Hill*

Superba

Strada

New Culture Rev'n, Viet-Anh

Cafe Med

Royal China

Prince Albert Rd

Crown & Goose

ST JOHN'S WOOD

ST. JOHN'S WOOD

Zizzi

**3**

Rosmarino

Sofra

Carluccio's Caffè, Harry Morgan's

Aventure

Oslo Court

Richoux

*Regent's Park*

Wellington Road

Albany Street

Park Road

Graze

The Garden Café

Queen's Head
& Artichoke

Ben's Thai

St John's Wood Rd

Raoul's Café
Café Laville

Kandoo

Seashell

BAKER ST.

GT. PORTL

Red Pepper,
Green Olive,
Waterway

Don Pepe
Mandalay

MARYLEBONE

See Map 2

REGENT'S
PARK

**4**

Edgware Road

Winter Garden,
(The Landmark)

Marylebone Road

MARYLEBONE

WESTWAY

RD.

Baker Street

PADDINGTON

Praed St

Sussex Gdns

# MAP 8 – HAMPSTEAD, CAMDEN TOWN & ISLINGTON

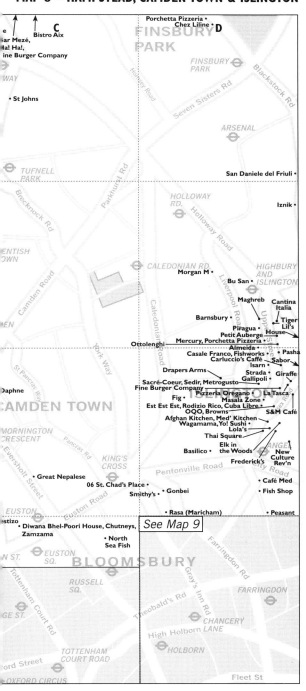

C

Bistro Aix

Bar Mezé,
Ha! Ha!,
Fine Burger Company

WAY

• St Johns

FINSBURY
PARK

Porchetta Pizzeria •
Chez Liline • D

FINSBURY
PARK

Blackstock Rd

Hornsey Road

Seven Sisters Rd

ARSENAL

TUFNELL
PARK

Brecknock Rd

Parkhurst Rd

HOLLOWAY
RD.

Holloway Road

San Daniele del Friuli •

Iznik •

KENTISH
TOWN

Camden Road

DEN

St Pancras Way

York Way

CALEDONIAN RD. •
Morgan M •

Caledonian Road

HIGHBURY
AND
ISLINGTON

Bu San • • Pasha

Maghreb        Cantina
Italia

Barnsbury •        • Tiger
Lil's

Piragua •        House
Petit Auberge •

Ottolenghi ·        Mercury, Porchetta Pizzeria •

Almeida •

Casale Franco, Fishworks • • • Sabor

Carluccio's Caffè

Drapers Arms        Isarn •        Strada • Giraffe

Sacré-Coeur, Sedir, Metrogusto        Gallipoli •

Fine Burger Company        Pizzeria Oregano • • La Tasca

Fig •        Masala Zone •

Est Est Est, Rodizio Rico, Cuba Libre •

OQO, Browns        S&M Café

Afghan Kitchen, Med' Kitchen •

Wagamama, Yo! Sushi •

Lola's •

Thai Square •

Elk in        New

Basilico •        the Woods        Culture

Frederick's        Rev'n

City Road

Daphne

CAMDEN TOWN

MORNINGTON
CRESCENT

Pancras Road

Eversholt Street

KING'S
CROSS

Pentonville Road

• Great Nepalese

06 St. Chad's Place •        • Café Med

Smithy's •  • Gonbei        • Fish Shop

EUSTON

Euston Road

Mestizo

• Diwana Bhel-Poori House, Chutneys,
Zamzama        • Rasa (Maricham)        • Peasant

See Map 9

EUSTON        • North
SQ.        Sea Fish

UN ST.        BLOOMSBURY

Tottenham Court Rd

RUSSELL
SQ.

Farringdon Rd

FARRINGDON

GE ST.        Theobald's Rd        Gray's Inn Rd

CHANCERY
LANE

High Holborn

ord Street        TOTTENHAM
COURT ROAD

HOLBORN

OXFORD CIRCUS        Fleet St

# MAP 9 – THE CITY

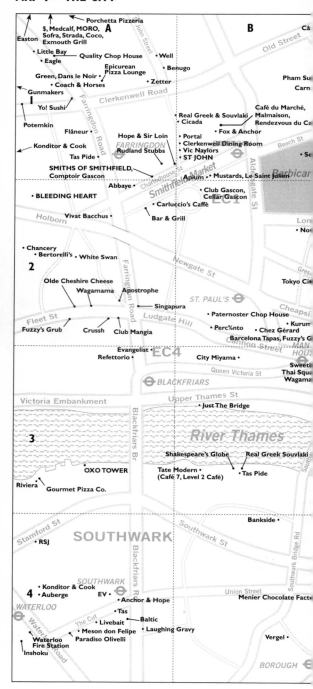

**A**

Porchetta Pizzeria

Easton

$, Medcalf, MORO, Sofra, Strada, Coco, Exmouth Grill

Little Bay — Quality Chop House
Eagle

Green, Dans le Noir
Epicurean Pizza Lounge
Coach & Horses

Gunmakers

Yo! Sushi

Potemkin

Flâneur

Konditor & Cook

Tas Pide

SMITHS OF SMITHFIELD, Comptoir Gascon

Abbaye •

• BLEEDING HEART

Holborn

Vivat Bacchus •

• Chancery
• Bertorelli's
• White Swan

Olde Cheshire Cheese
Wagamama    Apostrophe

Fleet St
Fuzzy's Grub    Crussh    Club Mangia

Evangelist
Refettorio •

EC4

Victoria Embankment

**3**

Riviera    Gourmet Pizza Co.

OXO TOWER

Stamford St    SOUTHWARK

• RSJ

SOUTHWARK
**4**    • Konditor & Cook
• Auberge    EV •    • Anchor & Hope
WATERLOO            • Tas
Waterloo    • Livebait    Baltic
Fire Station    • Meson don Felipe    • Laughing Gravy
Inshoku    Paradiso Olivelli

John Street

**B**

Old Street

• Well

• Benugo

Clerkenwell Road

• Zetter

Pham Su
Carn

Café du Marché,
• Real Greek & Souvlaki    Malmaison,
• Cicada    • Fox & Anchor    Rendezvous du Ca

Hope & Sir Loin    • Portal    Beech St
Rudland Stubbs    • Clerkenwell Dining Room
• Vic Naylors    • Se
• ST JOHN

Chartersouse Street    Apium • • Mustards, Le Saint Julien    Barbican

• Club Gascon,    Aldersgate St
Cellar Gascon

• Carluccio's Caffè

Bar & Grill    Lon
• No

Newgate St

Gres

Tokyo Cit

ST. PAUL'S ⊖

Ludgate Hill    Singapura    Cheapsi

• Paternoster Chop House    • Kurum
• Perc%nto    • Chez Gérard    MAN.

Barcelona Tapas, Fuzzy's G
Cannon Street    HOU.

City Miyama •    Sweetii

Queen Victoria St    Thai Squa
Wagama

⊖ BLACKFRIARS

Upper Thames St
• Just The Bridge

River Thames

Shakespeare's Globe    Real Greek Souvlaki

Tate Modern •    • Tas Pide
(Café 7, Level 2 Café)    Sou

Bankside •

Southwark St

Blackfriars Rd

Union Street    Southwark Bridge Rd
Menier Chocolate Facto

Vergel •

BOROUGH ⊖

# MAP 9 – THE CITY

# MAP 10 – SOUTH LONDON (& FULHAM)

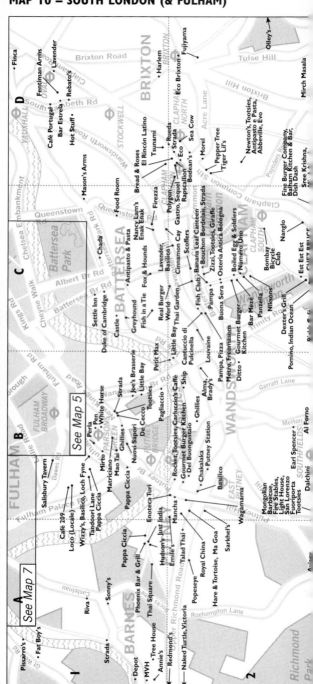

## MAP 11 – EAST END & DOCKLANDS

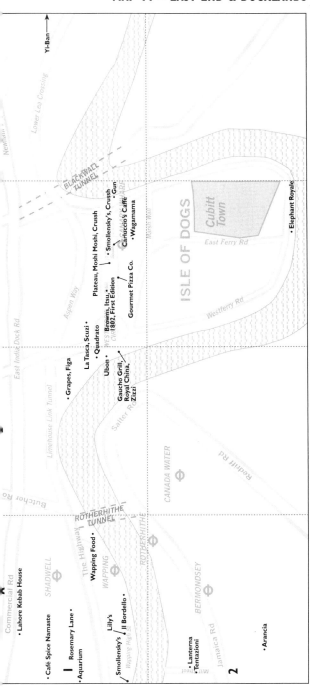

Yi-Ban →

Lower Lea Crossing

Newham

BLACKWALL TUNNEL

East India Dock Rd

Aspen Way

Plateau, Moshi Moshi, Crussh • Smollensky's, Crussh • Gun

• Carluccio's Caffè • Wagamama

ISLE OF DOGS

Cubitt Town

East Ferry Rd

• Elephant Royale

La Tasca, Scuzi • Browns, Itsu, • WES 1802, First Edition • Quadrato • Gourmet Pizza Co.

• Grapes, Figa

Ubon •

Gaucho Grill, Royal China, Salter Rd. • Zizzi

Westferry Rd

Limehouse Link Tunnel

Butcher Ro

ROTHERHITHE TUNNEL

CANADA WATER

Redhill Rd

Commercial Rd
• Lahore Kebab House

• Café Spice Namaste

• Rosemary Lane •

• Aquarium

SHADWELL

The Highway

Wapping Food •

WAPPING

Smollensky's •
Lilly's •
• Il Bordello

Wapping High St

ROTHERHITHE

BERMONDSEY

Jamaica Rd

• Lanterna
• Tentazioni

Mill St

• Arancia

2